Motor Vehicle Calc and Science

PART 2 *SI Units*

R. C. CHAMPION, F.I.M.I., M.I.R.T.E.
Head of Engineering Trades Department,
Paddington Technical College

E. C. ARNOLD, M.I.M.I., M.I.R.T.E.
Former Course Tutor, Automobile Engineering,
Southgate Technical College

EDWARD ARNOLD

© R. C. Champion and E. C. Arnold 1970

First published 1955
by Edward Arnold (Publishers), Ltd,
25 Hill Street, London, W1X 8LL
Second edition 1967
Reprinted 1968
Third edition 1970
Reprinted 1972, 1974

ISBN 0 7131 3233 7

*Printed in Great Britain by Richard Clay (The Chaucer Press), Ltd,
Bungay, Suffolk*

Preface to First Edition

This book has been written as a continuation of Part I, which dealt with simple basic calculations and science of the motor vehicle. Trigonometry, algebra and logarithms have now been explained and their application to automobile engineering has been shown in the worked examples. It has been the authors' intention to apply the calculations to every-day problems which the service engineer and mechanic meet during the course of their work.

The science section covers many subjects, as the motor mechanic requires a wide range of scientific knowledge to service efficiently the modern motor vehicle. Each subject has worked examples, and exercises are provided at the end of each chapter for the student's own practice. The authors have often been asked by students for more exercises to solve themselves and we hope that these books will satisfy their need.

Parts 1 and 2 cover the Motor Vehicle Mechanics and Technicians Examinations of the City and Guilds of London Institute and similar examinations set by other boards. Many of the exercises are past examination questions of professional examining boards, and the authors are grateful to the following for their co-operation and permission to print these questions:

City and Guilds of London Institute, London.
The Institute of the Motor Industry, London.
Union of Lancashire and Cheshire Institutes, Manchester.
Northern Counties Technical Examinations Council, Newcastle upon Tyne.
East Midland Educational Union, Nottingham.
Union of Educational Institutes, Birmingham.

Preface to Third Edition

The reception accorded to the first and second edition of Parts 1 and 2 of this book has convinced the authors of its usefulness to the teachers and students for whom it was written.

The new editions of both Part 1 and Part 2 use the new SI metric system throughout (see page vii of Part 1); both Parts have been thoroughly revised in order to meet the requirements of the motor industry and the examining bodies who will be using SI units in the future.

This revision has given the authors the opportunity of rearranging, deleting and adding further topics to cover the revised syllabus for Motor Vehicle Mechanics and Technician courses of the City and Guilds of London Institute and other examining bodies.

The authors are once again most grateful to the examining bodies mentioned for granting them permission to include questions from previous examination papers.

R. C. C.
E. C. A.

Contents

CHAPTER

PAGE

1. LOGARITHMS 1
   Use of tables—evaluation of formulae.

2. INVOLUTION AND EVOLUTION 10
   Indices—powers—roots—logarithms—slide rule.

3. FRICTION 20
   Effect of friction—types of friction—coefficient of friction—
   angle of friction—inclined and horizontal planes—friction in
   bearings—plate clutches—brakes—frictional torque—power
   lost and heat generated.

4. LUBRICATION AND VISCOSITY 43
   Viscosity—measurement of viscosity—grades of lubricant—
   classification—S.A.E. and index numbers—detergents—
   cold sludging and oxidation—grease as a lubricant—
   flash point—additives.

5. BEARINGS AND LOADS ON BEARINGS . . . 56
   Journal bearings—loads and bearing pressures—ball and
   roller bearings, radial and thrust bearings—taper roller and
   needle bearings—geometry of bearings—load on king-pins.

6. TRANSMISSION OF MOTION AND POWER . . . 69
   Transmission of power by belt, chain and gear wheel—
   velocity and gear ratio—efficiency of drive—steering box.

7. MACHINES 99
   Simple machines—velocity ratio, mechanical advantage and
   efficiency—types of machine, lifting jack, worm and axle,
   chain blocks, hydraulic press and jack—hydraulic braking
   system—law of a machine.

CHAPTER   PAGE

8. PROPERTIES OF GASES 121

Absolute temperature and pressure—Boyle's and Charles' law—compression pressure and ratio—specific heat of gases —adiabatic and isothermal expansion.

9. LIQUIDS 146

Pressure due to head—flow of liquids through orifice—coefficient of contraction, velocity and discharge—flow of oil through gear-type pump—Archimedes' Principle—relative density and density—the venturi.

10. FUELS 157

Types of fuel and classification—chemical symbols and formulae—air-fuel ratios—octane and cetane numbers— relative density—anti-knock and fuel dopes—heating value— flash point.

11. ENGINE TESTING 173

Types of engine test—methods of testing—dynamometers— indicators—fuel and air measurement—exhaust gas analysis— flame rate and air–fuel ratio—efficiency—heat balance— Willans line.

12. FORCES ON A VEHICLE 211

Speed, velocity and displacement—relative velocity—angular velocity—acceleration—centripetal acceleration—mass— rolling, gradient and air resistance—momentum—impulse— direct impact—potential and kinetic energy—conservation of energy—rotating mass—radius of gyration—moment of inertia —circular motion—centripetal and centrifugal force—centre of gravity above ground level—overturning speed of vehicles on corners—skidding when cornering—distribution and transfer of load when cornering and braking.

13. PERIODIC MOTION AND BALANCING 264

Spring vibration—simple harmonic motion—road-wheel balancing—engine balancing

14. BENDING AND TWISTING 280

Simple bending—bending moments—torsion and angle of twist.

CHAPTER   PAGE

15. MATERIALS 294

Ferrous and non-ferrous-factor of safety—elements and alloys —testing of metals—heat treatment—soldering, brazing and welding.

16. ELECTRICITY 318

Specific resistance—coil ignition—condenser—dynamo and dynamo control—cut-out and regulators—alternator—starter motor.

17. MISCELLANEOUS 337

Springs—valve force and acceleration—torque reaction and couples—tractive effort and gear-ratio—universal joints— force on piston and connecting rod—crankshaft torque— forces on a lever—piston speed and gas velocity—drilling machine speeds and feeds.

APPENDIX 359

Tables of logarithms and antilogarithms . . . 360

Tables of natural sines, cosines and tangents . . 364

Index 371

1 Logarithms

Logarithms enable multiplication and division to be converted into the easier processes of addition and subtraction, thus reducing labour and saving time. The student should regard logarithms as a useful tool. He should endeavour to learn how to use them efficiently and not be too concerned as to how and why they work. However, since the driver of a car is more efficient for knowing how the 'wheels go round', the explanation given at the end of this chapter should enable students to understand how logarithms do their work.

There are two systems of logarithms in use, but we are concerned only with that system called **common**, which can be defined as follows.

The common logarithm of a number is the index of the power to which 10 must be raised in order to equal the number. The figure 10 is the base on which the system of common logarithms rests, i.e. the figure 10 is considered as the starting-point.

The logarithms of all numbers from 10 to 99 have been carefully calculated and compiled and a table to four figures, called four-figure logarithms, is given at the end of this book. We shall see how to use the tables later in this chapter, so now let us examine the composition of a logarithm.

A logarithm consists of two parts:

(*a*) a whole number portion called the **characteristic** followed by—
(*b*) the decimal portion called the **mantissa**.

The characteristic can be positive or zero or negative; the mantissa is, however, always positive. The characteristics are not given in the table, but they are found by inspection, as will be shown later.

The mantissa is found by consulting the table. For any given number of four figures the mantissa is always the same, no matter where the decimal point appears in the number; only the characteristic is affected by the position of the decimal point in the number. Thus, the mantissa of 3768; 376·8; 37·68; 3·768; 0·3768; 0·03768, and so on, is the same for each.

Use of Tables

In order to find the mantissa when the number has not more than four figures, we proceed:

(*a*) Find the first two figures of the number, whose logarithm is required, in the left-hand vertical line numbered 0 to 99 inclusive.

(*b*) Find the third figure of the number in the horizontal line at the top of the page numbered 0 to 9 inclusive; in the column under this figure and opposite to the first two figures found, a four-figure number will be found; this logarithm number covers the first three figures of the number.

(*c*) Find the fourth figure of the number in the right-hand horizontal line numbered 1 to 9 inclusive; in the column under this figure and in line with the four-figure number previously found is one or two figures. This figure or figures is added to the four-figure number previously found in order to complete the mantissa.

Example (see the two lines of a logarithm table below).

Find (1) the mantissa of the logarithm of 376·8 and
   (2) the logarithm of 376·8.

(1) (*a*) Look in the left-hand column for the figures 37; opposite these and under 6 (the third figure) we find the four-figure number 5752.

(*b*) Under 8 (the fourth figure) in the right-hand column and in line with 5752 we find the figure 9. This figure 9 is added to 5752, making 5761; thus the mantissa of the logarithm of 376·8 is 5761.

(2) To complete the logarithm we have to find the characteristic, and to do this we proceed:

As the original number is greater than one, then the characteristic will be positive and one less than the number of figures to the left of the decimal point, i.e. 2. Thus, the complete logarithm is 2·5761.

	0	1	2	3	4	5	6	7	8	9	1 2 3 4	5	6 7 8 9
37	5682	5694	5705	5717	5729	5740	5752	5763	5775	5786	1 2 3 5	6	7 8 9 10
38	5798	5809	5821	5832	5843	5855	5866	5877	5888	5899	1 2 3 5	6	7 8 9 10

Example. Find the logarithm of 0·0345, using the tables at the end of the book.

(*a*) Look in the left-hand column for the figures 34; opposite these and under 5 (the third figure) we find 5378, which is the required mantissa.

(*b*) To complete the logarithm we have to find the characteristic, and to do this we proceed:

As the original number is less than one the characteristic will be negative and one more than the number of noughts following the decimal point. Here, only one nought follows the decimal place; thus the characteristic is negative 2, usually called **bar** 2. To avoid confusion it is customary to place the negative sign above the negative figure, thus $\bar{2}$, because only the characteristic is negative. Remember the mantissa is *always* positive. Therefore the complete logarithm of 0·0345 is $\bar{2}$·5378.

In order to avoid using the wrong characteristic the following points should always be remembered.

Positive Characteristics

When the original number is equal to or greater than one the characteristic will be positive and it will be one less than the number of figures in front of the decimal point. For example, the logarithm of 37·5 is 1·5740, and the logarithm of 3·75 is 0·5740. The logarithm of 1 is 0·0000, the logarithm of 10 is 1·0000, the logarithm of 100 is 2·000 and so on.

Negative Characteristics

A simple method of finding the negative characteristic is to count the decimal point as $\bar{1}$ and add to it $\bar{1}$ for each nought following the decimal point, e.g. 0·$\bar{0}\bar{0}$345, making a total of $\bar{3}$.

Multiplication of Logarithms

By adding the logarithms of two or more numbers together, the logarithm of their product is found. The number corresponding to this logarithm, which is obtained from the table of **antilogarithms**, is the product required. A table of antilogarithms will be found at the end of this book and the following examples show the method of using this table as well as the method of multiplication by logarithms.

A simple form of solving the calculation is by using the logarithms in a tabulated layout as shown below.

Example. Multiply 6·25 by 25·4.

Number	*Logarithm*
6·25	0·7959
25·4	1·4048
	2·2007

This logarithm answer has to be changed into an ordinary number by means of the table of antilogarithms. The process is similar to that of finding the logarithm of a number, and we proceed:

(1) Take the mantissa only and find its antilogarithm in the table.

(2) The number in the table corresponding to ·200, the first three figures of the mantissa, is 1585.

(3) To complete the antilogarithm under the figure 7 at the head of the right-hand column and in line with 1585 is the figure 3. This 3 is added to 1585 to give 1588, which completes the antilogarithm.

(4) To complete the conversion to an ordinary number we must consider the characteristic 2, because the value of the characteristic governs the position of the decimal point. To place the decimal point correctly we add one to the characteristic, which in this example will now be 3, i.e. $2 + 1$, and counting from the left-hand side of the antilogarithm obtained we place the decimal point after the third figure as shown— 158·8.

Thus $6·25 \times 25·4 = \underline{158·8}$

Example. Find the value of $0·00017 \times 2700 \times 0·25$.

Number	Logarithm
0·00017	$\bar{4}·2304$
2700	$3·4314$
0·25	$\bar{1}·3979$
	$\bar{1}·0597$

The following explanation should enable the student to grasp the method of obtaining the negative characteristic ($\bar{1}$), in this example.

After adding the mantissa there is 1 to carry to the characteristic column; now this 1 is positive because the mantissa is always positive. The characteristic column thus contains positive 3, plus 1 carried, which equals 4 and negative 4, plus negative 1, which equals $\bar{5}$. The result of 4 and $\bar{5}$ is clearly $\bar{1}$, e.g. if a man pays £4 off a £5 debt he still owes £1 or is minus £1.

The antilogarithm of ·0597 is 1148. Then the antilogarithm of $\bar{1}·0597$ is 0·1148.

Thus $0·00017 \times 2700 \times 0·25 = \underline{0·1148}$

Division by Logarithms

To divide one figure by another by means of logarithms we subtract the logarithm of the divisor from the logarithm of the dividend, and the result will be the logarithm of the quotient. The quotient itself is obtained from the antilogarithm tables.

Example. Divide 63·5 by 25·4.

Number	Logarithm
63·5	1·8028
25·4	1·4048
	0·3980

The antilogarithm of ·3980 is 2500. Then the antilogarithm of 0·3980 is 2·5.

Thus $\qquad\qquad$ 63·5 ÷ 25·4 = <u>2·5</u>

Example. Divide 24·37 by 635·1.

Number	Logarithm
24·37	1·3868
635·1	2·8029
	$\overline{2}$·5839

In this example, to subtract 0·8 from 0·3 in the mantissa we borrow 1 from the characteristic which makes it 0. To subtract the characteristics we change the sign of the bottom-line characteristic and add, thus $\overline{2}$ plus 0 equals $\overline{2}$.

The antilogarithm of ·5839 is 3836. Then the antilogarithm of $\overline{2}$·5839 is 0·038 36.

Thus $\qquad\qquad$ 24·37 ÷ 635·1 = 0·038 36

The following points concerning logarithms and antilogarithms should be memorized.

(1) Never confuse logarithms and antilogarithms: to avoid this, print **Anti** in red ink across the antilogarithm tables.

(2) When subtracting characteristics always change the sign of the bottom line and **add**.

(3) Always remember that the mantissa is positive.

The following example shows the method of working out problems containing both multiplication and division.

Example. Evaluate (find the value of) $\dfrac{84 \cdot 25 \times 105 \times 10 \cdot 05}{200 \times 0 \cdot 525}$.

Number		Logarithm	
84·25		1·9256	
105		2·0212	
10·05		1·0021	
	Numerator	4·9489	4·9489
200		2·3010	
0·525		1̄·7202	
	Denominator	2·0212	2·0212
			2̄·9277

The antilogarithm of ·9277 is 8467. Then the antilogarithm of 2·9277 is 846·7.

Explanation of Logarithms

We have seen in Chapter 2, Part I that the small figure placed to the right and above a number is called the index. This index figure indicates the power to which the number is to be raised. Now 10 is the base of the system of common logarithms, and with logarithms to the base 10 (in practice we do not show the base 10 in the working) we have the following:

$10^0 = \quad 1$, ∴ log $\quad 1$ is 0 $10^{-1} = 0 \cdot 1$, ∴ log 0·1   is 1̄

$10^1 = \quad 10$, ∴ log $\quad 10$ is 1 $10^{-2} = 0 \cdot 01$, ∴ log 0·01 is 2̄

$10^2 = \quad 100$, ∴ log $\quad 100$ is 2 $10^{-3} = 0 \cdot 001$, ∴ log 0·001 is 3̄

$10^3 = 1000$, ∴ log 1000 is 3

In general 10 is base, the index is the logarithm, e.g. $10^2 = 100$ or log 2 is 100, and 100 = the number. From the foregoing the student should understand how we arrive at the characteristic.

Students are often puzzled because we add logarithms to multiply and subtract them to divide. Suppose we multiply 10^2 by 10^3, i.e. 100×1000, we shall get 100 000 or 10^5; in other words we add the indices together, thus $10^2 \times 10^3 = 10^{2+3} = 10^5$. In the same way $10^3 \div 10^2 = \dfrac{1000}{100} = 10$ or 10^1, i.e. $10^{3-2} = 10^1$. From this it follows that when we add or subtract logarithms, what we are really doing is adding or subtracting the powers of the numbers.

If we take a number less than 10, say 7, we have to raise 10 to a lesser power than 1 so that the result equals 7. Now log 7 is 0·8451 and this indicates that by raising 10 to the power of 0·8451, we shall obtain 7, i.e. $10^{0.8451} = 7$. Log 70 is 1·8451, i.e. $10^{1.8451} = 70$; log 700 is 2·8451, and so on.

The logarithm of any number under 1 is $\bar{1}$·something, e.g. log 0·9 is $\bar{1}$·9542 and log 0·09 is $\bar{2}$·9542.

In Chapter 12 we shall deal with the forces of rotating parts, therefore a knowledge of the following methods is necessary.

The expressions likely to be met are:

(*a*) 2 cos θ; 2 sin θ; 2 tan θ, etc.
(*b*) cos 2θ; sin 2θ; tan 2θ.
(*c*) cos² θ; sin² θ; tan² θ.

It is usually convenient to use logarithms for these calculations.

Example. Let θ = 20°, then

(*a*) 2 cos θ = 2 × cos 20° = 2 × 0·9397 = $\underline{1·8794}$
   or log 2 + log cos 20° = 0·3010 + $\bar{1}$·9730 = 0·2740
        ∴ 2 cos 20° = $\underline{1·879}$.
(*b*) cos 2θ = cos (2 × 20°) = $\overline{\text{cos 40}°}$ = $\underline{0·7660}$.
(*c*) log cos² θ = 2 × log cos 20° = 2 × $\overline{\bar{1}·9730}$ = $\bar{1}$·9460
     ∴ cos² θ = $\underline{0·8831}$.

Note: in (*a*) it is *twice* the cos of the *angle*.
  In (*b*) it is *twice* the angle.
  In (*c*) it is the cos of the angle squared.

Example. Find the value of 4 + 3 cos θ when θ = 20°.

In this example, 4 must be added to the value of 3 cos θ:

$$3 \cos \theta = 3 \times \cos 20° = 3 \times 0·9397 = 2·8191$$
$$\text{Add} \quad 4$$
$$\overline{6·8191}$$

∴ 4 + 3 cos θ = $\underline{6·8191}$

Example. Find the value of $3 \sin^2 \theta$ when $\theta = 23° 30'$.

Let $\qquad\qquad x = 3 \sin^2 \theta$

Then $\qquad\quad \log x = \log 3 + (2 \log \sin \theta)$
$$= 0.4771 + (2 \times \bar{1}.6007)$$
$$= 0.4771 + \bar{1}.2014$$
$$= \bar{1}.6785$$
$$\therefore x = \underline{0.4769}$$

Example. Find the value of $\sin^2 \theta + 2 \cos \theta$ when $\theta = 74° 48'$.

Let $x = \sin^2 \theta$ and $y = 2 \cos \theta$.

Then $\qquad\qquad \log x = 2 \log \sin \theta$
$$= 2 \times \bar{1}.9845 = \bar{1}.9690$$
$$\therefore x = \underline{0.9311}$$

Then $\qquad\qquad \log y = \log 2 + \log \cos \theta$
$$= 0.3010 + \bar{1}.4186$$
$$= \bar{1}.7196$$
$$\therefore y = 0.5243$$
$$\sin^2 \theta + 2 \cos \theta = 0.9311 + 0.5243$$
$$= \underline{1.4554}$$

Exercise 1

1. Evaluate, using logarithms,

$$\frac{3.81 \times 12.2 \times 7.805 \times 0.137}{4.52 \times 3.06 \times 10.72} \qquad (0.3353)$$

2. The ratio of air to fuel by mass in an engine running on a weak mixture is given by the formula:

$$\frac{36.4 N_2}{8 CO_2 - 4 O_2 + 1.05 N_2}$$

where N_2, CO_2 and O_2 represent the proportions by volume of nitrogen, carbon dioxide and oxygen in a given volume of dried exhaust gas.

A test on a certain engine gave the following figures: N_2, 0.838; CO_2, 0.122; O_2, 0.04. Find the air-to-fuel ratio under these conditions.

(17.99 to 1)   (C. and G.)

3. Calculate, using logarithms: (*a*) 1.687×3.009; (*b*) $223 \times 0.005\,87$; (*c*) $223 \div 0.005\,87$.   ((*a*) 5.076; (*b*) 1.309; (*c*) 37 990)   (E.M.E.U.)

4. Calculate, using logarithms: (*a*) $\dfrac{68.5 \times 3.05}{285.7}$; (*b*) the area of a circle 21 mm diameter, taking $\pi = 3.142$.

((*a*) 0.7313; (*b*) 346.3 mm²)   (E.M.E.U.)

5. Using logarithms, calculate:

$$\frac{5 \cdot 03 \times 0 \cdot 7654}{6 \cdot 288}$$ (0·6122) (E.M.E.U.)

6. Write down the logarithms of: (*a*) 8010, 0·8971, 0·3462; (*b*) 93·85 ÷ 1·96.

((*a*) 3·9036; 1̄·9528; 1̄·5394; (*b*) 1·9724–0·2923)

(E.M.E.U.)

7. Evaluate by means of logarithms:

$$\frac{21 \cdot 68 \times 152 \cdot 7 \times 9 \cdot 7}{3 \cdot 8 \times 13 \cdot 68}$$ (617·7) (U.L.C.I.)

8. Evaluate by means of logarithms:

$$\frac{3173 \times 12 \cdot 46 \times 4 \cdot 375}{189 \cdot 2 \times 28 \cdot 45}$$ (32·13) (U.L.C.I.)

Involution and Evolution

In Chapter 1 the process of multiplication and division was reduced to addition and subtraction by the use of logarithms. In a similar way the process of involution and evolution can be reduced to multiplication and division by the use of logarithms.

Involution can be defined as the process of raising a number to any given power. To find the value of a number with an index we proceed:

(1) Find the log of the number.
(2) Multiply this log by the power figure (index) of the number.
(3) Find the antilog of this product.

Example. Find the value of $2 \cdot 371^5$.

Log of $2 \cdot 371$ is $0 \cdot 3749$

Multiply $0 \cdot 3749$ by the index figure:
$$0 \cdot 3749 \times 5 = 1 \cdot 8745$$

Antilog of $\cdot 8745$ is 7491. Then antilog of $1 \cdot 8745$ is $74 \cdot 91$
$$\therefore 2 \cdot 371^5 = \underline{74 \cdot 91}$$

Example. Find the value of $0 \cdot 345^4$.

Log of $0 \cdot 345$ is $\bar{1} \cdot 5378$

Multiply $\bar{1} \cdot 5378$ by the index figure:
$$\bar{1} \cdot 5378 \times 4 = \bar{2} \cdot 1512$$

Antilog of $\cdot 1512$ is 1417. Then antilog of $\bar{2} \cdot 1512$ is $0 \cdot 01417$
$$\therefore 0 \cdot 345^4 = \underline{0 \cdot 01417}$$

Note that after multiplying the mantissa by 4 we have positive 2 to carry, thus four times $\bar{1}$ equals $\bar{4}$ and $\bar{4}$ plus 2 equals $\bar{2}$, i.e. $(\bar{4} + 2 = \bar{2})$.

Example. Find the value of $5 \cdot 25^{0 \cdot 4}$.

Log of $5 \cdot 25$ is $0 \cdot 7202$

Multiply $0 \cdot 7202$ by the index figure:
$$0 \cdot 7202 \times 0 \cdot 4 = 0 \cdot 2881$$

Antilog of ·2881 is 1941. Then antilog of 0·2881 is 1·941

$$\therefore 5 \cdot 25^{0 \cdot 4} = \underline{1 \cdot 941}$$

Note that the solution of this example is practically impossible without the use of logarithms.

Example. Find the value of $5 \cdot 5^{0 \cdot 234}$.

Log of 5·5 is 0·7404

Multiply 0·7404 by the index figure:

$$0 \cdot 7404 \times 0 \cdot 234 = 0 \cdot 1733$$

Antilog of ·1733 is 1490. Then antilog of 0·1733 is 1·490

$$\therefore 5 \cdot 5^{0 \cdot 234} = \underline{1 \cdot 490}$$

In addition to the foregoing examples, the following should be noted. In the expression xyz^2 only z is squared, but in the expression $(xyz)^2$ *all* the letters are squared, i.e. $x^2y^2z^2$.

$$x^0 = 1; \qquad 1^1 = 1; \qquad x^{-1} = \frac{1}{x} \; ; \qquad 10^{-1} = \frac{1}{10}$$

$$2^0 = 1; \qquad 1^2 = 1; \qquad x^{-2} = \frac{1}{x^2} \; ; \qquad 10^{-2} = \frac{1}{10^2}$$

$$0 \cdot 9^0 = 1; \qquad 1^4 = 1; \qquad x^{\frac{1}{2}} = \sqrt{x}; \qquad 10^{-3} = \frac{1}{10^3}$$

$$x^0y^0z^0 = 1; \qquad 1^{0 \cdot 3} = 1; \qquad x^2 = \frac{1}{x^{-2}}$$

In the foregoing we have stated that $x^0 = 1$; the proof of this statement is as follows.

If we divide a quantity having an index by itself the result always has an index of 0, e.g. $x^2 \div x^2 = x^{2-2} = x^0$; also the result of dividing any two equal quantities is always 1, e.g. $x^2 \div x^2 = 1$. Thus it follows that any quantity with ^{0} for its index is equal to 1, therefore $x^0 = 1$.

It has been stated also that $x^{-1} = \frac{1}{x}$. The proof of this statement is as follows.

If we divide a letter having an index by the same letter with a higher index, then the index of the result is negative, e.g. $x^2 \div x^3 = x^{-1}$. Dividing x^2 by x^3 we have $\frac{x \times x}{x \times x \times x}$, by cancelling, this equals $\frac{1}{x}$ and since $x^2 \div x^3 = x^{-1}$, therefore $x^{-1} = \frac{1}{x}$.

Index figures are often used for very large or very small numbers. Thus the modulus of elasticity, E, was stated to be 207 000 N/mm^2;

this can be written as 207×10^3. The coefficient of expansion of copper is 0·000 017 1 per °C; this can be written as $1·71 \times 10^{-5}$.

Example. $17\ 800\ 000 \times 0·000\ 009\ 53$ can be written as

$$1·78 \times 10^7 \times 9·53 \times 10^{-6}$$
$$= 1·78 \times 9·53 \times 10^{7-6}$$
$$= 1·78 \times 9·53 \times 10$$

When the index of the number is **negative** and the number is greater than unity the process of involution is performed as shown in the following example.

Example. Find the value of $5·5^{-0·4}$.

Rewrite $5·5^{-0·4}$ in its equivalent form $\dfrac{1}{5·5^{0·4}}$, i.e. $1 \div 5·5^{0·4}$ and proceed:

(1) log of 1 is   0·0000
(2) log of 5·5 is   0·7404
(3) Multiply by the index $0·7404 \times 0·4 = 0·2962$
(4) Subtract log of $5·5^{0·4}$ from log of 1:

$$0·0000 - 0·2962 = \bar{1}·7038$$

Antilog of ·7038 is 5056. Then antilog of $\bar{1}·7038$ is 0·5056

$$\therefore\ 5·25^{0·4} = \underline{0·5056}$$

When the index of a number is negative and the number is less than unity the process of involution is performed as shown in the following example.

Example. Find the value of $0·625^{-0·2}$.

In this example we do not write $0·625^{-0·2}$ in its equivalent form as shown in the last example, but proceed:

(1) log of 0·625 is $\bar{1}·7959$ or $-1 + 0·7959$.
(2) By subtracting 0·7959 from the -1 we get $-0·2041$, thus making the mantissa a negative quantity.
(3) Multiply $-0·2041$ by the index figure, thus

$$-0·2041 \times -0·2 = 0·040\ 82,$$

so negative mantissa × negative index gives a positive answer.

(4) Antilog of ·040 82 is 1098. Then antilog of 0·040 82 is 1·098

$$\therefore\ 0·625^{-0·2} = \underline{1·098}$$

The following worked examples should be carefully studied to avoid mistakes when working out similar examples.

Example. Find the value of $5·58^3 + 125^{2·5}$.

The method of working out this example is:

(1) Raise each number to its respective power, using logarithms.
(2) Find the antilog of each product and add them together to give the answer.

(1) log of 5.58^3 is 0.7466×3 $= 2.2398$
log of $125^{2.5}$ is 2.0969×2.5 $= 5.2423$

(2) antilog of 2.2398 is 173.7
antilog of 5.2423 is $174\,700.0$

then $173.7 + 174\,700.0 = 174\,873.7$

$\therefore 5.58^3 + 125^{2.5} = \underline{174\,873.7}$

Example. Find the value of $5.58^3 \times 125^{2.5}$.

The method of working this example is:

(1) Raise each number to its respective power, using logarithms.
(2) Add these products together and find the antilog of the result.

Number		*Logarithm*
5.58^3	$0.7466 \times 3 =$	2.2398
$125^{2.5}$	$2.0969 \times 2.5 =$	5.2423
		7.4821

antilog is 3035

$\therefore 5.58^3 \times 125^{2.5} = \underline{30\,350\,000}$

Example. Find the value of $\dfrac{5.58^3 \times 125^{2.5}}{3.5^{2.7}}$.

The method of working this example is:

(1) Raise each number to its respective power, using logarithms.
(2) Add the products of the top line and subtract the product of the bottom line.
(3) Find the antilog of the result.

Number		*Logarithm*	
5.58^3	$0.7466 \times 3 =$	2.2398	
$125^{2.5}$	$2.0969 \times 2.5 =$	5.2423	
	Numerator	7.4821	7.4821
$3.5^{2.7}$	$0.5441 \times 2.7 =$	$\overline{1}.4691$	
	Denominator	$\overline{1}.4691$	$\overline{1}.4691$
			6.0130

Antilog is 1030

$\therefore \dfrac{5.58^3 \times 125^{2.5}}{3.5^{2.7}} = \underline{1\,030\,000}$

Evolution can be defined as the extraction of roots and to find the root of a number we proceed:

(1) Find the log of the number.
(2) Divide this log by the root figure (index) of the number.
(3) Find the antilog of this result.

Example. Find the value of $\sqrt[3]{23\cdot37}$.

$$\text{log of } 23\cdot37 \text{ is } 1\cdot3687$$
$$\text{divide by the index: } 1\cdot3687 \div 3 = 0\cdot4562$$
$$\text{antilog of } 0\cdot4562 \text{ is } 2859$$
$$\therefore \sqrt[3]{23\cdot37} = \underline{2\cdot859}$$

Example. Find the value of $\sqrt[4]{0\cdot673}$.

$$\text{log of } 0\cdot673 \text{ is } \bar{1}\cdot8280$$
$$\text{divide by the index: } \bar{1}\cdot8280 \div 4$$

As we cannot divide $\bar{1}$ by 4 as it now stands, the $\bar{1}$ must be modified. The following explanation and working should make the matter clear.

If we add a figure to a number and then subtract the same figure from this number the result is the number with which we started, thus:

$$\bar{1}\cdot8280 = \bar{4} + 3\cdot8280, \text{ we have 'put in' (added) } \bar{3} \text{ and 3,}$$
then
$$\bar{4} + 3\cdot8280 \div 4 = \bar{1} + 0\cdot9570 = \bar{1}\cdot9570.$$
$$\text{Antilog } \cdot9570 \text{ is } 9057$$
$$\therefore \sqrt[4]{0\cdot673} = \underline{0\cdot9057}$$

Example. Find the value of $\sqrt[2\cdot5]{0\cdot6875}$.

$$\text{Log of } 0\cdot6875 \text{ is } \bar{1}\cdot8373$$
Divide by the index:
$$\bar{1}\cdot8373 \div 2\cdot5$$
$$\bar{2}\cdot\bar{5} + 2\cdot3373 \div 2\cdot5 \text{ (}\bar{1}\cdot5 \text{ and } 1\cdot5 \text{ added) will give}$$
$$\bar{1} + 0\cdot9349 = \bar{1}\cdot9349$$
$$\text{Antilog of } \cdot9349 \text{ is } 8608$$
$$\therefore \sqrt[2\cdot5]{0\cdot6875} = \underline{0\cdot8608}$$

Example. Find the value of $\sqrt[3]{5\cdot3^{2\cdot4} \times 8\cdot9^{3\cdot2}}$.

Number		Logarithm
$5\cdot3^{2\cdot4}$	$0\cdot7243 \times 2\cdot4 =$	$1\cdot738\ 32$
$8\cdot9^{3\cdot2}$	$0\cdot9494 \times 3\cdot2 =$	$3\cdot038\ 08$
		$4\cdot776\ 40$

$$4\cdot7764 \div 3 = 1\cdot5921$$
$$\text{Antilog of } \cdot5921 \text{ is } 3909$$
$$\therefore \sqrt[3]{5\cdot3^{2\cdot4} \times 8\cdot9^{3\cdot2}} = \underline{39\cdot09}$$

Example. Find the value of $1 - \left(\dfrac{1}{5 \cdot 5}\right)^{0 \cdot 4}$.

Now
$$1^{0 \cdot 4} \text{ is } 1$$
$$\text{Log of } 1^{0 \cdot 4} \text{ is } 0 \cdot 0000$$
$$\text{Log of } 5 \cdot 5^{0 \cdot 4} \text{ is } 0 \cdot 7404 \times 0 \cdot 4 = 0 \cdot 2962$$
$$\text{Log } 1^{0 \cdot 4} - \log 5 \cdot 5^{0 \cdot 4} = 0 \cdot 0000 - 0 \cdot 2962$$
$$= \bar{1} \cdot 7038$$
$$\text{Antilog of } \bar{1} \cdot 7038 \text{ is } 0 \cdot 5056$$
then
$$1 - 0 \cdot 5056 = 0 \cdot 4944$$
$$\therefore 1 - \left(\frac{1}{5 \cdot 5}\right)^{0 \cdot 4} = \underline{0 \cdot 4944}$$

Log—Log

A labour-saving process for finding powers and extracting roots is the '**log of a log**' method. The following examples should make this method clear.

Example. Find the value of $15^{0 \cdot 2345}$.

(1) Find the log of the index.
(2) Find the log of the number.
(3) Find the log of the log of the number.
(4) Add the log of the index to the log of the log of the number and find the antilog of this addition.
(5) Find the antilog of the antilog of the addition.

(1) Log of $0 \cdot 2345$ is $\bar{1} \cdot 3701$
(2) Log of 15 is $1 \cdot 1761$
(3) Log of $1 \cdot 1761$ is $0 \cdot 0705$
(4) $\bar{1} \cdot 3701 + 0 \cdot 0705 = \bar{1} \cdot 4406$
    Antilog of $\bar{1} \cdot 4406$ is $0 \cdot 2758$
(5) Antilog of $0 \cdot 2758$ is 1887
    $\therefore 15^{0 \cdot 2345} = \underline{1 \cdot 887}$

Example. Find the value of $0 \cdot 7854^{0 \cdot 2345}$.

$$\text{Log } 0 \cdot 7854^{0 \cdot 2345} \text{ is } 0 \cdot 2345 \log 0 \cdot 7854$$
$$\text{is } 0 \cdot 2345 \times \bar{1} \cdot 8951$$
$$\text{is } 0 \cdot 2345 \times -0 \cdot 1049$$
$$\text{is } -0 \cdot 0246 \text{ (by logs)}$$
$$\text{is } \bar{1} \cdot 9754$$
$$0 \cdot 7854^{0 \cdot 2345} \text{ is antilog } \bar{1} \cdot 9754$$
$$\therefore 0 \cdot 7854^{0 \cdot 2345} = \underline{0 \cdot 9450}$$

Example. Find the value of $^{2\cdot345}\!\sqrt{64}$.

(1) Find the log of the index.
(2) Find the log of the number.
(3) Find the log of the log of the number.
(4) Subtract the log of the index from the log of the log of the number and find the antilog of this subtraction.
(5) Find the antilog of the antilog of the subtraction.

(1) Log of 2·345   is 0·3701
(2) Log of 64   is 1·8062
(3) Log of 1·8062   is 0·2567
(4) 0·2567 − 0·3701 = $\bar{1}$·8866
    Antilog of $\bar{1}$·8866 is 0·7702
(5) Antilog of 0·7702 is 5891
    ∴ $^{2\cdot345}\!\sqrt{64} = \underline{5\cdot891}$

The Slide Rule

A well-known engineer once said that, with a slide rule, arithmetic was fun! The student should regard the slide rule not as fun but as a quick and accurate method of calculation. The main operations of the slide rule are multiplication and division, but it can be used for square and cube roots, logarithms, trigonometrical functions of angles and log–log values.

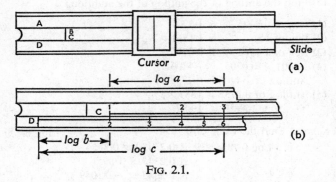

FIG. 2.1.

Fig. 2.1 (*a*) shows the construction of the rule with the slider extended. Scale A and scale B on the upper edge of the slider are identical; they number or have graduations from 1 to 100. Scale C, on the lower edge of the slider, and scale D are identical; these number from 1 to 10.

The construction of the rule is based on common logarithms and, since the log of 1 is 0, all four scales begin with 1; the graduations are proportional to the logarithm of the numbers. Numbers 1 to 10 occupy half of scale A and the whole length of scale D. It is recommended that scales C and D are used for multiplication and division as the larger scale is more accurate.

To multiply, move the slider until 1 on C scale is opposite the multiplicand on D scale, move the **cursor** until the *line* is over the multiplier on C scale, the answer is read under the cursor line on D scale.

To divide, find the number to be divided on D scale, place the cursor line over it and move the slider until the divisor on C scale is also under the cursor line. The answer is read off the D scale opposite to 1 on the C scale.

It is sometimes found that 1 on C scale cannot be used because it is beyond the range of scale D, then 10 is used as it is numerically equal to 1. Fig. 2.1 (*b*) shows how this is achieved for multiplication and division, the mantissa is added or subtracted.

Let $a = 3$; $b = 2$ and $c = 6$:

$$\log a + \log b = \log c \quad \text{or} \quad (3 \times 2 = 6)$$

$$\log c - \log b = \log a \quad \text{or} \quad \left(\frac{6}{2} = 3\right)$$

Square roots. The cursor line is placed over the number on scale A and the square root is shown under the cursor line on scale D.

To square a number the foregoing operation is reversed.

A book of instructions is supplied with each slide rule; these should be carefully read and the suggested exercises carried out. If difficulty is found in fixing the decimal point it may be disregarded during the calculations and fixed by finding a rough answer.

Exercise 2

1. (*a*) Without using logs, find the value of:

$$\left(\tfrac{2}{3}\right)^{-1} \quad \text{and} \quad \tfrac{1}{3}^{-4} - (5)^0$$

(*b*) Use logs to find the value of:

$$\frac{\sqrt{843 \cdot 7}}{8 \cdot 3 \times \sqrt{3}}$$

((*a*) 1·5 and 80; (*b*) 2·02)   (I.M.I.)

2. Given that log 2 = 0·3010 and that log 3 = 0·4771, find the value of log $\sqrt[5]{0·6}$.   ($\bar{1}$·9556)   (I.M.I.)

3. Calculate, using logarithms (*a*) 5·86^2, (*b*) $\sqrt[3]{1·76}$.

((*a*) 34·34; (*b*) 1·208)   (E.M.E.U.)

4. Use logarithms to find the value of *x* in the equation

$$\sqrt{\frac{7·06 \times 2·832}{(0·3417 + 0·0583)}} = 7·07x$$

(*x* = 1)   (U.L.C.I.)

5. Using logarithms, calculate:

$$(0·592)^3; \sqrt{386}$$

(0·2074; 19·64)   (E.M.E.U.)

6. Using logarithms, find the value of the following:

(*a*) 387·5^3 × 0·084^2

(*b*) 9·367 × $\sqrt[3]{0·0876}$

(*c*) $\dfrac{42·31 \times 92·32^2}{\sqrt[2]{493·1}}$

((*a*) 410 700; (*b*) 4·16; (*c*) 16 240)

7. (*a*) Evaluate: 100$^{1·24}$; $\sqrt[5]{100}$

(*b*) By means of logarithms evaluate:

$$\frac{\sqrt{467·2} \times \sqrt[3]{7·3}}{\sqrt[3]{467·2} \times \sqrt{7·3}}$$

((*a*) 302; 2·512; (*b*) 2)   (N.C.T.E.C.)

8. Using logarithms, find the value of:

$$\frac{0·3789}{0·0421} - \frac{12·84}{2·568}$$

(4)   (U.L.C.I.)

9. Find the value of $\frac{4}{3}\pi r^3$ when $\pi = 3·142$ and $r = 2·90$.

(102·2)   (U.E.I.)

10. Calculate the value of:

$$\frac{4·5 \times 100\pi^2 \times 0·7071}{32·2 \times 9}$$

(10·83)   (U.L.C.I.)

11. If $V^{1·0646} = \dfrac{479}{P}$, calculate *V* when *P* = 30.   (13·5)   (U.E.I.)

12. By means of logarithms or otherwise, find the value of:

(a) $\dfrac{9 \cdot 32 \times 0 \cdot 761}{\sqrt{18 \cdot 2}}$

(b) $(18 \cdot 56)^{\frac{1}{3}}$

(c) $(1 \cdot 34)^{1 \cdot 2}$

(d) $(19 \cdot 75)^2 - (16 \cdot 75)^2$

((a) 1·663; (b) 1·794; (c) 1·421; (d) 109·5)   (U.E.I.)

13. Find (using logs) $0 \cdot 0387^{-1 \cdot 4}$.   (94·9)   (E.M.E.U.)

14. Find the value of y when:

$$y = \frac{23 \cdot 31}{4} + \sqrt{[(5 \cdot 708)^2 \div (3 \cdot 393 \times 27 \cdot 18)]}$$

($y = 6 \cdot 422$)   (U.L.C.I.)

15. The air standard efficiency of an engine working on the constant volume cycle is given by the expression $1 - \left(\dfrac{1}{r}\right)^{0 \cdot 4}$, where r is the compression ratio. The thermal efficiency practically attainable is given approximately by $1 - \left(\dfrac{1}{r}\right)^{0 \cdot 236}$.

Express the latter as a percentage of the air standard efficiency for a compression ratio of 9·5.   (69·4 per cent)   (C. and G.)

16. (a) The final velocity V in m/s of a moving body is given by:

$$V^2 = U^2 + 2as$$

Using logarithms, find the value of V when $U = 14 \cdot 51$, $a = 2 \cdot 323$ and $s = 65 \cdot 52$.

(b) Evaluate: $\dfrac{347 \sqrt[3]{347}}{\sqrt{347}}$

((a) 22·7; (b) 130·9)   (N.C.T.E.C.)

3   Friction

Friction is a frictional force, resisting or preventing the sliding movement between two surfaces in contact. This resisting force is known as the **force of friction** and it acts in a direction opposite to the resultant motion between the surfaces. The theory is that friction is due to the **roughness** of the moving surfaces in contact, and the work lost in overcoming this is changed into heat energy.

The force of friction is often useful; for example, the clutch used for the transmission of power, brakes used for stopping or retarding a vehicle rely on friction, also the propulsion of the vehicle by **adhesion** between the tyre and road.

Frictional losses which occur in bearings and moving parts of the power unit and transmission are a waste of energy and a loss of useful power. This loss can be reduced by using oil or grease between the surfaces in contact. Further reduction can be obtained by replacing the sliding motion of a plain bearing with a rolling motion, that is, using a ball or roller bearing.

The bearings of the engine are separated by a film of oil, supplied continuously by a pressure pump. This reduces friction to a minimum and carries away heat from those bearings which cannot be cooled by any other method. The pistons and rings, however, do not receive such efficient lubrication, and they are responsible for about 60 per cent of the total frictional losses.

Three distinct and different conditions can exist between the surfaces of moving parts.

Dry friction. In the complete absence of any form of lubricant the friction, rate of wear and heat generated is high. This type of friction is used for brakes and clutches.

Boundary friction. The film of lubricant is not complete and the surfaces are only partially separated; the friction, rate of wear and heat generated is less than in the condition of dry friction. This type of friction exists on pistons, rings and valve stems.

Fluid friction. This is the complete separation of the surfaces by a film of lubricant. It is the ideal condition and reduces friction, rate of wear and heat generated to a minimum.

Laws relating to Friction between Dry Surfaces

The following laws relate to the behaviour of two smooth dry surfaces, moving with a uniform velocity and held in contact by a uniform load or constant force.

1. The friction force is **directly proportional** to the total force between the surfaces in contact.

2. The friction force depends on the nature and surface finish of the materials in contact.

3. The friction force is **independent** of the area of the surface in contact for any given load.

4. The friction force is **independent** of the relative velocity of the moving parts as long as the velocity is not high.

Careful experiments have shown that these laws are approximately true, and their accuracy is sufficient for most calculations.

Static friction is the friction of **rest**; it is always higher than the friction produced once the object has started to move. An example of this is the pistons in the engine cylinders; considerable force is required to move them but, once moving, the resistance is less.

Sliding or kinetic friction is the friction which exists after movement has started; for example, when pistons are moving.

The Angle of Friction

Fig. 3.1 shows a block of material resting on a smooth flat surface. This block produces a gravitational force W acting vertically downwards [kg g (1 kg × 9·81) N]. T is the reaction of the surface on the block; therefore $W = T$. (For calculations we usually accept the factor 9·8.)

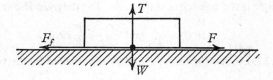

Fig. 3.1.

When motion is maintained by the pull F, the force of friction F_f is equal and opposite; if F and F_f are not in line, a turning moment is introduced. The first law of friction states that the force of friction F_f is proportional to the force between the two surfaces in contact, thus F_f varies as T. When uniform motion takes place F is also proportional to W.

The ratio of $\dfrac{F_f}{T}$ is known as the **coefficient of friction** and is denoted by the Greek letter μ (mu).

Since $F = F_f$ and $W = T$, then $\dfrac{F_f}{T} = \dfrac{F}{W}$

$$\therefore \text{ Coefficient of friction } \mu = \frac{F}{W} \quad \text{or} \quad F = \mu W$$

Fig. 3.2 (*a*) shows the resultant R of the two forces F_f and T. As the value of the force of friction increases, then the angle θ increases also,

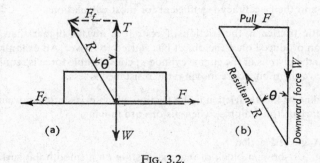

FIG. 3.2.

since the inclination of vector R to the normal reaction increases. The magnitude of this angle is called the angle of friction and the tangent of this angle is the coefficient of friction. The diagram shows that

$$\tan \theta = \frac{F_f}{T} \quad \text{and} \quad \frac{F_f}{T} = \frac{F}{W} \text{ or } \mu$$

Fig. 3.2 (*b*) shows the forces F and W represented by the triangle of forces, the angle $\tan \theta$ is equal to the relation $\dfrac{F}{W}$, which equals kinetic friction.

Example. A block of mass 20 kg requires a pull of 49 newtons to move it at a uniform speed on a horizontal smooth surface. What is the coefficient of friction between the block and surface?

$$\text{Coefficient of friction } \mu = \frac{\text{Horizontal pull}}{\text{Downward force}} \left(\frac{F}{W}\right)$$

$$= \frac{49 \text{ (N)}}{20 \times 9 \cdot 8 \text{ (kg g)}} = \underline{0 \cdot 25}$$

Example. The maximum horizontal retarding force applied by the brakes of a motor vehicle to bring it to the point of skidding is 5880 N. The mass of the vehicle is 1 tonne. What is the coefficient of friction between the tyres and road?

The mass of 1 tonne will produce a vertical downward force of $1 \times 1000 \times 9 \cdot 8 = 9800$ N.

$$\text{Coefficient of friction } \mu = \frac{\text{Horizontal force}}{\text{Downward force}}$$

$$= \frac{5880}{9800} = \underline{0 \cdot 6}$$

The Inclined Plane

The following experiment is carried out with laboratory apparatus. The plane on which the block rests is tilted until the block slides down the plane at a uniform velocity; this angle of the plane to the horizontal is the **angle of friction**.

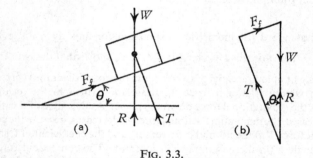

Fig. 3.3.

Fig. 3.3 shows a block resting on a plane inclined to the horizontal at an angle θ. This angle is small and the block will not move, it rests on the plane supported by friction. The gravitational force $W \sin \theta$ down the plane is less than the resisting frictional force $T \tan \alpha$, because tan θ is less than tan α the coefficient of friction μ (see text for Fig. 3.4). The normal component $T = W \cos \theta$ in this example. Vector F_f on the force diagram represents only that part of the frictional force up the plane required just to maintain the block at rest.

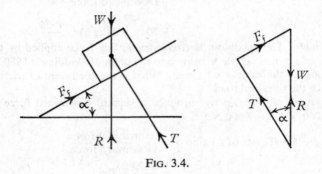

FIG. 3.4.

Fig. 3.4 shows the plane tilted at an angle α to the horizontal, and this angle causes the block to slide down the plane at a uniform speed. The gravitational force $W \sin \alpha$ down the plane is equal to the frictional resisting force $T \tan \alpha$ up the plane. The normal component $T = W \cos \alpha$ in this example.

By substitution, $W \sin \alpha = T \tan \alpha$
$$= W \cos \alpha \tan \alpha$$

The standard trigonometrical expression for any given angle A is $\frac{\sin A}{\cos A} = \tan A$ or $\sin A = \cos A \tan A$. This shows that the two forces in this example are equal. Vector F on the force diagram represents the maximum frictional force up the plane, which in this example equals the gravitational force down the plane. As the angle of the plane is **increased**, the maximum frictional force F_f **decreases**, because the component force T to the normal is decreasing and the coefficient of friction μ or angle α (in these examples) is constant. The component force T decreases because it is the product of the force W and cosine of the angle at which the plane is tilted (cos values decrease as the angles increase).

Fig. 3.5 shows the plane tilted at an angle ϕ to the horizontal. The angle ϕ is greater than the angle of friction α and the block accelerates down the plane. Gravitational force $W \sin \phi$ down the plane is greater than the resisting frictional force $T \tan \alpha$ up the plane by an excess force shown as the **vector** x on the force diagram.

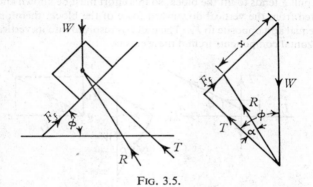

FIG. 3.5.

Gravitational force $F + x$ down the plane $= W \sin \phi$

Frictional resisting force F_f up the plane $= T \tan \alpha$

$= W \cos \phi \tan \alpha$

Accelerating force x down the plane $= W \sin \phi - F_f$

$= W \sin \phi - W \cos \phi \tan \alpha$

$= W(\sin \phi - \cos \phi \tan \alpha)$

$= W(\sin \phi - \mu \cos \phi)$

since $\tan \alpha = \mu$ (the coefficient of friction).

The accelerating force $F = ma$ (see Chapter 12)

The acceleration a down the plane $= \dfrac{F}{W}$

Substituting $W(\sin \phi - \mu \cos \phi)$ for F,

$$\text{acceleration } a = \frac{W(\sin \phi - \mu \cos \phi)g}{W}$$

$$= g(\sin \phi - \mu \cos \phi)$$

Horizontal Plane

A block resting on a horizontal surface is shown in Fig. 3.6; it is to be moved by a pull F acting in a direction of $\phi°$ to the horizontal. The pull F tends to lift the block, so this effort must be known and subtracted from the vertical downward force of the block, therefore F is not equal and opposite to F_f. The pull F is resolved into its vertical and horizontal components to find these effects.

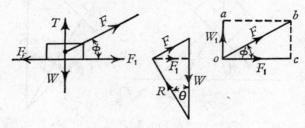

FIG. 3.6.

Method 1. Construct a force diagram, Fig. 3.6. Then W_1 is the vertical component which must be subtracted from the vertical downward force and F_1 is the horizontal pull, which is equal to the force of friction.

Method 2.

Vertical component $oa = bc$

$$\sin \phi = \frac{bc}{bo}$$

$$\therefore bc = bo \sin \phi$$

$$\therefore W_1 = F \sin \phi$$

Horizontal component oc.

$$\cos \phi = \frac{oc}{ob}$$

$$\therefore oc = ob \cos \phi$$

$$\therefore F_1 = F \cos \phi$$

Force between contact surfaces $= W - W_1$

Pull parallel to surface $F_1 = F \cos \phi$

Coefficient of friction $\mu = \dfrac{\text{Pull parallel to plane}}{\text{Force between surfaces}}$

$$= \frac{F \cos \phi}{W - F \sin \phi}$$

Example. A casting of mass 126·5 kg requires an effort of 350 N to drag it along a horizontal floor. The angle of the direction of the effort is 20° to the floor. What is the coefficient of friction between the casting and floor?

Downward gravitational force produced by mass of casting = $126·5 \times 9·8 = 1240$ N.

$$\text{Vertical component} = F \sin 20°$$
$$= 350 \times 0·342 \text{ N}$$
$$\therefore W_1 = \underline{119·7 \text{ N}}$$
$$\text{Force between surfaces} = W - W_1$$
$$= 1240 - 119·7 \text{ N}$$
$$= \underline{1120·3 \text{ N}}$$
$$\text{Horizontal component } F_1 = F \cos 20°$$
$$= 350 \times 0·9397 \text{ N}$$
$$\text{Effort parallel to floor} = \underline{328·895 \text{ N}}$$
$$\text{Coefficient of friction } \mu = \frac{\text{Effort parallel to floor}}{\text{Force between surfaces}}$$
$$= \frac{328·9}{1120·3}$$
$$= \underline{0·2937}$$

The Journal Bearing

The shaft or journal which rotates in the bearing rests on the bottom of the bearing when stationary, but when rotating it tends to 'climb' up the inside of the bearing in a direction opposite to its rotation. The working position of the shaft is at a point where the forces R, W and μR produce equilibrium.

Let R represent the reaction of the bearing on the shaft

$W =$ the downward load

$\mu R =$ tangential frictional force

Then the force diagram, Fig. 3.7, shows that $\tan \phi = \dfrac{\mu R}{R}$ or μ, the coefficient of friction between shaft and bearing. We see that, as the frictional force decreases, the tangent of the angle decreases and the point of contact A between the shaft and bearing approaches the vertical centre line of the bearing and shaft.

The vertical reaction at point A is R_A, and it is equal in magnitude to the downward load W when the shaft is rotating. The retarding frictional torque is the product of R_A and its perpendicular distance BO. The distance BO is the radius of a circle known as the friction circle and the angle OAB as the friction angle, which is equal and opposite to ϕ.

Then, retarding frictional torque $= R_A \times$ BO
$$= W \times \text{BO}$$

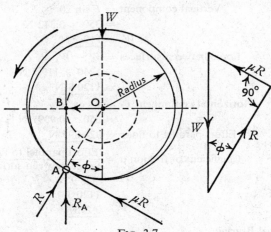

FIG. 3.7.

The distance BO $= r \sin \phi$, but the value of this angle is always small and, since the values for the small angles of sin and tan are almost identical, $\sin \phi$ can be substituted by $\tan \phi$, so if r = radius

then   BO $= r \tan \phi$

The retarding frictional torque $= W \times$ BO
$$= W \times r \tan \phi$$
$$= Wr\mu$$

The work lost due to friction during one revolution of the shaft
$$= \text{Frictional torque} \times \text{Angle in radians}$$
$$= Wr\mu \times 2\pi$$
$$= 2\pi\mu Wr \text{ J (when } r \text{ is in metres)}$$
∴ Work lost per min $= 2\pi\mu Wr$ (rev/min) J
∴ Power lost $= \dfrac{2\pi\mu Wr \text{ (rev/min)}}{60}$ (watts)

The heat generated per minute due to friction = Work lost per min.

Values for the Coefficient of Friction

Cast iron on cast iron . . .	0·15
Mild steel on cast iron . . .	0·20
Mild steel on brass . . .	0·15
Mild steel on mild steel . . .	0·14
Mild steel on white metal (oiled) .	0·003–0·04
Ball and roller bearings (oiled) .	0·0015–0·004
Moulded linings	0·25–0·3
Woven linings	0·3–0·35
Cork inserts (oiled) . . .	0·16

Example. The average downward load on the 76 mm diameter main bearings of a c.i. engine is 13·35 kN. If the coefficient of friction is 0·012, find the following when the engine speed is 1650 rev/min: (*a*) power lost due to friction; (*b*) heat generated per min due to friction.

Data
$$\mu = 0·012$$
$$W = 13·35 \text{ kN}$$
$$r = 0·038 \text{ m (radius of shaft)}$$
$$\text{rev/min} = 1650$$

(*a*)   Power lost $= \dfrac{2\pi\mu W r \text{ rev/min}}{60}$

$$= \frac{2 \times 3·1416 \times 0·012 \times 13·35 \times 0·038 \times 1650}{60}$$

$$= \underline{1·052 \text{ kW}}$$

(*b*)   Heat generated = Work done/min
$$= 1·052 \times 60 \text{ kJ}$$
$$\therefore \text{ Heat generated/min} = \underline{63·12 \text{ kJ}}$$

Example. The disc brake fitted to a motor car has one friction pad pressing on each side of the disc at a mean radius of 150 mm. The coefficient of friction between the pads and disc is 0·3, and the force applied

to each pad when braking is 3560 N. If the rolling radius of the road
wheel is 330 mm and it rotates at 560 rev/min, find: (*a*) frictional
torque; (*b*) horizontal retarding force; (*c*) heat generated by the brake
per minute.

Data $F = \mu F_a$

$F_a = 3560$ N

$\mu = 0\cdot3$

$r = 0\cdot15$ m (mean radius of disc)

$R = 0\cdot33$ m (radius of wheel)

rev/min $= 560$

There is a pad on each side of the disc, so the formula is multiplied by
two.

(*a*) Frictional torque $=$ Force $\times$ radius $\times$ 2

$= F \times r \times 2$

$= \mu F_a \times r \times 2$

$= 0\cdot3 \times 3560 \times 0\cdot15 \times 2$ Nm

$= \underline{320\cdot3 \text{ Nm}}$

(*b*) Horizontal retarding force $= \dfrac{\text{Frictional torque}}{\text{Road-wheel radius}}$

$= \dfrac{320\cdot3}{0\cdot33} \left(\dfrac{\text{Nm}}{\text{m}}\right)$

$= \underline{970\cdot7 \text{ N}}$

(*c*) Heat generated/min $=$ Work done/min

$=$ Torque $\times 2\pi$ rev/min

$= 320\cdot3 \times 2 \times 3\cdot1416 \times 560$ kJ/min

$= \underline{1127 \text{ kJ}}$

Clutches

The clutch, fitted to the transmission system of a motor car, is a
means of disconnecting and connecting the engine to the gear-box.
With frictional plate clutches of the axial type, the frictional contact
pressure between the driving and driven members is in a direction
parallel to the engine crankshaft. Most vehicle manufacturers fit a
clutch manufactured by one of a few proprietary firms. The clutches

are usually the single-plate type, although multiplate types are used for motor cycles and some motor vehicles. When the clutch is engaged it must be able to slip smoothly until the engine and gear-box speeds are synchronized, then the drive must be positive without slip at the maximum torque delivered by the engine. Heat generated during the slipping period must be easily dissipated so as not to lower the coefficient of friction of the lining or disc material.

Calculations of Torque and Power transmitted by a Clutch

Symbols used:

F_a = Total spring force (N)

F = Tangential force (N)

T = Torque (Nm or Nmm)

r_1 = External radius of disc (mm)

r_2 = Internal radius of disc (mm)

μ = Coefficient of friction

n = Number of pairs of frictional faces in contact (2 for a single-plate clutch)

rev/min = revolutions per minute

Fig. 3.8 shows an elementary form of clutch. A disc of friction material is riveted to the flange of the driving member, and this is held in contact with the driven member by springs which exert a force F_a.

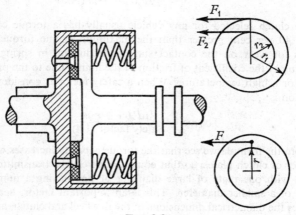

Fig. 3.8.

Torque transmitted during rotation is the product of the tangential force F and its perpendicular distance from the centre. For calculation purposes this value of F i.e. $\left(\dfrac{F_1 + F_2}{2}\right)$ is considered to act at the mean or average radius r, which is half the sum of the two radii or $\dfrac{r_1 + r_2}{2}$.

The torque is the tangential force multiplied by mean radius or:

$$\text{Torque} = F\left(\frac{r_1 + r_2}{2}\right) \qquad \text{Eq. 1}$$

Frictional torque is the actual torque transmitted by the contact surfaces, and it depends on the force exerted by the springs and the coefficient of friction between the surfaces.

$$\text{The tangential force } F = \mu F_a \qquad \text{Eq. 2}$$

Substituting this value of F in Eq. 1,

$$\text{Torque} = \mu F_a\left(\frac{r_1 + r_2}{2}\right) \qquad \text{Eq. 3}$$

The modern clutch has more than one pair of contact surfaces, so the symbol n is added to Eq. 3.

$$\therefore \text{Torque} = \mu F_a\left(\frac{r_1 + r_2}{2}\right) n$$

$$= \tfrac{1}{2}\mu F_a(r_1 + r_2)n \ \text{(Nm)}$$

The clutch selected for any vehicle usually has a torque capacity about 40 per cent greater than the maximum engine torque. This allows for wear on the contact surfaces, reduction in spring force, lowering of the coefficient of friction of the linings due to the presence of oil or a high temperature. When a safety factor is considered the equation is:

$$\text{Torque} = \frac{\tfrac{1}{2}\mu F_a(r_1 + r_2)n}{\text{Safety factor } (1\cdot 4)}$$

From the formula we see that the torque capacity increases with the number of clutch plates, so that equal torque can be transmitted by a clutch with one plate of large diameter or one having a number of plates of a smaller diameter. This is an important factor, because it reduces the diametrical dimensions of the flywheel and clutch, and also affects acceleration and speed of gear changing.

The formula for power transmitted by a clutch is the same as that used for the power absorbed by a dynamometer (see Part I).

$$\therefore \text{ Power } (P) = \frac{2\pi \text{ rev/min } T}{60}(\text{W})$$

or
$$\text{Torque} = \frac{P \times 60}{2\pi \text{ rev/min}}\text{Nm}$$

From these equations the following may be deduced:

The power varies as both the engine speed and the torque, so that an engine whose speed is increased but had its torque decreased continues to deliver the same power.

If the power remains constant the torque varies inversely as the engine speed. This is the reason for the robust construction of the slow-speed engine and the lighter construction of the high-speed engine.

Clutch-plate Pressure

The intensity of pressure on the clutch friction plate material must not cause the structure of the material to collapse or be destroyed in any way. If the clutch is designed with a low plate pressure the area of contact must be large, if the pressure is high the rate of wear increases. Maximum pressure for the woven type of lining is about 0.14 N/mm^2, and 0.28 N/mm^2 is the safe limit for the moulded lining.

$$\text{Intensity of pressure} = \frac{\text{Total spring force}}{\text{Contact area of one plate}}$$

$$= \frac{F_a}{\frac{\pi}{4}(D^2 - d^2)} \text{ N/mm}^2$$

Example. An engine running under full-load conditions develops its maximum torque at 1200 rev/min when the engine power is 15 000 W.

Find: (*a*) Torque transmitted by clutch.

(*b*) Maximum capacity of clutch if the safety factor is 40 per cent.

(*a*) Power $(P) = \dfrac{2\pi \text{ rev/min } T}{60}$ (W)

$$\therefore \text{ Torque } T = \frac{P \times 60}{2\pi \text{ rev/min}}$$
$$= \frac{15\,000 \times 60}{2 \times 3.1416 \times 1200} \text{ Nm}$$
$$= \underline{119.3 \text{ Nm}}$$

(*b*) Maximum permissible torque

$$= \text{Torque transmitted} \times 1\cdot4$$
$$= 119\cdot3 \times 1\cdot4 \text{ Nm}$$
$$= \underline{167\cdot02 \text{ Nm}}$$

Example. A single-plate clutch is required to transmit a maximum torque of 108 Nm. The friction rings are 220 mm external diameter, 125 mm internal diameter and the coefficient of friction is 0·25. What force must be exerted by each of the nine clutch springs?

Data Torque T = 108 Nm

External radius r_1 = 0·11 m

Internal radius r_2 = 0·0625 m

Pairs of friction surfaces n = 2

Coefficient of friction μ = 0·25

Torque $T = \frac{1}{2}\mu F_a(r_1 + r_2)n$

$$\therefore \text{ Spring force } F_a = \frac{T}{\frac{1}{2}\mu(r_1 + r_2)n}$$

$$= \frac{108}{0\cdot5 \times 0\cdot25(0\cdot11 + 0\cdot0625) \times 2} \left(\frac{\text{Nm}}{\text{m}}\right)$$

$$= \underline{2504 \text{ N}}$$

This is the total spring force; therefore, by dividing by 9, the force exerted by each spring is found.

$$\text{Force exerted by one spring} = \frac{\text{Total force}}{\text{Number of springs}}$$

$$= \frac{2504 \text{ N}}{9}$$

$$= \underline{278 \text{ N}}$$

Example. A multiplate clutch operating in an oil bath has 5 steel plates and 4 phosphor-bronze rings. The rings are 150 mm external diameter and 100 mm internal diameter. Six springs each exert a force of 710 N. Find the torque capacity of the clutch if the coefficient of friction is 0·08.

With this type of problem a simple sketch of the plate arrangement will ensure the correct number for the symbol n.

Data   Spring force F_a $= 710 \times 6$ N
  External radius r_1 $= 0 \cdot 075$ m
  Internal radius r_2 $= 0 \cdot 05$ m
  Pairs of contact surfaces $n = 8$

$$\begin{aligned}
\text{Torque } T &= \tfrac{1}{2}\mu F_a(r_1 + r_2)n \\
&= 0 \cdot 5 \times 0 \cdot 08 \times 710 \times 6(0 \cdot 075 + 0 \cdot 05) \times 8 \text{ Nm} \\
&= 0 \cdot 5 \times 0 \cdot 08 \times 4260 \times 0 \cdot 125 \times 8 \text{ Nm} \\
&= \underline{170 \cdot 4 \text{ Nm}}
\end{aligned}$$

Example. A single-plate clutch is designed to transmit a torque of 195 Nm. The friction rings are 200 mm by 145 mm, and the total spring force is 3735 N. Find: (a) Coefficient of friction, (b) Clutch-plate pressure.

Data   Spring force F_a $= 3735$ N
        External radius r_1 $= 0 \cdot 10$ m
        Internal radius r_2 $= 0 \cdot 0725$ m
        Torque $= 195$ Nm

Note. Clutch-ring dimensions are always given in diameters, unless otherwise stated.

(a) Torque T $= \tfrac{1}{2}\mu F_a(r_1 + r_2)n$

$$\begin{aligned}
\therefore \mu &= \frac{T}{\tfrac{1}{2}F_a(r_1 + r_2)n} \\
&= \frac{195}{0 \cdot 5 \times 3735(0 \cdot 10 + 0 \cdot 0725) \times 2}\left(\frac{\text{Nm}}{\text{Nm}}\right) \\
&= \underline{0 \cdot 3026}
\end{aligned}$$

(b) Plate pressure $= \dfrac{\text{Total spring force}}{\text{Contact area of one ring}}$

$$\begin{aligned}
&= \frac{F_a}{\dfrac{\pi}{4}(D_2 - d_2)} \\
&= \frac{3735}{0 \cdot 7854(0 \cdot 200^2 - 0 \cdot 145^2)} \text{ N/m}^2 \\
&= \frac{3735}{0 \cdot 7854 \times 0 \cdot 018\ 96} \text{ N/m}^2 \\
&= \underline{250 \cdot 8 \text{ kN/m}^2}
\end{aligned}$$

Example. A single-plate clutch having the following specification is fitted to a commercial vehicle. What is the maximum permissible torque it can transmit?

Data

Spring force	= 467 N
Number of springs	= 16
Clutch rings	= 405 mm × 290 mm
Coefficient of friction μ	= 0·3
Safety factor	= 40 per cent

$$\text{Torque } T = \frac{\frac{1}{2}\mu F_a(r_1 + r_2)n}{\text{Safety factor}}$$

$$= \frac{0·5 \times 0·3 \times 467 \times 16(0·2025 + 0·145) \times 2}{1·4} \text{ Nm}$$

$$= \frac{0·5 \times 0·3 \times 7472 \times 0·3475 \times 2}{1·4} \text{ Nm}$$

$$= \underline{556·4 \text{ Nm}}$$

The actual torque was divided by 1·4 to give the permissible torque which the manufacturer would use as a maximum.

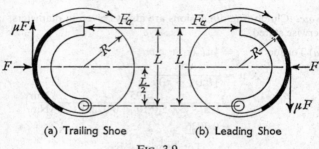

(a) Trailing Shoe (b) Leading Shoe

FIG. 3.9.

Theory of the Elementary Internal-expanding Brake Shoe

The forces acting on a **leading** and a **trailing** shoe when the brake is actuated are shown in Figs. 3.9 (*a*) and (*b*).

F_a represents the force from the actuating mechanism and produces a force F between shoe and drum. When the drum is rotating the force F produces a frictional force μF as shown in Fig. 3.9 (*b*). Fig. 3.9 (*b*) also shows that the points of application F and μF represent a mean position along the length of the shoe.

Let us examine the operation and the method of calculating the brake torque of the leading shoe, using Fig. 3.9 (*b*).

Leading Shoe

To calculate the braking torque of the leading shoe, we proceed:

Taking moments about the shoe pivot,

$$\text{Clockwise} = (F_aL) + (\mu FR)$$
$$\text{Anticlockwise} = \frac{LF}{2}$$

Because the shoe is in equilibrium under these conditions:

$$\text{Anticlockwise moments} = \text{Clockwise moments}$$
$$\frac{LF}{2} = (F_aL) + (\mu FR)$$

Dividing each side by F, we have

$$F = \frac{F_aL}{\dfrac{L}{2} - \mu R}$$

Now, braking torque $T_l = \mu FR$

$$\therefore T_l = \mu \left(\frac{F_aL}{\dfrac{L}{2} - \mu R} \right) R$$

Let us examine the operation and method of calculating the braking torque of the trailing shoe, using Fig. 3.9 (*a*).

Trailing Shoe

To calculate the braking torque of the trailing shoe, we proceed: Taking moments about the shoe pivot,

$$\text{Clockwise} = \left(\frac{FL}{2} \right) + (\mu FR)$$
$$\text{Anticlockwise} = F_aL$$

Because the shoe is in equilibrium also under these conditions,

$$\text{Clockwise moments} = \text{Anticlockwise moments}$$
$$\left(\frac{FL}{2} \right) + (\mu FR) = F_aL$$

Dividing each side by F, we have:

$$F = \frac{F_a L}{\frac{L}{2} + \mu R}$$

Since braking torque $T_t = \mu F R$

$$T_t = \mu \left(\frac{F_a L}{\frac{L}{2} + \mu R} \right) R$$

Example. A brake drum is 250 mm diameter. The pivots for the brake shoes and the points of application of the forces actuating the shoes are each at 100 mm from the axis of rotation. Assuming that the pressure distribution over the brake lining is equal to a single force acting radially and that the coefficient of friction is 0·25, calculate the braking torque exerted by an operating force of 890 N on: (a) the leading shoe; (b) the trailing shoe.

To calculate the braking torque T_l for the leading shoe we must first determine the value of F, Fig. 3.9 (b).

$$F = \frac{F_a L}{\frac{L}{2} - \mu R}$$

$$= \frac{890 \times 0·2}{0·10 - (0·25 \times 0·125)}$$

$$= \frac{178}{0·068\ 75}$$

$$\therefore T_l = \frac{178 \times 0·25 \times 0·125}{0·6875}$$

$$= \underline{81\ \text{Nm}}$$

To calculate the braking torque T_t for the trailing shoe, we must first find the value of F, Fig. 3.9 (a).

$$F = \frac{F_a L}{\frac{L}{2} + R}$$

$$= \frac{890 \times 0·2}{0·10 + (0·25 \times 0·125)}$$

$$= \frac{178}{0·131\ 25}$$

$$\therefore T_t = \frac{178 \times 0·25 \times 0·125}{0·131\ 25}$$

$$= \underline{42·4\ \text{Nm}}$$

It should be noted that T_l is much greater than T_t; hence the adoption of the two-leading-shoe type of brake.

Exercise 3

1. The brakes of a car are capable of locking all four wheels. The coefficient of friction between the tyres and road surface is 0·4.

Find the greatest slope on which the car will stand without moving down the slope. (21° 48′)

2. A single dry-plate clutch has annular facings 250 mm external and 150 mm internal diameter. The total spring force is 3560 N and the coefficient of friction is 0·25. Calculate the maximum torque which the clutch can transmit. (178 Nm)   (C. and G.)

3. Give three examples of useful application of friction in a motor car and state the approximate coefficient of friction between the surfaces concerned. (C. and G.)

4. A car has a mass of 1271 kg. The coefficient of friction between the tyres and the road is 0·4. What is the maximum retarding force which can be used to stop it without causing it to skid? If the actual retarding force at the ground is 0·75 of the maximum and is constant, how many joules of work are done in bringing the car to rest in a distance of 18·5 m? If all the work is converted into heat, how many joules are generated? (4984 N; 69 153 J; 69·153 kJ)   (E.M.E.U.)

5. The friction disc of a single-plate clutch has a face area of 27 100 mm² and a mean radius of 115 mm. If the spring pressure per m² of area is not to exceed 124 000 N and the coefficient of friction is 0·3, calculate the maximum power that could be transmitted by the clutch at 2000 rev/min. (48·56 kW)   (C. and G.)

6. (*a*) What is friction? Give two examples in motor-engineering practice where a high coefficient of friction is an advantage and two examples where friction is wasteful and harmful.

(*b*) A car has a mass of 1271 kg. The coefficient of friction between road and tyres is 0·6. What is the greatest force that can be used to stop the car on a horizontal road without causing it to skid?

(7476 N)   (E.M.E.U.)

7. A single dry-plate clutch has annular facings 200 mm external and 125 mm internal diameter. The clutch is required to transmit 67·8 Nm at the point of slipping when the coefficient of friction is 0·30. Calculate the total spring force necessary. (1391 N)   (C. and G.)

8. The average side thrust on a piston during the power and compression stroke is a force of 356 N, thrust during exhaust and induction strokes is 124 N. If the coefficient of friction between the piston and cylinder wall is 0·025 and the piston speed 460 m/min, what is the power lost to friction if the engine has six cylinders? (276 W)

9. A motor car of mass 1·2 tonne is fitted with tyres having a rolling radius of 330 mm, the wheel bearings have a mean diameter of 63·5 mm; their coefficient of friction is 0·0025.

What power is required to overcome bearing friction when the speed of the car is 90 km/h? (70·71 W)

10. The thrust along a connecting rod is 10 680 N when the angularity of the rod is 11° 32′. The coefficient of friction between the piston and cylinder wall is 0·02.

What force on the piston crown is required to overcome the friction?

If the piston speed at this instant is 365·8 m/min, what power is required to overcome the friction? (42·72 N; 259·45 W)

11. A motor-cycle clutch has three plates fitted with cork inserts and they run in an oil bath, their mean radius is 60 mm and coefficient of friction is 0·16.

What spring force is required, if the power transmitted at maximum torque is 12·68 kW, the engine speed is 3400 rev/min, and gear reduction between engine and clutch is 2 to 1? (1236·4 N)

12. A single-plate clutch works between the flywheel face and a spring-loaded pressure plate. The mean diameter of the friction ring is 228 mm and the coefficient of friction between the ring and driving surfaces is 0·3. Calculate the spring force required on the pressure plate to transmit 26·11 kW at 2500 rev/min. (1457 N) (C. and G.)

13. Define the coefficient of friction.

A block of mass 45·4 kg rests on a plane inclined at 10° to the horizontal. If there is no friction between the surfaces, what is the least force which is necessary to move the block up the plane?

If the coefficient of friction between the block and the plane is 0·2, what additional force will be required? (78·47 N; 89 N) (I.M.I.)

14. A body of mass 90·8 kg is pulled along a horizontal plane at uniform speed by a force of 178 N inclined upward at 30° to the horizontal. Find the work done by this force in moving the body 3 m along the plane and determine the coefficient of friction for the materials in contact. (534 Nm; 0·1924) (I.M.I.)

15. Explain what is meant by the 'angle of friction' and show that the tangent of this angle is equal to the coefficient of friction.

A mass of 45·4 kg rests on an inclined plane of angle 20°. If the friction is just sufficient to prevent the mass from sliding down the plane, determine the coefficient of friction between the surfaces in contact.

(0·364)   (I.M.I.)

16. Find the equivalent in joules of work done per minute when a vehicle of mass 1529 kg has all its wheels locked and comes to rest in 8 s after travelling 13·75 m. Take the coefficient of friction between the tyres and road as 0·82.   (1268 kJ/min)   (N.C.T.E.C.)

17. A disc brake running at 600 rev/min has one friction block pressing on each side of the disc at an effective radius of 200 mm. The force acting on each block is 890 N and the coefficient between the block and the disc is 0·3. Calculate: (*a*) the friction torque acting on the disc brake shaft; (*b*) the work done per minute by this torque.

((*a*) 106·8 Nm; (*b*) 402·6 kJ/min)   (N.C.T.E.C.)

18. A 50 mm diameter shaft bearing carries a load equivalent to a force of 1000 N. A lever is attached to the shaft and a force of 2·25 N, applied at right angles to the end of the lever and at a distance of 250 mm from the centre of the shaft, will just turn the shaft slowly. Calculate the coefficient of friction between the shaft and bearing. If the shaft is rotated at 2800 rev/min calculate the work lost to friction per minute.

(0·022; 9677 J)   (U.E.I.)

19. A disc brake running at 450 rev/min has one friction block pressing on each side at an effective radius of 190 mm. The force acting on the block is 665 N and the coefficient of friction between each block and the disc is 0·25. Calculate: (*a*) the friction torque acting on the brake-disc shaft; (*b*) the work done per minute by this torque.

((*a*) 63·18 Nm; (*b*) 198·66 kJ)   (U.E.I.)

20. A shaft bearing, 63·5 mm diameter, carries a load of mass 47·24 kg, the shaft makes 3200 rev/min. If the coefficient of friction between the shaft and bearing is 0·022, calculate the work lost in friction per minute in joules.   (6531 J)   (U.E.I.)

21. If the force between the brake-shoes and drum on a motor vehicle is 1112 N and the coefficient of friction between them is 0·4, how many joules of work are done against friction in 60 revolutions of the drum? The diameter of the drum is 305 mm. How many heat units does this quantity of work represent?

(25 580 J; 25·58 kJ)   (E.M.E.U.)

22. Make a sketch of a simple mechanically expanded brake and indicate the forces acting on the leading and trailing shoes when the brake is applied.

If the distance between the shoe fulcrum and the point of application of the actuating force, equal to 445 N, is 150 mm, determine the value of the braking torque acting on the drum. Assume that the shoes are centrally positioned in the drum and that the coefficient of friction between the lining and the 200-mm diameter drum is 0·4.

(76·3 Nm; 23·22 Nm)

4   Lubrication and Viscosity

Lubrication

The main purpose of **lubrication** is to reduce friction and wear by separating two bearing surfaces, in relative motion, with a lubricant.

Lubrication can be divided into two general types. The first is called **fluid** or 'thick-film' lubrication. This is the ideal condition, in which two bearing surfaces in relative motion are always completely separated by a layer of lubricant. In practice this condition is never perfectly realized, but it exists (approximately) in the main bearings and big-end bearings of an engine.

The second is called **boundary** or 'thin-film' lubrication. This is the condition where some lubricant is present but the two bearing surfaces in relative motion are not completely separated by the thin film of lubricant; this film may be less than 0·006 35 mm thick. Boundary lubrication exists in engine-cylinder bores directly after starting up a cold engine.

Motor Vehicle Lubrication

Engine. All modern engine lubrication systems depend for their effectiveness on the continuous circulation of a considerable quantity of oil through the bearings. Oil is required not only to lubricate but also to carry heat away from the bearings. Therefore a considerable excess of oil, over that needed to maintain the necessary oil film, must be supplied.

Maintenance of the oil film is affected by both the working temperature of the engine and the climatic conditions. Under tropical conditions a thicker grade of oil is used to ensure an adequate oil film, but under more temperate conditions a thinner grade of oil can be used. Vehicle manufacturers usually recommend *winter*, *summer* and *tropical* grades of oil. If the grade of oil used is too heavy, then it may be difficult to start the engine at low temperatures owing to the excessive 'drag' of the moving parts of the engine. On the other hand, the use of a thin grade of oil may cause a breakdown of the oil film, resulting in rapid wear and possible seizure of the working parts.

Transmission. Special oils are used in the gear box and the rear axle. These oils are capable of withstanding the high pressures concerned without squeezing the oil out from between the gear teeth, thus avoiding undue metal-to-metal contact which would otherwise cause excessive wear and damaged surfaces.

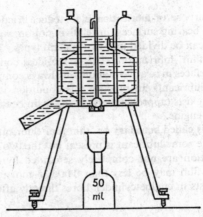

50 ml

FIG. 4.1.

Viscosity

The terms 'thick' and 'thin' when applied to oils are too vague, and the term **viscosity** is generally used when referring to this property of an oil. Viscosity is a measure of an oil's resistance to flow or simply the stickiness of an oil. A high-viscosity oil denotes a thick oil, and a low-viscosity oil denotes a thin oil. To make practical comparisons the viscosity of oils is measured by noting the time taken for a given volume of oil, at a stated temperature, to flow through a calibrated jet; the apparatus used is called a **viscometer**. In Great Britain the **Redwood** viscometer is generally used, see Fig. 4.1. With this apparatus the time taken for 50 millilitres of oil to flow through a jet of 1 mm² area is noted. Readings are usually recorded at temperatures of 20°C, 60°C and 90°C; the viscosity of the oil is stated in Redwood seconds. In U.S.A.

the **Saybolt** viscometer is used and the viscosity is stated in Saybolt Universal seconds.

Temperature Effect on Viscosity, see Fig. 4.2

The viscosity of an oil changes with temperature. Increasing temperature causes an oil to 'thin', thus the viscosity of the oil is lowered. Falling temperature causes an oil to 'thicken', thus the viscosity of the oil is raised.

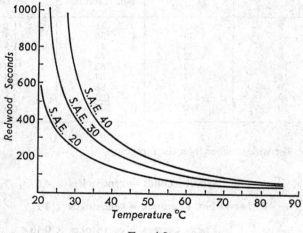

FIG. 4.2.

When plotting the viscosity–temperature relationship of a lubricant on linear graph paper the curve will be approximately hyperbolic in shape. If, however, it is plotted on logarithmic graph paper or on the standard viscosity–temperature chart the result is a straight line. A lubricant need then only be tested at two temperatures; the two points are located on the graph or chart paper and a straight line drawn through them. The viscosity at any temperature can be read off the line, see Fig. 4.3, p. 52.

Various types of viscometer are used, and viscosity is expressed in different units. In the petroleum industry kinematic viscosity has been standardized. The unit of viscosity is the **stoke,** named after George Stokes because of his work on viscous flow early in the nineteenth century. The stoke is a large unit, so that the centistoke is generally used $\left(\frac{1}{100} \text{ stoke}\right)$.

Conversion to other units may be made by using a conversion chart. Approximate conversion can be made by using the following table:

Kinematic viscosity, centistokes	Saybolt Universal seconds	Redwood No. 1, seconds	Engler degrees
2	33	31	1·1
4	39	36	1·3
6	46	41	1·5
8	52	46	1·7
10	59	52	1·8
15	77	68	2·3
20	98	86	2·9
30	140	125	4·1
50	230	205	6·6

For viscosities higher than the foregoing,

$$\text{Saybolt seconds} = \text{centistokes} \times 4·6$$

$$\text{Redwood No. 1 seconds} = \text{centistokes} \times 4·1$$

$$\text{Engler degrees} = \text{centistokes} \times 0·13$$

Viscosity Numbers

Because the general classification of oils by the terms light, medium, heavy and so on vary between different oil companies, these terms are considered too vague to be serviceable. Therefore the **S.A.E.** (the Society of Automotive Engineers, an American institution) has classified crankcase and transmission oils into grades dependent on their viscosity. Each grade is given a number called an S.A.E. number, and the viscosity of any oil with an S.A.E. number must be within certain limits at a given temperature. It must be pointed out, however, that S.A.E. numbers refer to viscosity only and they do not consider any other property of the oil. The numbers do not, in any way, indicate the *quality* of an oil.

S.A.E. Numbers (Crankcase Oils)

S.A.E. numbers of oils are often quoted according to their viscosity and a list is given of the principal grades used for crankcase oils.

S.A.E. No.	Viscosity Range, Redwood Seconds			
	−20°C		90°C	
	Min.	Max.	Min.	Max.
5	..	3 520	..	..
10W	5 250	10 560	..	..
20W	10 560	42 000	..	..
20	..	..	43	55
30	..	..	55	67
40	..	..	67	83
50	..	..	83	112

In general, low numbers indicate low viscosity and high numbers indicate high viscosity. Each oil is graded at one particular temperature, but oils of the same S.A.E. number may have vastly different viscosities at a higher or a lower temperature.

Viscosity Index

Most engine manufacturers issue their own specification for crankcase oils. These specifications usually give narrow limits for viscosity readings at 20°C, 60°C and 90°C, to ensure that the oil used has the least possible change of viscosity with temperature rise and fall. A method has been adopted for estimating this degree of change, and oils are given numbers known as their **Viscosity Index** (V.I.).

A low or zero viscosity index given to an oil indicates a large variation in viscosity with temperature change.

A high, 100 or 100 plus, viscosity index given to an oil indicates a small variation in viscosity with temperature change.

In general, a poor-quality oil has a high viscosity when cold and a low viscosity when hot. An oil of this grade would have a zero viscosity index. A high-quality oil maintains its viscosity level and would have an index number of 100–115.

Practical Application of S.A.E. Numbers (Crankcase Oils)

The table above gives seven grades of crankcase oil ranging from S.A.E. 5 to S.A.E. 50. In Great Britain, for car and commercial engines in good condition, the S.A.E. 5 and 10W grades appear to be coming into general use. It is claimed that not only is low-temperature starting greatly improved but the saving in fuel and the increase in maximum power is between 2 and 8 per cent for each. In some instances, however, this improvement may be partially offset by an increase in oil consumption and wear. It is interesting to note that at least one heavy commercial vehicle manufacturer is recommending the S.A.E. 5 grade of crankcase oil for both winter and summer use.

The S.A.E. 20W and 20 grades are often used all the year round for engines in good condition.

The S.A.E. 30 grade is a popular summer oil for most engines.

The S.A.E. 40 grade is used in hard slogging petrol engines during the summer.

The S.A.E. 50 grade is used for old engines in order to reduce oil consumption.

These assumptions are now disappearing because of the introduction of multi-grade oils (see p. 51).

Flash Point

Flash point is the temperature at which oil will burn or give off ignitable gases. For lubricating oils, these temperatures range from 175° to 260°C.

Properties of Oil

It is not possible to gauge the quality or suitability of an oil by touch or sight. Exact chemical tests alone can determine whether an oil has the necessary lubricating properties for the duties concerned. Some of these properties will be explained, and we shall consider them in two parts, namely body and flow quality.

Body concerns the resistance to oil-film 'breakdown' during the application of heavy loads. For example, when the power stroke begins in an engine the bearing loads rapidly increase from about 2000 kN/m² to about 10 000 kN/m²; oil body prevents these loads 'squeezing-out' the oil film from between the shaft and the bearing. Oil body cushions the shock loads, helps to maintain a good seal between the piston rings and cylinder bore, an adequate oil-film on all bearings under load is also maintained.

Flow quality concerns the ease with which an oil flows through the oil pipe-lines and spreads over the bearing surfaces. Body and flow quality appear to have opposing characteristics, because the less viscous an oil becomes the less body it will have. The oil used in any engine must have sufficient body to perform the foregoing tasks, and yet the oil must have sufficient flow qualities to pass easily through all oil-ways, filters, etc., and spread effectively over all the bearing surfaces. Rising temperatures cause the oil to lose body and gain in flow quality, but lower temperatures cause the oil to gain body and lose in flow quality. Under normal working conditions the temperature of the engine oil is between 50° and 70°C, but under extreme load conditions the temperature may rise higher for a short time. Heavy duty engines are often fitted with an oil cooler in order to maintain the oil at a reasonable temperature.

Detergent Oils (Crankcase)

Detergent oils have been developed during recent years in order to cope with the severe operating conditions of the high-speed petrol and compression-ignition engine.

In particular, piston-ring 'sticking' and piston 'coating' has become evident; these conditions are caused by the exposure of the oil to excessive temperatures, which cause an accumulation of varnish-like material to appear on the pistons and in the ring grooves. Other effects are the formation of sludge, the coating and etching of bearings, and the general deterioration of the oil as a lubricant. The use of detergent oils has obviated these troubles and led to satisfactory operation (see following section on additives).

Additives

There are two main classes of additive:

(1) Those materials used to modify the base oil.
(2) Those materials used to improve the performance of the oil in use.

Additives in class 1 are:

(*a*) **Viscosity index improvers**
(*b*) **Pour point depressants**
(*c*) **Anti-foam agents**

Additives in class 2 are:

(*a*) **Detergent dispersants**
(*b*) **Oxidation inhibitors**
(*c*) **Film strength additives**
(*d*) **Extreme pressure additives**

Viscosity-index Improvers

It was mentioned earlier that a high-quality oil maintains its viscosity level as its temperature rises, and it could have a viscosity index (V.I.) of 100–115.

V.I. improver additives are becoming more and more widely used to raise the V.I. of oil to over 120. These improvers are products having a long chain-like molecular structure. As the temperature increases the V.I. improver becomes more soluble in the oil, and thus increases its viscosity relative to the oil itself.

When between 4–8 per cent of the V.I. improver is added, the viscosity of the oil decreases at a much slower rate than that of a similar 'straight' oil, between the temperatures of −20° and 90°C.

Pour-point Depressants

The pour point of a lubricating oil is determined by finding the lowest temperature to which the oil can be cooled before it ceases to flow when a special test-tube containing the oil is tilted after cooling. This test gives an indication of the lowest temperature for the satisfactory use of an oil.

Gear oils are tested for their 'channel' point, which determines the ability of a gear oil to adhere to the moving gears.

Anti-foam Agents

Oil foaming or frothing is a problem in certain engines and gear boxes; it applies particularly to automatic transmission units, giving inefficient torque-converter and gear-changing operations.

A silicone fluid is very effective as an anti-foam additive, and is widely used.

Detergent–Dispersants

Detergent oils were previously mentioned in this chapter, but the modern detergent–dispersant is not only capable of dealing with high-temperature conditions but can also deal with low-temperature operating problems. As engine powers have increased in recent years new problems have arisen with light-load operation, especially at reduced temperatures. Under these conditions by-products of partially burned fuel together with moisture from condensed 'blow-by' gases combine to form very heavy deposits of sludge inside the engine crankcase.

These formations of sludge demand additives with increased detergency. In general, most modern detergent oils have the necessary detergency for both high- and low-temperature operating conditions.

Oxidation Inhibitors

Because oils are in contact with the air they deteriorate by oxidation, and the higher the temperature to which an oil is subjected, the more rapidly it oxidizes. The rate of oxidation about doubles for each 10°C rise at the higher temperatures.

The most widely used material is known as **zinc dialkyl dithiophosphate**, which improves film strength and has anti-scuffing properties in addition to its oxidation-inhibiting properties.

Film-strength Additives

In addition to the foregoing additive mentioned under oxidation inhibitors, many organic sulphur, phosphorus and chlorine compounds have film-strength-increasing properties which prevent breakdown of the oil film, thus reducing the possibility of metal-to-metal contact.

Extreme-pressure Additives

These additives increase the load-carrying ability of an oil and also cater for boundary lubrication conditions as found in rear axle gears.

The more highly additive treated oils are used for hypoid gear lubrication and are known as **Hypoid** oils; the additive generally used is of the sulphur–phosphorus–chlorine type.

Gear oils having lower amounts of additive are used for spiral bevel gears and gear boxes. These are known as **E.P.** oils, and, for these oils, additives of the chlorine type are generally used.

Basically, E.P. oil is blended to resist extreme pressure, while the hypoid oil resists shearing action.

Multi-grade Oils

Engine oils now produced are graded as S.A.E. 5W/20, 10W/30, 20W/40 and 20W/50. These oils are known as constant-viscosity or, more commonly, multi-grade oils. By suitable use of V.I. improvers oils can be produced which have the following characteristics.

Take, for example, the S.A.E. 10W/30 oil. At $-20°C$ this oil will have the same viscosity as a S.A.E. 10W oil, while at 90°C it will have the same viscosity as a S.A.E. 30 oil; Fig. 4.3 shows multi-grade oil relationships.

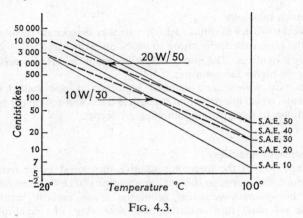

FIG. 4.3.

Transmission Oils

For transmission lubrication the following four grades of oil are in general use: S.A.E. 80, 90, 140 and 250.

Transmission oils must not 'channel' at low temperatures, i.e. the lubricant should not become semi-solid so that a channel is cut by the rotating gears. If channelling does occur during service all the oil is pushed to the sides of the gear casing. If it does not fall back quickly into the track of the rotating gears these and the bearings will be starved of oil.

Gear-box Lubrication

The 'crash'-type gear box usually uses a heavy oil of the S.A.E. 140 grade, but in some gear boxes oils are used which have the ability to withstand higher tooth pressures, and these oils reduce the 'scuffing' of the gear-tooth surface during early life; these are known as E.P. (**extreme-pressure**) oils.

The synchromesh gear box, fitted to cars, uses an engine oil of the S.A.E. 30/40/50 grade. When this type of gear box is used for commercial vehicles a light gear oil of the S.A.E. 80/90 grade, an engine oil of the S.A.E. 50 grade or a light E.P. oil is used. The epicyclic gear box uses a low-viscosity oil similar to the S.A.E. 30/40 grade of engine oil.

Automatic transmission units use a specially developed oil of about S.A.E. 20/30 grade.

Rear Axle Lubrication

The spiral bevel axle on cars uses the S.A.E. 90 grade, commercial vehicles with the same type of axle normally use the S.A.E. 140 grade of gear oil.

The worm gear axle operates at high temperatures because of the pronounced sliding action and the high contact pressures. Therefore, most vehicle manufacturers insist on the use of compounded oils which have been subjected to a solvent refining process and the addition of certain compounds, e.g. chlorine, sulphur and phosphorus.

The hypoid axle requires a specially developed hypoid oil about the S.A.E. 70–140 grade because of the high rubbing speeds and contact pressures connected with this type of final drive.

Chassis Lubrication

A variety of lubricants are used for chassis lubrication, these range from a gear oil of the S.A.E. 140/225 grade to a high-temperature, heavy-duty soda or lime-soda base grease.

Most cars and light commercial vehicles use a gear oil of the S.A.E. 140 grade or a soft lime-base grease of the water-resisting type which has a melting point of about 100°C.

Heavy commercial vehicles use a medium grease made with a heavier oil and having a greater lime-soap content. This type of grease is less readily squeezed out of bearings operating under high pressure, and it helps to seal bearings against the entry of water, dust and mud.

A high-melting-point grease is used for wheel-hub lubrication, and these greases have a melting point of about 160°C. This point is usually sufficient to withstand the effects of the heat flow from the brake drums; this heat tends to have a separating effect on the hub grease.

Exercise 4

1. Low-viscosity oils are now being used for new engines. Explain the advantages derived from their use.

State your views on the recommendation of oils suitable for old and somewhat worn engines. Describe what you understand by the terms given below relating to different grades of oil, and state the purposes for which they are most likely to be used in vehicle lubrication.

S.A.E. 20; S.A.E. 30; S.A.E. 50; S.A.E. 90.   (C. and G.)

2. State briefly what you know about extreme pressure oils, stating for what purpose they are used and the precautions desirable in service.
(C. and G.)

3. How are the following parts of a motor car lubricated: (*a*) differential gear; (*b*) connecting-rod big-end bearings; (*c*) wheel hub bearings; (*d*) dynamo armature bearings; (*e*) spring shackles; (*f*) carburettor control linkage joints?   (C. and G.)

4. What is meant by the term 'forced lubrication'? Give a sketch showing the path of the oil to the principal bearing surfaces of a four-cylinder engine with three-bearing crankshaft.   (C. and G.)

5. Discuss the use of extreme-pressure lubricants in the transmission (gear box and rear axle) and sketch one type of oil seal employed with these lubricants.   (E.M.E.U.)

6. How are the following parts of a car lubricated: (*a*) dynamo bearings; (*b*) connecting-rod bearings; (*c*) universal joints; (*d*) track-rod joints?   (U.L.C.I.)

7. What is meant by the term 'viscosity index'?

8. Sketch and describe some form of lubricating-oil filter and explain how it is cleaned.   (C. and G.)

9. Define the two types of lubrication which can occur in practice.

10. Consider two engine oils of high quality, one of the low-viscosity type and the other of medium-viscosity type. State the conditions under which each would be most suitable for a petrol engine. Sketch in section and describe one of the following units: (*a*) an oil bath air-cleaner; (*b*) an externally fitted oil filter.   (C. and G.)

11. Referring to a lubricating oil, explain the terms 'viscosity' and 'flash point'.

State how the properties of a lubricating oil are affected by temperature, and describe how, in a car engine, the temperature of the oil may be prevented from becoming excessive.   (E.M.E.U.)

12. What are detergent oils and what advantages accompany their use in high-speed compression-ignition engines?   (I.M.I.)

13. What is the difference between an E.P. oil and a hypoid oil? Give reasons why an E.P. oil should not be used in a hypoid-type rear axle.

14. Explain the following terms used in connection with lubricating oils: (*a*) viscosity; (*b*) detergent; (*c*) multi-grade; (*d*) extreme-pressure.
(U.E.I.)

15. Describe an experiment to determine the viscosity of a lubricating oil over a suitable range of temperature.

Sketch and describe the apparatus used and show how the results are used to obtain viscosity values. (C. and G.)

16. State the principal factors affecting oil consumption in a high-speed engine in good mechanical condition.

Explain the effect of high-temperature operating conditions on the physical and chemical properties of the oil.

Describe briefly how engine-oil consumption is usually controlled.
(C. and G.)

17. Modern engines normally use low-viscosity oils. Why is this? What are additives and what is their purpose? (U.L.C.I.)

18. Define: (*a*) a detergent lubricating oil; (*b*) an extreme-pressure lubricant; (*c*) a grease.

Give an application for which each is suitable and state the reasons.
(I.M.I.)

5 Bearings and Loads on Bearings

All bearing assemblies are concerned with three main parts:

(1) The bearing, which is usually stationary.
(2) The moving part, e.g. a rotating shaft, a piston and so on.
(3) A film of lubricant between the bearing and the moving part.

We have seen in the last chapter that it is impossible to maintain a perfect oil film at all times. Therefore bearing materials are used which avoid failure when the occasional metal-to-metal contact occurs. In general, the best combination of materials for resisting wear is where the hardness of the materials used differ considerably. The abrasive matter or particles, which we must accept as ever present in the lubricant, becomes embedded easily into the softer surface of the bearing assembly and thus tend to remain out of harm's way. The hard surface of the bearing assembly is often harder than the abrasive matter, which is crushed without appreciable wear occurring to the hard surface.

The best combination for resisting wear is a 'glass-hard' steel shaft running in a soft white metal bearing, e.g. a camshaft running in white metal bushes.

Types of Fit

There are several types of fit which range from a free-running fit to a force or shrink fit.

A **free fit** is where the shaft diameter is slightly smaller than the bearing diameter.

A **force** or **shrink** fit is where the shaft diameter is slightly larger than the bearing diameter, e.g. a gudgeon pin and certain types of aluminium-alloy pistons at normal room temperature, about 15°C.

Allowance is the difference between the shaft diameter and the bearing diameter. For any given nominal size the allowance will vary according to the type of fit.

Interference is the amount by which the shaft diameter exceeds the bearing diameter.

Tolerance is the difference permitted between the maximum and minimum dimensions of a part, e.g. the size of a big-end bearing could be 50·0125–49·9875 mm, i.e. 0·0125 mm on either side of 50 mm. This gives a tolerance of 0·025 mm, or 50 mm plus or minus 0·0125 mm, usually expressed as 50 mm ± (plus or minus) 0·0125 mm.

Clearance is the free space between the bearing and the shaft.

Minimum clearance is the difference between the minimum diameter of the bearing and the maximum diameter of the shaft. Maximum clearance is the difference between the maximum diameter of the bearing and the minimum diameter of the shaft.

Nominal dimension is the measurement which gives the size of the part, e.g. a small-end bearing of 20·5 mm diameter.

Plain Bearings

A simple type of **plain** bearing can be defined as a cylindrical hole lined with bearing metal or fitted with a bearing bush. These materials reduce friction in the bearing and they enable an easy replacement to be made when excessive wear occurs.

Engine bearings are usually the plain or bushed type, and they work under most exacting conditions of speed and load. The most heavily loaded engine bearings are the big- and small-end bearings of the connecting rod and main bearings of the crankshaft.

The big-end bearing consists of 'half' (split) steel or bronze shells lined with white metal. Most modern engines are fitted with the thin-shell prefinished type of bearing which consists of a steel shell about 1·55 mm thick, lined with white metal whose thickness is only about 0·255–0·385 mm. Suitable thin-shell bearings are also used for the main bearings.

Thin-shell bearings have a long life and they are readily assembled or replaced without boring, scraping or hand fitting of any kind. In fact, it is damaging to carry out any of this work because of the fine tolerances and the excellence of the surface finish obtained by means of diamond boring or broaching.

Students are sometimes puzzled because a comparatively soft material (white metal) is used for engine bearings. The reasons for using white metal are as follows:

(a) Should the oil supply to the bearings cease, the white metal melts and gives the driver warning by 'knocking'. This enables the engine to be stopped quickly, and thus avoids damage to the crankpin or crankshaft journal.

(b) Bearings made from white metal are comparatively easy and inexpensive to renew.

(c) White metal allows abrasive matter to become easily embedded.

(d) The heat conductivity of white metal is fairly high.

The small-end bearing of the connecting rod is usually a phosphor–bronze bush.

The camshaft usually rotates in plain white-metal bushes or in unbushed holes formed in suitable bosses in the cast-iron crankcase.

In the operation of engines where extra heavy duty and loading occurs, lead–bronze and copper–lead bearings are used.

These types of bearing have a larger clearance than the white-metal bearing because of:

(a) The high coefficient of expansion of the alloys used.

(b) The higher frictional properties of the alloys which thus produce more frictional heat.

(c) The need to give an adequate flow of oil in order to carry away the frictional heat.

(d) Any small high spots are not as easily rubbed away as they are with white-metal bearings.

Sintered bronze is a bearing material consisting of 90 per cent copper and 10 per cent tin, both in powder form. Graphite is added and the mixture is moulded into bushes by a hydraulic process at pressures of about 275 000 kN/m². These mouldings are then **sintered** (furnace heated at 700°C) followed by quenching in oil. A density of about 70 per cent is obtained, and the porous nature of the bushes enables oil to be held, thus giving the bushes a self-lubricating property.

Sintered bronze is used extensively for dynamo shaft bushes, distributor spindle bushes and brake pivot bushes. Sintered bronze bushes can withstand bearing pressures up to 14 000 kN/m² and are useful where lubrication is difficult or undesirable, e.g. in clutch assemblies.

Plastics (synthetic polymers) are used for motor-vehicle bearings, especially for suspension and steering parts; these plastics include **Fluon** and **Nylon**.

Fluon is usually known as p.t.f.e., which stands for polytetrafluoroethylene. It has many desirable properties, including low coefficient of friction and wide service temperature range ($-200°C$ to about $+300°C$).

It is unaffected by solvents, including water, and requires no lubrication. For motor-vehicle work, however, certain modifications are necessary as follows:

The actual bearing is made up of three bonded layers—

(*a*) a backing strip of steel;

(*b*) a middle layer of porous bronze, the pores solidly filled with a mixture of p.t.f.e. and lead;

(*c*) a surface layer about 0·025 mm thick of the same p.t.f.e.–lead mixture.

In use a film of p.t.f.e. mixture is transferred to the opposite mating surface, and this film, as well as a thin surface layer on the bearing, is maintained throughout the working life of the bearing. This type of bearing combines a low coefficient of friction, high compressive strength, good heat conductivity, excellent resistance to wear and no lubrication is required; in fact, they are often called 'dry bearings'.

Nylon has a low coefficient of friction and can be used as a bearing material which also does not require lubrication. The resistance to wear of nylon bearings under heavy loads is far less than that of the fluon type, but nylon costs much less.

Nylon is used in steering ball-joints and other moving parts under fairly light loads.

Bearing Pressure Calculations

To calculate the pressure on engine bearings we must consider the following:

(*a*) The **gas pressure** on the piston crown, in kN/m^2, denoted by p_g.

(*b*) The area of the piston crown (bore), in m^2, denoted by $\frac{\pi}{4}d^2$.

(*c*) The force on the piston crown, in kN, denoted by F.

(*d*) The **projected** area of the bearing surface, in m^2, denoted by A_p.

Note that in all bearing-pressure calculations we use the projected area of the bearing, i.e. the length of the bearing multiplied by its diameter. We do *not* calculate the surface area of the curved portion of the bearing, see Fig. 5.1.

(e) The bearing pressure in kN/m² denoted by p_b.

Using the foregoing symbols, we obtain the formula for determining bearing pressure.

$$p_b = p_g \times \frac{\pi d^2}{4} \text{ kN} \div A_p \text{ m}^2$$

$$= F \div A_p \text{ kN/m}^2$$

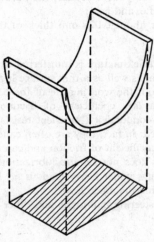

Fig. 5.1.

Example. An engine cylinder has a bore of 90 mm, and the maximum gas pressure reached is 3450 kN/m². The small-end bearing of the connecting rod is 25 mm diameter by 30 mm long. Calculate the small-end bearing pressure in kN/m².

Then $p_b = \dfrac{p_g \pi d^2}{4 A_p}$

$$= \frac{3450 \times 3 \cdot 1416 \times 0 \cdot 09 \times 0 \cdot 09}{0 \cdot 025 \times 0 \cdot 03 \times 4} \text{ kN/m}^2$$

$$= \underline{29\ 300 \text{ kN/m}^2}$$

Example. The maximum load on a big-end bearing of 63·5 mm diameter is 12 kN. If the allowable bearing pressure is 3445 kN/m², what length of bearing is required?

The projected area of the bearing is equal to the maximum load divided by the allowable pressure. The projected area divided by the diameter of the bearing gives the length of the bearing.

Then
$$A_p = \frac{12 \text{ kN}}{3445 \text{ kN/m}^2}$$

$\therefore$ Length of bearing $= \dfrac{12 \text{ kN}}{3445 \text{ kN/m}^2} \div 0.0635 \text{ m}$

$= \underline{0.054\ 86 \text{ m or } 54.86 \text{ mm}}$

Example. The maximum torque exerted by a propeller shaft in low gear is 488 Nm. Calculate the load and pressure on the universal-joint needle roller bearings, given the following data:

Mean radius of universal-joint cross (see Fig. 5.2) 22·85 mm
Diameter of cross-pins 14·5 mm
Length of cross-pin 9·5 mm

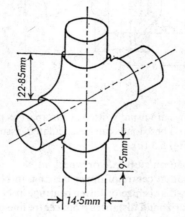

Fig. 5.2.

Let $T =$ torque exerted by propeller shaft, in Nm
$r =$ mean radius of cross, in metres
$d =$ diameter of cross-pin, in metres
$l =$ length of cross-pin, in metres
$p_b =$ bearing pressure, in kN/m²
$F =$ load per pin, in N

Then $\quad F = \dfrac{T}{4r} = \dfrac{488 \text{ Nm}}{4 \times 0.022\,85 \text{ m}} = 5338 \text{ N or } 5.338 \text{ kN}$

Also $\qquad\qquad\qquad A_p = dl \quad$ and $\quad A_p = \dfrac{F}{p_b}$

Then $\qquad 0.0145 \times 0.0095 \text{ m}^2 = \dfrac{5.338 \text{ kN}}{p_b \text{ kN/m}^2}$

$$\therefore p_b = \dfrac{5.338}{0.0145 \times 0.0095} = \underline{38\,750 \text{ kN/m}^2}$$

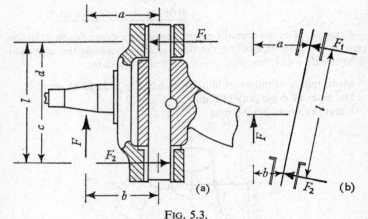

Fig. 5.3.

King-pin Bearings

King-pin bearings are usually fitted as far apart as possible to reduce the loads on them. These loads can be calculated, assuming no king-pin inclination. See Fig. 5.3 (*a*).

Let $\qquad F =$ load on stub axle or wheel, in N

$\qquad F_1 =$ load at centre of upper bearing, in N

$\qquad F_2 =$ load at centre of lower bearing, in N

a and $b =$ horizontal distances from centre line of king-pin to line of action of F, in mm

$\qquad l =$ distance between centres of bearings, in mm

Then $\qquad\qquad\qquad Fa = F_2 l$

$$\therefore F_2 = \dfrac{Fa}{l}$$

$$Fb = F_1 l$$

$$\therefore F_1 = \dfrac{Fb}{l}$$

Also, by taking moments,

$$F_1 l = Fb$$
$$F_2 l = Fa$$

From Fig. 5.3 (*a*), $l = c + d$ and the total length l is always used irrespective of the varying lengths of c and d.

Example. In a certain motor vehicle the vertical load on one stub axle is 1500 N acting at a point 75 mm from the vertical centre line of the king-pin. If the distance between the centres of each king-pin bush is 150 mm, calculate the load on each king-pin bush.

Let $\qquad F_1 =$ load on top bush, in N

$\qquad\qquad F_2 =$ load on bottom bush, in N

then $\qquad F_1 = 1500 \times \dfrac{75\text{N}}{150} = \underline{750\ \text{N}}$

$\qquad\qquad F_2 = 1500 \times \dfrac{75}{150}\ \text{N}$

$\qquad\qquad\quad = \underline{750\ \text{N}}$

In practice, it is usual to find that king-pins are given king-pin inclination. This inclination gives unequal loads on the king-pin bushes (see Fig. 5.3 (*b*)), so that, by taking moments, we have the following:

$$F_1 l = Fb$$
$$F_2 l = Fa$$
$$\therefore F_1 = \frac{Fb}{l} \quad = \quad F_2 = \frac{Fa}{l}$$

Example, see Fig. 5.3 (*b*). In a certain motor vehicle the load on one stub axle is 2490 N. The distance l is 75 mm, b is 70 mm and a is 80 mm. Find the loads on the king-pin bearings.

Let $\qquad F_1 =$ load on top bearing, in N

$\qquad\qquad F_2 =$ load on lower bearing, in N

then $\qquad F_1 = 2490 \times \dfrac{70}{75}\ \text{N}$

$\qquad\qquad\quad = \underline{2324\ \text{N}}$

$\qquad\qquad F_2 = 2490 \times \dfrac{80}{75}\ \text{N}$

$\qquad\qquad\quad = \underline{2656\ \text{N}}$

Ball and Roller Bearings

Ball and roller bearings were introduced to reduce friction by substituting **rolling** friction for the sliding friction found in plain bearings.

There are several types of ball and roller bearings in general use:

(1) **The Single-Row Deep Groove Radial or Journal Bearing.** This bearing is shown in Fig. 5.4 (*a*). The outer 'race' path A is a ring of

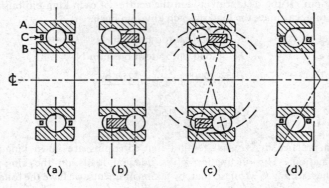

Fig. 5.4.

hardened steel with a groove formed on its inner circumference. The inner race path B is a similar ring, but it is provided with a groove on its outer circumference. Hardened steel balls fit between the two rings, and the outer race path can turn relatively to the inner path, the balls meanwhile roll round the grooves.

The balls are prevented from rubbing each other by the cage C. The groove radii conform closely to the radii of the balls, and by this construction the maximum carrying capacity for the complete bearing is obtained. Although designed for radial loads, journal bearings will take a limited amount of end thrust, and they are sometimes used as a combined journal and thrust bearing.

(2) **The Double-row Journal Bearing.** This bearing is a variation of the single-row journal bearing (see Fig. 5.4 (*b*)). Two grooves are formed in each race path, and each groove is fitted with a row of balls. These bearings are fitted to increase load-carrying capacity, and they are often used where space is limited.

(3) **The Double-row, Self-aligning Journal Bearing.** This bearing has two rows of balls, and the groove of the outer race path is ground to form part of a sphere whose centre is on the axis of the shaft (see Fig. 5.4 (*c*)). This bearing can withstand a certain amount of misalignment caused by shaft deflection.

(4) **The Combined Radial and One-way Thrust Bearing.** This bearing is designed to take end-thrust, in one direction only, in addition to the radial loads (see Fig. 5.4 (*d*)). Bearings of this type are often mounted in pairs and are often used in rear axles. They are sometimes fitted as clutch-withdrawal thrust bearings, and under this condition it is essential for them to be fitted correctly, otherwise the bearing will fall to pieces at the first operation of the clutch pedal.

(5) **The Parallel-roller Journal Bearing.** In this type of bearing cylindrical rollers (see Fig. 5.5 (*a*)), having a length equal to the dia-

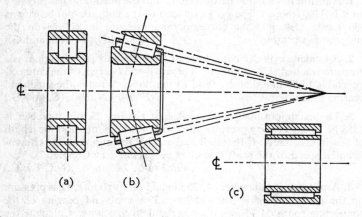

(a)   (b)   (c)

FIG. 5.5.

meter of the roller, are used. This bearing can withstand a heavier radial loading than the corresponding ball journal bearing of the same dimensions, but it cannot carry end-thrust without modification.

(6) **The Taper-roller Bearing** (see Fig. 5.5 (*b*)). The rollers and race paths of this bearing are conical in shape, with a common **apex** intersecting at a single point on the centre line of the shaft; this ensures correct rolling, and this condition is maintained by the engagement of the outer ends of the roller with the flanges of the inner race path. This

type of bearing will resist even greater thrust loads than radial loads, and they are often used in pairs face to face.

The taper-roller bearing is particularly effective for differential assemblies, rear and front wheel hubs. Some form of adjustment is usually provided to avoid undue slackness or tightness and to give preload.

(7) **The Needle-roller Bearing** (see Fig. 5.5 (*c*)). In this type of bearing the rollers have a length of at least three roller diameters, and they are packed in cages between the inner and the outer sleeves; in some instances, however, the cage and one of the sleeves is omitted.

This type of bearing is often used in universal joints, gear-boxes and brake camshafts; they are useful in positions where space is limited.

Exercise 5

1. A piston has a diameter of 75 mm, and the maximum gas pressure on it is 3790 kN/m². The projected area of the gudgeon-pin bearing is 580 mm². Calculate the corresponding pressure in kN/m² on the gudgeon-pin bearing. (28 870 kN/m²) (C. and G.)

2. An engine cylinder has a bore of 63·5 mm and the maximum gas pressure reached is 3445 kN/m². The small-end bearing of the connecting rod is 15·85 mm diameter and 25 mm long. What is the small-end bearing pressure in kN/m²? (27 540 kN/m²) (C. and G.)

3. The maximum load on a crankshaft bearing 75 mm diameter is 3558 N. If the bearing pressure allowed is 482·5 kN/m², find the length of bearing required. If the shaft makes 1800 rev/min, find the circumferential speed of the shaft in metres per second (see Chapter 7).
(98·3 mm; 7·07 m/s) (N.C.T.E.C.)

4. A piston has a diameter of 125 mm, and the maximum gas pressure on the piston crown is 3100 kN/m². The small-end bearing of the connecting rod is 31·75 mm diameter and 38 mm long. Calculate the small-end bearing pressure in kN/m². (31 530 kN/m²)

5. Both the taper-roller bearing and the double-row self-aligning ball bearing embody a geometrical principle upon which they depend for their accurate working. Make careful freehand drawings showing clearly the geometrical principle involved in each type of bearing.
(C. and G.)

6. A piston has a diameter of 125 mm and the maximum gas pressure on the piston crown is 2895 kN/m². The big-end bearing of the connecting rod is 63·5 mm diameter and 63·5 mm wide. Calculate the big-end bearing pressure in kN/m². (8810 kN/m²)

7. What type of bearing is used in each of the following cases: (*a*) connecting rod big-end; (*b*) connecting rod small-end; (*c*) clutch-spigot bearing; (*d*) front wheel hubs; (*e*) camshaft bearings? (U.L.C.I.)

8. Lead bronze is now frequently used in place of white metal lined shells, because in certain circumstances white metal cracks and breaks away from the shell. What are the circumstances?

In many cases one-half of a bearing is white metal and the other half is lead bronze. In such construction, which half is lead bronze in: (*a*) the main bearings; (*b*) the big-end bearings.

Give your reasons. (C. and G.)

9. The main and big-end bearings of an i.c. engine are lined with white metal. Give reasons for this and explain the need for these bearings to be fitted to the crankshaft to fine limits of clearance.

(E.M.E.U.)

10. Sketch and describe the following types of bearings: (*a*) thrust bearing; (*b*) journal bearing; (*c*) taper-roller bearing. (E.M.E.U.)

11. (*a*) What geometrical conditions must be satisfied by the rollers of a taper-roller bearing?

(*b*) Under what conditions of loadings are such bearings employed?

(*c*) Give a sketch of a taper-roller assembly, showing how the races are secured and how adjustment may be made. (C. and G.)

12. What is meant by 'tolerance' in the dimensions of a machine part? Explain the difference between 'tolerance' and 'allowance'.

The dimensions of a hole are given as $25 + 0.015$ and $25 - 0.0000$ mm, and the shaft intended to fit it as $25 + 0.0000$ and $25 - 0.015$ mm. What are the maximum and minimum allowances? Sketches may be used to illustrate your answer.

(0.03 mm max.; 0.0000 mm min.) (E.M.E.U.)

13. (*a*) State the properties desirable in a bearing metal used for plain bearings in an internal-combustion engine. Say why copper-lead alloy is often used for compression-ignition engine bearings.

(*b*) Why are ball and roller bearings widely used on motor vehicles?

(*c*) Make a detailed sketch showing how taper-roller bearings are arranged to take the thrust on the swivel pins of heavy vehicles.

(C. and G.)

14. In a certain motor vehicle the load on each king-pin bush is 810 N and their centres are 140 mm apart. Calculate the load on the stub axle at a distance 90 mm from the vertical centre line of the king-pin which has no inclination. (1260 N)

15. In a certain motor vehicle the load on one stub axle is 1780 N.

The distance *l* is 250 mm, *b* is 68·5 mm and *a* is 84 mm. Find the loads on the king-pin bearings, see Fig. 5.3 (*b*). (488 N; 598 N)

16. (*a*) Explain the difference between a 'force fit' and a 'clearance fit'.

(*b*) A shaft size on a drawing is shown as $25 \pm {0.040 \atop 0.025}$ mm diameter. Explain what this means, calculate the tolerance on the shaft and state the nominal size of the shaft. (0·065 mm; 25 mm) (U.E.I.)

17. Give examples where the following types of bearings would be used on a motor vehicle and state why the particular type of bearing is suitable: (*a*) ball journal; (*b*) ball thrust; (*c*) tin-based plain; (*d*) needle roller; (*e*) oil-less. (U.L.C.I.)

6 Transmission of Motion and Power

In motor vehicles the turning effort of the engine crankshaft is transmitted by various mechanisms to the road wheels, dynamo, distributor, water-pump, fan, fuel-pump, etc.

Belt drive

Motion and power can be transmitted from one rotating shaft to another by means of pulleys and an endless belt, see Fig. 6.1. The pulley A, which gives motion to the belt, is called the **driving** pulley, or

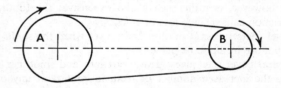

FIG. 6.1.

simply **driver**; the pulley which receives the motion is called the **driven** pulley, or simply **driven**. The application of belt drive to the modern motor vehicle is usually limited to the dynamo, fan and water-pump.

Chain Drive

The chain is a positive form of drive and consists of a **sprocket** and **chain wheel** which are connected by an endless chain. The sprocket is considered as the driver and the chain wheel as the driven member.

Gear Drive

Belts tend to slip, chains stretch and become noisy in operation. Therefore, to ensure a drive which cannot slip and is reasonably quiet, the method of transmitting rotary motion by **gear wheels** has been generally adopted for most types of motor-vehicle transmissions.

Types of Gear

Spur gears are the simplest form of gear-wheel drive, and they are generally used to transmit motion and power between parallel shafts. This type of gear is found in two general forms:

(*a*) **Straight-cut** teeth, where the teeth are set at right angles to the face and parallel to the axis of the gear wheel.

(*b*) **Helical** cut teeth which are set at an angle both to the face and the axis of the gear wheel. This arrangement enables a greater number of teeth to be in contact at any one time when compared with the straight tooth form. This fact, coupled with the larger tooth area, results in smooth running, continuous motion, silence and a reduced tooth loading.

(*c*) The term **spiral** gears refers to helical gear wheels whose axes are at right angles but are not in the same plane.

(*d*) **Worm** gears are a development of spiral gears and connect shafts at right angles to each other.

The chief advantages of worm gearing are: silence of operation under all conditions, durability, wide range of velocity ratios. This type of gear, however, is rather heavy and expensive; the tooth-contact sliding friction causes some loss of efficiency.

(*e*) **Bevel** gears transmit motion and power when the shafts are not parallel but are in the same plane.

The **spiral** bevel gear gives greater strength and smoother running owing to the increased number of teeth in contact at any one time when compared with the straight type of bevel gear.

(*f*) **Hypoid** gears are a development of bevel gearing, the chief difference being the offset of the pinion axis in relation to the crown-wheel axis. The pinion is usually fitted below the crown-wheel axis; this enables the propeller shaft to be lowered, thus avoiding floor 'tunnels'. This offset of the pinion causes sliding at the tooth-contact surfaces in the direction of the tooth length; the sliding motion increases with an increase of offset. The greater tooth strength of the hypoid gearing enables smaller gears to be used when compared with the corresponding spiral bevel drive of equal strength.

Velocity Ratio

The velocity or speed ratio of two rotating shafts connected by belts, chains or gears can be defined as the number of times one shaft revolves while the other shaft makes one complete revolution.

The revolutions of any two belt pulleys in motion are inversely proportional to their diameters. For example, when a pulley of 150 mm diameter is driven through one complete revolution by another pulley of 75 mm diameter, then the 75 mm diameter pulley will turn through two complete revolutions. Therefore,

$$\text{Velocity ratio} = \frac{\text{Revolutions of driver pulley}}{\text{Revolutions of driven pulley}} = \frac{\text{Dia. of driven pulley}}{\text{Dia. of driver pulley}}$$

that is

$$\frac{2}{1} = \frac{150}{75} = 2 \text{ to } 1$$

From the foregoing, the following formula has been derived:

$$\frac{N}{n} = \frac{d}{D}$$

where N = number of revolutions of driver pulley
n = number of revolutions of driven pulley
D = dia. of driver pulley
d = dia. of driven pulley

Example. On a certain engine the fan–dynamo pulley of the crankshaft is 150 mm diameter and the driven pulley on the dynamo is 100 mm. If the rev/min of the engine are 3000, calculate the rev/min of the dynamo shaft.

Now

$$\frac{N}{n} = \frac{d}{D}$$

hence

$$\frac{3000}{n} = \frac{100}{150}$$

$$\therefore n = \frac{150 \times 3000}{100} = \underline{4500 \text{ rev/min}}$$

From this example the following should be noted:

(*a*) When the diameter of the driver pulley is smaller than the diameter of the driven pulley, then the speed of the driven pulley is always less than the speed of the driver pulley.

(*b*) When the diameter of the driver pulley is larger than the diameter of the driven pulley, then the speed of the driven pulley is always more than the speed of the driver pulley.

The velocity ratio of chain drive depends on the number of teeth of the sprocket and the chain wheel:

$$\frac{\text{Revolutions of sprocket}}{\text{Revolutions of chain wheel}} = \frac{\text{Number of teeth in chain wheel}}{\text{Number of teeth in sprocket}}$$

This velocity ratio can be expressed by means of a formula:

$$\frac{N}{n} = \frac{t}{T}$$

where N = number of revolutions of the sprocket (driver)

   n = number of revolutions of the chain wheel (driven)

   T = number of teeth of sprocket

   t = number of teeth of chain wheel

Example. The crankshaft sprocket on a certain engine has 25 teeth and the camshaft chain wheel has 50 teeth. The sprocket and the chain wheel are connected by means of a chain. If the engine speed is 2000 rev/min, what is the speed of the camshaft?

Now $\dfrac{N}{n} = \dfrac{t}{T}$

hence $\dfrac{2000}{n} = \dfrac{50}{25}$

$$\therefore n = \frac{2000 \times 25}{50} = \underline{1000 \text{ rev/min}}$$

Velocity Ratio of Gears

The velocity ratio of a pair of gear wheels in motion depends on the number of teeth in the driven and the driver gears, thus:

$$\frac{\text{Revolutions of driver gear}}{\text{Revolutions of driven gear}} = \frac{\text{Number of teeth in driven gear}}{\text{Number of teeth in driver gear}}$$

or the velocity ratio of driven to driver gear is:

$$\frac{N}{n} = \frac{t}{T}$$

where N = number of revolutions of driver gear

   n = number of revolutions of driven gear

   T = number of teeth of driver gear

   t = number of teeth of driven gear

Example. The timing gear wheel on a certain engine crankshaft has 24 teeth and the meshing gear wheel on the camshaft has 48 teeth.

If the engine speed is 2400 rev/min, calculate the speed of the camshaft.

Now

$$\frac{N}{n} = \frac{t}{T}$$

hence

$$\frac{2400}{n} = \frac{48}{24}$$

$$\therefore n = \frac{2400 \times 24}{48} = \underline{1200 \text{ rev/min}}$$

Gear Terms

Fig. 6.2 shows a number of the terms used to denote various parts of a gear wheel.

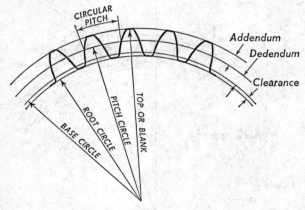

Fig. 6.2.

Outside diameter. This is the diameter of the gear wheel measured across the tops of two diametrically opposed teeth, or the gear blank diameter.

Pitch circle. This is the circumferential line drawn through the points where the teeth make contact.

Pitch diameter. This is the diameter of the pitch circle. When the term 'diameter of gear' is used, it refers to the pitch diameter, which is often used in gear calculations.

Circular pitch. This is the length of the arc from the face of one tooth to the face of the next tooth measured along the pitch circle.

The module. This is the pitch diameter of the gear in millimetres divided by the total number of gear-wheel teeth. For example, a gear wheel has a pitch diameter of 100 mm and contains 25 teeth. The module will be $\frac{100}{25} = 4$.

Root diameter. This is the diameter of the gear from the bottom of the space between two teeth to the bottom of the space diametrically opposite, or the root circle diameter.

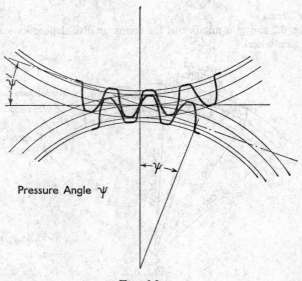

Pressure Angle ψ

Fig. 6.3.

Addendum. This is the radial height of the tooth outside the pitch circle.

Dedendum. This is the radial height of the tooth inside the pitch circle.

Pressure angle. The pressure angle is the angle between a line normal to the two gear teeth at the point of contact and a common tangent to the two pitch circles, Fig. 6.3. As the pressure angle increases, the flanks of the teeth become more curved and the teeth more pointed.

The **involute** tooth form with a pressure angle of 20° is generally used for motor-vehicle gears.

Gear wheels having teeth of involute form will all mesh together, because the pitch diameter, module, circular pitch and number of teeth are relative to each other irrespective of the size of gear wheel.

Terms used in gear-wheel calculations:

Let N = number of teeth in gear wheel (driven)
n = number of teeth in pinion (driver)
C = circular pitch, in millimetres
D = pitch dia. of gear wheel, in millimetres
d = pitch dia. of pinion, in millimetres
M = the module
L = distance between gear centres, in millimetres
r = gear ratio

Then   Number of teeth N or $n = \dfrac{D}{M}$ teeth

Pitch dia. $D = NM$ mm
Pitch dia. $d = nM$ mm

Circular pitch $C = \dfrac{\pi D}{N \text{ or } n}$ mm

Distance between gear centres $L = \dfrac{1}{2}(D + d) = (N + n)\dfrac{M}{2}$ mm

Total number of teeth in gear wheel and pinion

$$N + n = \frac{2L}{M}$$

Gear ratio $r = \dfrac{N}{n}$

∴ Number of teeth in gear wheel $N = rn$ teeth

$$\frac{2L}{M} = N + n = rn + n = n(r + 1)$$

∴ Number of teeth in pinion $n = \dfrac{2L}{M} \div (r + 1)$ teeth

∴ Number of teeth in gear wheel $N = \dfrac{2Lr}{M} \div (r + 1)$ teeth

Example. Two gear wheels with teeth $6M$ are to work at 186 mm centres. Their gear ratio is to be about 1·5 to 1. Calculate:

(a) the actual gear ratio;
(b) the number of teeth in gear wheel and pinion;
(c) the number of teeth in each gear in order to obtain a gear ratio of 1·5 to 1.

We must first find the values of (b):

$$N + n = \frac{2L}{M} = \frac{2 \times 186}{6} = 62 \text{ teeth}$$

$$n = \frac{2L}{M} \div (r + 1) = \frac{62}{1\cdot5 + 1} = \frac{62}{2\cdot5} = 24\cdot8, \text{ say } \underline{25 \text{ teeth}}$$

$$\therefore N = 62 - n = 62 - 25 = \underline{37 \text{ teeth}}$$

$$\therefore \text{ Actual } r = \frac{37}{25} = \underline{1\cdot48 \text{ to } 1}$$

To obtain a ratio of 1·5 to 1, the gear centres could be reduced to 180 mm, when $\frac{2L}{M}$ is then 60.

$$\therefore n = \frac{60}{2\cdot5} = 24 \quad \text{and} \quad N = 60 - 24 = 36$$

(a) <u>1·48 to 1</u>

(b) <u>37 and 25</u>

(c) <u>36 and 24</u>

Gear Trains

A number of gear wheels in mesh for a **speed reduction** or a **speed multiplication** is called a gear **train** or simply gearing; these are either 'simple' or 'compound'.

In **simple trains** all the gear wheels are in the same plane, i.e. level with each other when they are viewed edgewise. The simplest train of this type consists of two gears only (see Fig. 6.4 (*a*)).

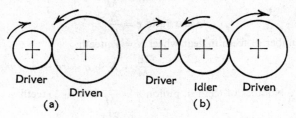

Fig. 6.4.

Where shafts must rotate in the same direction, a third or odd number of wheels may be introduced (see Fig. 6.4 (*b*)). These gear wheels are called **idle** wheels or simply 'idlers' because they have no effect on the velocity ratio of the train. Thus, in a simple train there may be any number of idlers, each with any number of teeth, without altering the ratio of the train. But an odd number of idlers gives the same direction of rotation to both the driver and the driven gears or shafts, whereas an even number of idlers reverses the direction of the driven gear or shaft. Simple gear trains are found in the timing gear of some o.h.v. engines.

Compound trains of gear wheels consist of two or more simple trains in series and the driven gear wheel of one train is fixed on the same shaft as the driver of the next train. Idlers may be introduced into the train, but they have no effect on the velocity ratio. Thus, neglecting idlers, all the gear wheels of a compound train are either drivers or driven; there are always an equal number of each, drivers or driven, and they all affect the velocity ratio of the train.

In the motor vehicle, gear trains are used, in general, for three purposes:

(1) To drive various parts at different speeds and yet keep the parts in correct 'timing'. For example, the camshaft, the distributor or the magneto of an engine.

(2) The drive may be turned through an angle, e.g. the rear axle final drive.

(3) One shaft can be made to drive another shaft at a different speed, thus producing a variation in torque. The torque in two shafts is inversely proportional to their rates of revolution, i.e. if by means of gearing, one shaft drives another shaft at half speed, then the torque in the driven shaft will have twice the torque of the driver shaft. Thus, torque can be increased by reduction gearing and similarly reduced by multiplication gearing; this is the principle of the gear box.

The velocity ratio of gear trains is:

$$\text{Velocity ratio} = \frac{\text{Product of number of teeth of all driven wheels}}{\text{Product of number of teeth of all driver wheels}}$$

$$= \frac{\text{Driven}}{\text{Drivers}}$$

Gear-box Ratios

The velocity ratio or **gear ratios**, as they are usually called, of a motor-vehicle gear box are generally obtained by means of compound gear trains. The calculation of these ratios usually concerns a speed reduction of the mainshaft.

Example. In a certain gear box the constant-mesh wheels have 14 and 30 teeth. The low-gear wheel on the mainshaft has 28 teeth and the low-gear wheel on the layshaft has 16 teeth. Calculate the low-gear ratio.

In problems concerning the calculation of gear ratios it is an advantage to draw a diagram (see Fig. 6.5).

$$\text{Velocity or gear ratio} = \frac{\text{Product of all teeth on driven gears}}{\text{Product of all teeth on driver gears}}$$

$$= \frac{30 \times 28}{16 \times 14}$$

$$= 3\cdot75 \text{ to } 1$$

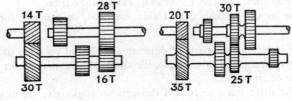

FIG. 6.5.   FIG. 6.6.

Example. In a four-speed gear box the constant-mesh wheels have 20 and 35 teeth. The second-gear mainshaft wheel has 30 teeth and the meshing layshaft wheel has 25 teeth. Calculate the second-gear ratio.

See Fig. 6.6.   Second-gear ratio $= \dfrac{35 \times 30}{25 \times 20}$

$$= 2\cdot1 \text{ to } 1$$

Top gear is usually called the 'direct' drive, because the engine crankshaft and the gear-box mainshaft are coupled directly together. The gear ratio is therefore 1 to 1.

A number of modern vehicles are fitted with **overdrives** which enable the propeller shaft to rotate at a higher speed than the crankshaft. A typical overdrive gear ratio is 0·72 to 1, i.e. the engine crankshaft turns 0·72 of a revolution to every one complete revolution of the propeller shaft.

Epicyclic Gearing

The diagram, Fig. 6.7, is used to illustrate the principle of **epicyclic** gearing of which we shall examine five applications. The **annulus** is a ring gear with internal teeth, the **sun wheel** is the inner gear often fitted to the engine driving shaft. Meshing with both annulus and sun wheel are three or more **planet wheels** usually linked and attached to the driven shaft.

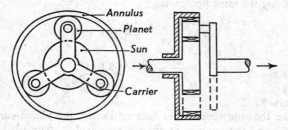

Fig. 6.7.

Application 1

If the annulus is held by means of a friction band, when the sun wheel is rotated clockwise by the engine, then the planet wheels will roll round between the two clockwise and at the same time turn on their studs anticlockwise. The **planet carrier**, and therefore output shaft, turn clockwise also, but at a reduced speed, relative to the driving shaft, thus giving a gear reduction whose ratio is calculated as follows:

Let S = number of teeth in sun wheel
A = number of teeth in annulus
P = number of teeth in one planet wheel
r = gear ratio

Then $r = \dfrac{S + A}{S}$ and $A = S + 2P$

or $r = 1 + \dfrac{A}{S}$

Example. If $S = 24$ and $A = 48$, what is the gear ratio and P for the planet wheels?

$$r = \frac{S + A}{S} \qquad\qquad A = S + 2P$$

$$= \frac{24 + 48}{24} \qquad\qquad 48 = 24 + 2P$$

$$\qquad\qquad\qquad \therefore P = (48 - 24) \div 2$$

$$= \underline{3 \text{ to } 1} \qquad\qquad\qquad = \underline{12 \text{ teeth}}$$

Application 2

Assume the sun wheel to be held stationary and the annulus rotated clockwise by the engine. The carrier will rotate clockwise also and again rotate the output shaft. The gear reduction ratio in this application, using the same figures, is:

$$r = \frac{S + A}{A} = \frac{S}{A} + 1$$

$$= \frac{24 + 48}{48} = \underline{1 \cdot 5 \text{ to } 1}$$

Application 3

Assume the sun wheel to be held stationary, the planet carrier as the driver and the annulus as the driven member, then we have an **overdrive** whose gear ratio is:

$$r = \frac{A}{S + A}, \text{ using the same figures as before,}$$

$$= \frac{48}{48 + 24} = \underline{0 \cdot 66 \text{ to } 1}$$

Application 4

Assume the planet carrier to be held stationary, the sun wheel as the driver and the annulus as the driven member, then we have a reverse gear whose reduction ratio is:

$$r = \frac{A}{S}, \text{ using the same figures as before,}$$

$$r = \frac{48}{24} = \underline{2 \text{ to } 1}$$

Application 5

To obtain direct drive the driven shaft is locked to the driving shaft, usually by means of a friction clutch. This gives a ratio of 1 to 1.

Dual Epicyclic Gears

Automatic transmissions designed with two forward and one reverse gear often use this type of gear, see Fig. 6.8.

The system has one annulus, two sun gears, two sets of planets and one carrier.

Low gear. The power flow is $S_1 \longrightarrow P_1 \longrightarrow P_2 \longrightarrow S_2$ (stationary), $P_2 \longrightarrow C_1$. The **low** band is applied, the high clutch and reverse clutch are released.

High gear. Direct drive with **high** clutch engaged, the low band and reverse clutch released.

Reverse gear. The power flow is $S_1 \longrightarrow P_1 \longrightarrow P_2 \longrightarrow S_2$ (stationary), $P_2 \longrightarrow C_1$. The **reverse** clutch is engaged, so the annulus is held, the low band and high clutch are released.

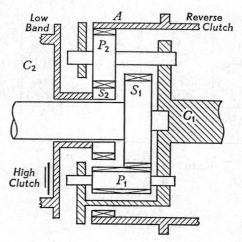

Fig. 6.8.

Calculations

To calculate the gear ratios of Fig. 6.8, let the number of teeth be $S_1 - 33$, $S_2 - 27$, $P_1 - 21$, $P_2 - 30$ and $A - 87$.

Low gear

	S_1	A	S_2	P_1	P_2	C_1
Give all $+1$ rev Hold C_1	$+1$	$+1$	$+1$	$+1$	$+1$	$+1$
Give $S_2 - 1$ rev	$\dfrac{S_2 P_2 P_1}{P_2 P_1 S_1}$		-1	$\dfrac{S_2 P_2}{P_2 P_1}$	$\dfrac{S_2}{P_2}$	0
	$1 + \dfrac{S_2 P_2 P_1}{P_2 P_1 S_1}$		0			$+1$

$$\text{Ratio} = 1 + \frac{S_2}{P_2} \times \frac{P_2}{P_1} \times \frac{P_1}{S_1} \text{ to } 1$$

$$= 1 + \frac{S_2}{S_1} \text{ to } 1$$

$$= 1 + \frac{27}{33} \text{ to } 1$$

$$= 1\frac{27}{33} \text{ to } 1 \quad \text{or} \quad \underline{1\cdot 82 \text{ to } 1}$$

Reverse Gear

	S_1	A	S_2	P_1	P_2	C_1
Give all $+1$ rev Hold C_1	$+1$	$+1$	$+1$	$+1$	$+1$	$+1$
Give $A - 1$ rev	$\dfrac{-A}{P_2}\dfrac{P_2P_1}{P_1S_1}$	-1		$\dfrac{AP_2}{P_2P_1}$	$\dfrac{-A}{P_2}$	0
	$1 + \dfrac{-A}{P_2}\dfrac{P_2P_1}{P_1S_1}$	0				$+1$

$$\text{Ratio} = 1 + \frac{-A}{P_2} \times \frac{P_2}{P_1} \times \frac{P_1}{S_1} \text{ to } 1$$

$$= 1 + \left(\frac{-A}{S_1}\right) \text{ to } 1$$

$$= 1 + \left(\frac{-87}{33}\right) \text{ to } 1$$

$$= \frac{-54}{33} \text{ to } 1 \quad \text{or} \quad \underline{-1\cdot 63 \text{ to } 1}$$

The negative sign indicates rotation in an anticlockwise direction.

Rear-axle Ratios

In most motor vehicles there is a further reduction in velocity or gear ratio before the turning effort of the gear-box mainshaft is applied to the road wheels; this reduction is called the rear-axle or final-drive ratio. In rear axles fitted with bevel gears, i.e. a crown wheel and pinion, the gear ratio is found as follows:

(1) Count the number of teeth in both crown wheel and pinion.
(2) Divide the number of teeth in the crown wheel by the number of teeth in the pinion. The following example makes the method of calculation clear.

Example. A motor-vehicle rear axle is fitted with a crown wheel which has 33 teeth, the corresponding pinion has 6 teeth. Calculate the rear-axle ratio.

$$\text{Rear-axle ratio} = \frac{\text{Number of teeth in crown wheel}}{\text{Number of teeth in pinion}}$$

$$= \frac{33}{6} = \underline{5 \cdot 5 \text{ to } 1}$$

In the worm-type rear axle the velocity or gear ratio is found by dividing the number of teeth on the worm wheel by the number of 'starts' on the worm.

Example. A heavy commercial vehicle rear axle is fitted with a worm wheel which has 37 teeth, the corresponding worm has 6 starts. Calculate the rear-axle ratio.

$$\text{Rear-axle ratio} = \frac{\text{Number of teeth, worm wheel}}{\text{Number of starts, worm}}$$

$$= \frac{37}{6} = \underline{6 \cdot 16 \text{ to } 1}$$

To ensure uniform wear of the foregoing types of gearing, crown and worm wheels are made with an uneven number of teeth. In the last example the same parts come into contact only once during 37 revolutions of the worm shaft.

Double-reduction Drives

Double-reduction final drives are used on the heavier type of commercial and cross-country vehicles.

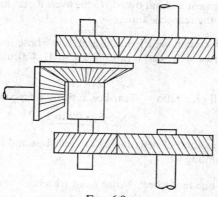

Fig. 6.9.

The first reduction is usually by bevel gears (crown wheel and pinion), and the other or final reduction may consist of spur gears, single or double helical gears, Fig. 6.9. In this arrangement the bevel gears are not subjected to the maximum final torque as they would be when fitted in a single-reduction drive. A large pinion and small-diameter crown wheel can be used, with consequent gain in strength and efficiency of the gears, and the axle casing can be made with more ground clearance than would be found with single-reduction axles of the same gear ratio.

Example. In a double-reduction axle the final reduction gears have 20 teeth and 45 teeth. The crown wheel has 48 teeth and the pinion 12 teeth.

Calculate the double-reduction gear ratio.

$$\text{Gear Ratio} = \frac{\text{Driven}}{\text{Drivers}}$$

$$= \frac{45 \times 48}{20 \times 12}$$

$$= \underline{9 \text{ to } 1}$$

Overall Gear Ratios

The **overall** or total velocity (gear) ratio can be calculated by multiplying together the gear-box ratio and the rear-axle ratio. In the normal vehicle arrangement without overdrive the overall gear ratio in top gear is the same as the rear-axle ratio.

Example. A certain vehicle has a gear box whose low-gear ratio is 4 to 1 and a rear axle whose ratio is 5·5 to 1. Calculate the overall gear ratio.

$$\text{Overall gear ratio} = \text{Gear-box ratio} \times \text{Rear-axle ratio}$$

$$= 4 \times 5 \cdot 5 = \underline{22 \text{ to } 1}$$

A practical method of determining the gear-box and rear-axle ratios without dismantling is:

(1) Jack up one rear wheel, wedge front wheels.
(2) Place the gear lever in the top-gear position.

(3) Place a chalk mark on the tyre of the raised rear wheel and chalk-mark the ground to correspond with the mark on the tyre.

(4) Make sure that the ignition switch is off and engage the starting handle.

(5) Rotate the engine crankshaft until the rear wheel has made two complete turns, at the same time noting the number of turns of the starting handle.

(6) The number of turns of the starting handle for two complete turns of the raised rear wheel gives the rear-axle ratio. Note that the number of turns of the rear wheel should always be brought to two, because with one wheel raised, the differential is working; this causes the raised rear wheel to revolve at twice its normal rate (see following example).

(7) To find the various gear-box ratios place the gear level in 1st, 2nd and 3rd gear positions as required and proceed as before. This operation gives the overall gear ratio of each gear, and the various gear-box ratios are found by dividing the overall gear ratio by the rear-axle ratio.

Example. One rear wheel of a certain vehicle is raised off the ground and the gear lever is placed in the top gear (direct drive) position. If, for 6 turns of the raised wheel, the starting handle has to be turned through 15 revolutions, what is the rear-axle ratio?

We can comply with the foregoing condition in (6) by multiplying the number of turns of the starting handle by two and then dividing this product by the number of turns of the raised rear wheel:

$$\text{Rear-axle ratio} = \frac{\text{Starting-handle turns} \times 2}{\text{Rear-wheel turns}}$$

$$= \frac{15 \times 2}{6} = \underline{5 \text{ to } 1}$$

Example. A vehicle has one of its rear wheels raised clear of the ground. With top gear engaged, the engine is turned by hand and is found to make 14 turns, while the raised rear wheel turns 5 times. With first gear engaged, 21 turns of the engine correspond to 2 turns of the rear wheel. Assuming direct drive through the gear box in top gear, calculate the rear-axle ratio and the first gear ratio of the gear box.

$$\text{Rear-axle ratio} = \frac{14 \times 2}{5} = \underline{5\cdot6 \text{ to } 1}$$

$$\text{Overall gear ratio, first gear} = \frac{21 \times 2}{2}$$

$$= 21 \text{ to } 1$$

$$\text{First gear ratio of gear box} = \frac{\text{Overall ratio}}{\text{Rear-axle ratio}}$$

$$= \frac{21}{5\cdot6} = \underline{3\cdot75 \text{ to } 1}$$

Torque and Speed in Final Drives

It has been already stated that torque can be increased by reduction gearing; therefore the torque transmitted by the engine through the gear box and propeller shaft to the final drive is increased in every gear-lever position except top (direct) and overdrive. The torque exerted by the propeller shaft is further increased by means of the gear reduction of the final drive. The torque of the final drive, provided a differential is fitted, is always equally divided between each axle shaft irrespective of the speed of the road wheels.

This does not apply to the limited-slip type of differential.

The speed of the propeller shaft is always less than the engine speed except when top (direct) or overdrive is engaged. The speeds of the axle shafts are always less than the speed of the propeller shaft because of the final-drive gear reduction.

The following examples show the methods of dealing with torque and speed problems.

Example. The rear axle of a car is fitted with a differential, and the torque driving the crown wheel is 220 Nm. When the car is turning a corner one rear wheel is rotating at 200 rev/min and the other wheel at 180 rev/min. What is the torque in each axle shaft and the work done per minute by each axle shaft?

The torque is equally divided between each axle shaft irrespective of their speeds, thus:

$$\text{Torque in each axle shaft} = \frac{220}{2} \, Nm$$

$$= \underline{110 \, Nm}$$

Although the torque is equal in each axle shaft, the work done by each shaft is not equal, thus:

(See Chapter 12, Part 1.)

Work done/min by outer shaft $= 2\pi\, T$ rev/min J

$$= 2\pi \times 200 \times 110 \text{ J}$$

$$= \underline{138\ 230 \text{ J}}$$

Work done/min by inner shaft $= 2\pi T$ rev/min J

$$= 2\pi \times 180 \times 110 \text{ J}$$

$$= \underline{124\ 400 \text{ J}}$$

Example. An engine develops a torque of 90 Nm at the flywheel at a speed of 1500 rev/min and drives through a gear box which has a low gear ratio of 3 to 1. If the efficiency of the drive is 90 per cent, what is the torque and speed of the propeller shaft?

The torque of the propeller shaft is increased by the gear reduction, but this torque is slightly reduced because the mechanical efficiency of the drive is only 90 per cent (see Chapter 12, Part 1).

Then,

Torque of propeller shaft $=$ Engine torque $\times$ Gear box
ratio $\times$ Efficiency

$$= 90 \times 3 \times \frac{90}{100} \text{ Nm}$$

$$= \underline{243 \text{ Nm}}$$

The speed of the propeller shaft is reduced by the gear reduction. Then,

Speed of propeller shaft $=$ Engine speed $\div$ Gear-box ratio
$$= 1500 \div 3 \text{ rev/min}$$
$$= \underline{500 \text{ rev/min}}$$

Loads on Gearing
Helical Gears

For example, when an engine camshaft is driven by helical gears end-thrust is produced on both the crankshaft and the camshaft. However, provision is always made to resist this end-thrust, the crankshaft usually having thrust flanges at one main bearing, while the camshaft is provided with a thrust button or plunger.

Another example is the end-thrust on the first-motion shaft of a gear box. This thrust is usually taken by a deep-groove journal ball bearing whose race paths are secured against endwise motion on the shaft and in the gear-box housing.

Spiral Bevel Gears (*Final Drive*)

Forces produced in this form of drive are perpendicular to the pitch angle of each gear. These forces are resolved into their components for the calculation of loads on bearings.

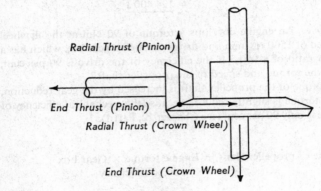

Radial Thrust (Pinion)

End Thrust (Pinion)

Radial Thrust (Crown Wheel)

End Thrust (Crown Wheel)

Fig. 6.10.

Fig. 6.10 shows that the end-thrust of the crown wheel is equal and opposite in direction to the radial load on the pinion, and the radial load on the crown wheel is equal and opposite to the end-thrust on the pinion.

The load on the bearing next to the pinion is much greater than the load on the bearing next to the companion flange. In fact, the load on this bearing is equal to the radial load caused by tooth pressure **plus** the load on the outer bearing of the pinion shaft.

Example. A pinion shaft is supported by two bearings, 115 mm apart, with the pinion outside the bearings. A load of 12 000 N acts on the pinion at a point 45 mm from the centre line of the nearer bearing and at right angles to the shaft. Calculate the load on each bearing.

Fig. 6.11 shows the pinion shaft and bearing arrangements. The load on bearing B is upwards and the load on bearing A is downwards (see Part 1, Chapter 11, Fig. 11.13 and example).

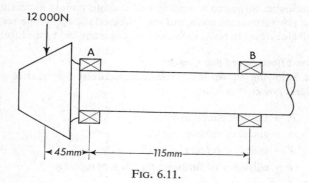

FIG. 6.11.

Let Rb = reaction to upward load on B, then:
Taking moments about A,

$$\text{Clockwise moments} = \text{Anticlockwise moments}$$
$$Rb \times 115 = 12\,000 \times 45$$
$$Rb = \frac{12\,000 \times 45}{115}$$
$$= 4696 \text{ N}$$
$$\therefore \text{Load on B} = \underline{4696 \text{ N}}$$

Taking moments about B,

$$\text{Clockwise moments} = \text{Anticlockwise moments}$$
$$A \times 115 = 12\,000 \times 160$$
$$A = \frac{12\,000 \times 160}{110}$$
$$= \underline{16\,690 \text{ N}}$$

Hypoid Gears

Because the axes of the crown wheel and pinion do not intersect, the thrust load on one component is not equal to the radial load on the other component, as it is in spiral bevel gears. During design the loads on the crown wheel and pinion must be calculated separately.

For a given ratio, a hypoid pinion is up to 30 per cent larger in diameter and the surface area of the teeth is greater than in the spiral bevel pinion. The increased surface area of the hypoid pinion enables a much higher torque to be transmitted without unduly increasing the contact pressure on the teeth, but the increased sliding motion requires a special lubricant to resist the shearing action applied to the lubricant.

Tractive Effort, Speed and Power
The following shows the connection between the tractive effort, speed and power of a vehicle.

Let T_e = tractive effort, in kN
v = speed of vehicle, in m/s
V = speed of vehicle, in km/h
e = efficiency of transmission, as a percentage

If a force of T_e kN is moved through a distance of v m in 1 s, then the rate of doing work = $T_e v$ kN m/s,

$$\therefore \text{Power (kW)} = T_e v \ (1 \text{ kNm/s} = 1 \text{ kW})$$

Now
$$v = \frac{1000}{3600}V$$

where 1000 = m in 1 km
3600 = s in 1 hour
Therefore
$$v = 0 \cdot 2777V$$
where V = km/h

Then, substituting $0 \cdot 2777V$ in place of v in the foregoing equation, we have:

$$\text{Power required at road wheels} = T_e V \, 0 \cdot 2777$$

and the Brake power (P_b) of the engine = $\dfrac{T_e V \, 0 \cdot 2777}{e}$

The power of the engine is always greater than the power at the road wheels because of the losses in the transmission.

Example. A six-cylinder engine of bore 70 mm and stroke 100 mm has a b.m.e.p. of 760 kN/m² at 2700 rev/min. If the corresponding road speed is 72 km/h and the transmission efficiency is 91 per cent, calculate the tractive effort at the road wheels. (C. and G.)

$$P_b = 760 \times 0.1 \times \frac{\pi}{4} \times 0.07^2 \times \frac{2700}{2} \times \frac{6}{60}$$

$$= 39.5 \text{ kW} \qquad \text{(See Chapter 11)}$$

Now
$$P_b = \frac{T_e V \times 0.2777}{e}$$

then
$$39.5 = \frac{T_e \times 72 \times 0.2777}{0.91}$$

$$\therefore T_e = \frac{39.5 \times 0.91}{72 \times 0.2777} \text{ kN}$$

$$= \underline{1.798 \text{ kN}}$$

Linear Speed

Consider a wheel rotating at a constant number of revolutions per minute (rev/min). A point on the rim of the wheel is travelling faster than a point nearer the centre which is stationary. The speed of any point on a rotating body is called **linear** speed, meaning the length or distance travelled by the point in one minute, one second, etc. Then: Distance covered by periphery of wheel in one revolution = πD where D = diameter of wheel, i.e. the circumference of the wheel under consideration.

$$\therefore \text{ Linear speed} = \text{Distance moved during one complete}$$
$$\text{revolution} \times \text{rev/min}$$

$$= \pi D \times \text{rev/min in m or mm/min}$$

The foregoing shows that the larger the diameter, the higher is the linear speed, e.g. the maximum speed of a vehicle can be increased by fitting oversize tyres, provided sufficient engine power is available.

Example. A motor vehicle travels at 50 km/h. What are the rev/min of the driving wheels whose diameter is 660 mm?

Assuming no slip between the tyres and road, the forward speed of the vehicle is equal to the linear speed of the wheels.

$$\text{Linear speed} = \pi D \times \text{rev/min}$$
$$= \pi \times 0.66 \times \text{rev/min m/min}$$

50 km/h must be converted to m/min:

$$\frac{50 \times 1000}{60} \text{ m/min}$$

$$\therefore \ \pi \times 0 \cdot 66 \times \text{rev/min m/min} = \frac{50 \times 1000}{60} \text{ m/min}$$

$$\therefore \ \text{rev/min} = \frac{50 \times 1000}{60 \times \pi \times 0 \cdot 66}$$

$$= \underline{400 \text{ rev/min}}$$

Example. A fan pulley, whose diameter is 100 mm and whose fan blade tips are 175 mm from the centre of the shaft rotates at 1500 rev/min.

Calculate: (*a*) the linear speed of the fan pulley, in m/min; (*b*) the linear speed of the fan tips in m/s.

(*a*)   Circumference of pulley $= \pi D$

$$= \frac{22}{7} \times 0 \cdot 1 \text{ m} = \frac{2 \cdot 2}{7} \text{ m}$$

Linear speed of pulley, in m/min = Circum. of pulley, in m $\times$ rev/ min

$$= \frac{2 \cdot 2}{7} \times 1500 \text{ m/min}$$

$$= \underline{471 \cdot 4 \text{ m/min}}$$

(*b*) The radius of the fan blades is 175 mm, therefore the effective diameter is 175×2 mm.

Linear speed of fan tips, in m/s = Circum. of fan blade circle, in m

$$\times \frac{\text{rev/min}}{60}$$

$$= \frac{22}{7} \times 0 \cdot 175 \times 2 \times \frac{1500}{60} \text{ m/s}$$

$$= \underline{27 \cdot 5 \text{ m/s}}$$

Example. The rim of a disc 75 mm diameter is held in contact with the rim of a pulley 415 mm diameter so that no slipping takes place between the surfaces in contact. The 75 mm disc is found to be turning at 1650 rev/min. Calculate the rev/min of the pulley and the linear speed of its rim in m/s.

Here we use the formula given on p. 71, i.e. $\dfrac{N}{n} = \dfrac{d}{D}$, then:

$$\frac{N}{1650} = \frac{0\cdot075}{0\cdot415}$$

$$N = \underline{298 \text{ rev/min}}$$

Linear speed of pulley rim = Circum. of pulley × rev/min

$$= \frac{\pi \times 0\cdot415 \times 298}{60} \text{ m/s}$$

$$= \underline{6\cdot5 \text{ m/s}}$$

Steering-box Calculations

The primary object of the steering box is to multiply the torque exerted through the steering wheel by the driver so that the vehicle can be steered with comparative ease.

The factors which govern the torque transmitted to the drop arm are as follows:

(a) The diameter of the steering wheel, which multiplies the torque for a given force applied to the steering by the driver.

(b) The gearing in the steering box, which multiplies the torque transmitted through the steering wheel by the driver.

(c) The torque is reduced by the inefficiency of the gearing because of friction.

In the examples which follow it is assumed that the driver uses both hands on the steering wheel and exerts an equal force with each hand.

The formula for calculating the torque in the drop-arm shaft is as follows:

$$T = F_a \times d \times r \times e$$

where T = torque, in Nm

F_a = force exerted by each hand on the steering wheel, in N

d = dia. of steering wheel, in metres

r = gear ratio of steering box

e = efficiency of gearing, per cent

It should be noted that the steering-wheel torque is the force of **one** hand multiplied by the diameter of the steering wheel, $F_a\, d$ If preferred, it can be written as $\left(\dfrac{F_a\, d}{2}\right) + \left(\dfrac{F_a\, d}{2}\right)$, i.e. (Force × Radius) + (Force × Radius).

Example. In a certain steering box the gear ratio is 15 to 1. Assuming an efficiency of 84 per cent, determine the torque on the drop-arm shaft when the driver applies a force of 22 N with each hand on a steering wheel of 0·46 m diameter.

$$T = F_a dre \text{ Nm}$$

$$= 22 \times 0{\cdot}46 \times 15 \times \frac{84}{100} \text{ Nm}$$

$$= \underline{127{\cdot}5 \text{ Nm}}$$

Angle of Drop arm

The angle moved through by the drop arm from its central position to full lock in one direction depends on the gear ratio of the steering box, the number of turns of the steering wheel and mechanical limitations in the design of the mechanism.

The formula for calculating the angle of the drop arm is as follows:

$$A = \frac{360n}{r}$$

where A = angle of drop arm from central to full lock, in degrees
n = number of turns of steering wheel
r = gear ratio of steering box

Example. The gear ratio of a steering box is 12 to 1 and the number of turns of the steering wheel to produce full lock from the central position is 1·2. Calculate the angular travel of the drop arm.

$$\sin A = \frac{360n}{r}$$

$$= \frac{360 \times 1{\cdot}2^{\circ}}{12}$$

$$= \underline{36^{\circ}}$$

Exercise 6

1. The rim of a disc 50 mm diameter is held in contact with the rim of a pulley 325 mm diameter so that no slipping takes place between the surfaces in contact. The 50 mm disc is found to be turning at 2210 rev/min. Calculate the rev/min of the pulley and the linear speed of its rim in m/s.   (340 rev/min; 5·79 m/s)   (C. and G.)

2. An engine develops a torque of 100 Nm at the flywheel at a speed of 2000 rev/min and drives through the gear box by the engine pinion having 19 teeth, layshaft wheels with 30 and 20 teeth and second gear pinion with 29 teeth. What is the speed and torque of the propeller shaft?   (875 rev/min; 229 Nm)   (C. and G.)

3. The tooth numbers in a four-speed gear box are arranged to be interchangeable, so that only four types of gearwheel are required. These tooth numbers are 20, 26, 33, 39. Calculate the gear ratios.
          (1st 3·55; 2nd 2·47; 3rd 1·53; top 1; *r* 4·615)   (C. and G.)

4. A vehicle is travelling at 100 km/h. The wheels are 710 mm diameter. What is the forward speed of periphery with respect to the ground: (*a*) at the highest point of the wheel; (*b*) at a height equal to the radius of the wheel; (*c*) at a height equal to three-quarters of the diameter of the wheel; (*d*) at the contact point on the ground?
   Calculate the rev/min of the wheel.
((*a*) 200 km/h; (*b*) 100 km/h; (*c*) 150 km/h; (*d*) 0 km/h; 747 rev/min)
                                                      (C. and G.)

5. Describe and compare the relative merits of the following types of gear:

(*a*) Straight bevel	(*b*) Straight spur
Spiral bevel	Helical spur
Hypoid bevel	Double helical spur

                                                      (C. and G.)

6. In a four-speed gear box the constant-mesh pinions have 20 and 35 teeth respectively. The second-gear mainshaft pinion has 30 teeth and the meshing layshaft gear 25 teeth. If the rear-axle ratio is 5·5 to 1, calculate the overall gear ratio in second gear.   (11·55)   (U.L.C.I.)

7. Show that if two toothed wheels are in gear their speeds are inversely proportional to their diameters or their number of teeth.
   Three spur wheels A, B and C on parallel shafts are in gear. A has 12 teeth, B 40 teeth and C 48 teeth. Find the speed of C when A makes 80 rev/min. What is the purpose of wheel B?
                                        (20 rev/min)   (U.L.C.I.)

8. A car has *one* of its rear wheels jacked up clear of the ground. With top gear engaged, the engine is turned by hand and it is found to make 11 turns while the jacked-up rear wheel turns 4 times. With first gear engaged, 19 turns of the engine correspond to 2 turns of the road wheel. Assuming direct drive through the gear box in top gear, calculate the rear-axle ratio and the first-gear ratio of the gear box.
                                        (5·5; 3·45)   (C. and G.)

9. The gear ratio of the final drive, being in doubt, is checked by jacking up of one wheel and putting the gear lever in direct gear; the number of turns of the starting handle corresponding to 10 revolutions of the raised wheel is 25. What is the rear-axle ratio?

(5)   (C. and G.)

10. The final drive gear ratio of a car is $4\frac{1}{2}$ to 1. In order to check this, one wheel is jacked up while the engine is turned when in 'top' gear by means of the starting handle. How many revolutions should the starting-handle make for one revolution of the rear wheel, the car remaining stationary?   (2·25)   (C. and G.)

11. If the torque transmitted to the crown wheel of a rear axle fitted with a differential is 115 Nm, what is the torque in the near-side and off-side axle shafts respectively when the car is turning in a radius of 10 m?   (57·5 Nm)   (C. and G.)

12. A gear-box mainshaft carries a pinion having 16 teeth which drives a gear wheel of 32 teeth. On the same shaft as this wheel is a pinion of 13 teeth which drives a gear wheel of 31 teeth through an idler wheel which has 10 teeth; the whole forming the reverse gear train in a gear box. If the engine makes 2200 rev/min, calculate the gear ratio for reverse gear and the speed of the propeller shaft.

(4·76; 462 rev/min)   (U.E.I.)

13. A dynamo, required to make 3800 rev/min is driven from an engine crankshaft making 3200 rev/min. If the effective diameter of the pulley on the dynamo is 140 mm, calculate the size of the pulley required on the crankshaft. Also calculate the speed of the belt in m/min.

(166·25 mm; 1672 m/min)   (U.E.I.)

14. An engine develops a maximum torque of 88 Nm and drives through a gear box having a first-speed reduction of 4·2 to 1 to the rear axle, where the final drive reduction is 5 to 1. If the efficiency of the drive is 85 per cent, what is the maximum torque in each axle shaft?

(785 Nm)   (C. and G.)

15. A vehicle with road wheels of 710 mm effective diameter has a final-drive bevel wheel with 57 teeth, the bevel pinion driven by the propeller shaft having 14 teeth. Calculate the propeller-shaft speed in rev/min when the vehicle travels at 50 km/h.

(1520 rev/min)   (U.E.I.)

16. The maximum safe speed for a certain type of belt is 21 m/s. The belt is used to drive a shaft the maximum speed of which is 1425 rev/min. Calculate the diameter of the pulley to be used. If the type of belt is changed so that the maximum safe belt speed can be increased by 15 per cent, calculate the new diameter of pulley to be used if the maximum speed of the shaft is to remain the same.

(282 mm; 324·3 mm)   (U.E.I.)

17. A four-start worm is driven by a propeller shaft at 2500 rev/min and meshes with a worm wheel on the rear-axle shafts. The worm wheel as 21 teeth. Calculate the speed of the vehicle if the effective diameter of the road wheels is 710 mm.   (63·72 km/h)   (U.E.I.)

18. A chain drive consists of a sprocket having 15 teeth driving a wheel having 42 teeth. The chain wheel is keyed on the same shaft as a second spocket having 17 teeth which drives the final chain wheel having 58 teeth. The 15-teeth sprocket runs at 3300 rev/min.

Calculate the rev/min of the 58-teeth wheel. The 58-teeth wheel is on the same shaft as a road wheel 0·6858 m effective diameter. Calculate the speed of the road-wheel rim in m/min and in km/h.

(345·4 rev/min; 744·2 m/min; 44·66 km/h)   (U.E.I.)

19. An air-compressor pulley is 305 mm diameter and makes 220 rev/min. The motor driving the compressor makes 1425 rev/min and has a pulley 125 mm diameter. Since a countershaft must be used, the motor pulley is arranged to drive a 356 mm diameter pulley on the countershaft. Calculate the diameter of the countershaft pulley which drives the compressor.   (134·1 mm)   (N.C.T.E.C.)

20. A pinion shaft is supported by two bearings 100 mm apart with the pinion outside the bearings. A load of 11 120 N acts on the pinion at a point 45 mm from the centre of the nearer bearing and at right angles to the shaft. Calculate the load on each of the bearings.

(16 124 N; 5004 N)   (C. and G.)

21. Sketch a simple epicyclic gear train consisting of a sun wheel, planet wheels and annulus gear. Explain carefully what happens when: (*a*) the annulus is prevented from rotating; (*b*) the planet wheel spider is prevented from rotating; and (*c*) the spider and annulus are locked together. Assume in each case that the sun wheel is being driven.

(U.L.C.I.)

22. A pinion having 18 teeth drives a gear wheel. The teeth are of standard involute form of 5 M and 20° pressure angle. If the velocity ratio of driver to driven is to be 1·5, calculate: (1) the number of teeth in the wheel; (2) the distance between the centres.

(27 teeth; 112·5 mm)   (C. and G.)

23. A gear wheel is to be about 150 mm in pitch diameter; its circular pitch is 14 mm. Find the number of teeth and exact pitch diameter.

(33 teeth; 147 mm)

24. An engine develops a brake torque of 115 Nm at 2500 rev/min and drives through a gear box having constant-mesh gears of 24 and 36 teeth respectively. The first gear wheel on the mainshaft has 45 teeth and the meshing pinion has 15 teeth. If the rear-axle reduction ratio is 4·5 to 1, determine: (*a*) the speed of the axle shafts, in rev/min; (*b*) the torque on the propeller shaft, in Nm.

((*a*) 123·4 rev/min; (*b*) 517·5 Nm)   (C. and G.)

25. A worm and wheel steering gear has a ratio of 14 to 1. Assuming an efficiency of 85 per cent, determine the torque on the worm-wheel shaft when the driver exerts a force of 18 N with each hand on a steering wheel of 400 mm diameter.   (85·68 Nm)

26. A commercial vehicle has a steering box whose gear ratio is 18 to 1. The angular travel of the drop arm for full lock is 35 degrees. How many turns of the steering wheel are required for full lock?

(1·75 turns)

7 Machines

A **machine** may be defined as a device which receives energy and uses or converts it to do work in a better way. The energy received by a machine may be in any form, and it is usually called the **power input**, applied force, power or effort. The output of a machine is called the **load** or **power output**.

Many forms of machine are found in common use, for example, the spanner which increases the muscular effort of the engineer to tighten a nut. The internal-combustion engine receives heat energy from the burning fuel, this is transformed into mechanical energy by the piston, connecting rod and crankshaft, eventually reaching the road wheels to propel the vehicle. All lifting machines, the crane, jack and hoist, are further examples; these are operated by gears, threads, hydraulic and compressed-air power. Lathes, drilling machines and milling machines receive power from electric motors, the energy is used for cutting or removing metal. The braking system of a vehicle receives its power input from the driver's foot; this is transmitted by rod, cable or fluid to the brake shoes, where work is done in retarding or stopping the vehicle.

The **symbols** used in machine calculations are:

F = The applied force, in newtons
s_1 = The distance moved by the applied force
W = The load or weight moved by the machine, in newtons
s_2 = The distance moved by the load
E = The efficiency
MA = Mechanical advantage or Force ratio
VR = Velocity ratio or Movement ratio

Efficiency of a Machine

In all machines a certain amount of power is wasted in overcoming friction between the moving parts; even in hydraulic machines there is fluid, gland and plunger cup friction. The power wasted should always be as small as possible, the lower the frictional losses, the higher will be the efficiency.

Calculations of Machines

When the power input is mechanical, work done is the product of force and distance moved by the force.

$$\therefore \text{Work 'put into' machine} = \text{Force} \times \text{Distance}$$
$$= Fs_1$$

Work done by the machine is the product of load and distance moved by the load.

$$\therefore \text{Work done by machine} = \text{Load} \times \text{Distance}$$
$$= Ws_2$$

If the input and output were equal, then $Fs_1 = Ws_2$. This, however, cannot be, since in all machines a certain amount of power is wasted in overcoming friction, and the useful work done by the machine is less than the work put into the machine. The ratio

$$\frac{\text{Work done by the machine}}{\text{Work put into the machine}}$$

is known as the **efficiency**, and it is always less than unity. If the answer is multiplied by 100 the result is expressed as a percentage.

Velocity Ratio (Movement Ratio)

In machines the movement of the driving or input part bears a definite relationship to the movement of the output or load. Consider the movement of a lever, the lifting jack and its lever, or the gear box and final drive of a motor vehicle. Movement at the input is usually greater than movement at the output and this ratio

$$\frac{\text{Movement at input}}{\text{Movement at output}}$$

is known as **velocity ratio**, VR, and expressed in symbols as $\frac{s_1}{s_2}$. Consider again the final drive of a car: if the propelling shaft rotates four and a half times to one revolution of the road wheels, the drive has a gear ratio or velocity ratio of 4·5 to 1.

Mechanical Advantage (Force Ratio)

It is often found that a machine will overcome a large resistance by the application of only a small force. An effort of about 20 N at the end of the operating handle of a hydraulic jack will lift a load of several tonne. This ratio

$$\frac{\text{Force at output or load}}{\text{Force at input or effort}}$$

is the **mechanical advantage**, *MA*, and is expressed in symbols as $\frac{W}{F}$.

Consider again the final drive. An input torque of 100 Nm is increased to over 400 Nm in the axle shafts; as the shafts rotate their torque increases but their speed decreases.

The efficiency has already been defined as

$$\frac{\text{Work done by the machine}}{\text{Work put into the machine}}$$

$$\therefore E = \frac{\frac{W}{F}}{\frac{s_1}{s_2}} \text{ or } \frac{MA}{VR}$$

Example. A set of chain lifting blocks requires a force or pull of 270 N to lift a mass of 661·22 kg. For every 0·9 m movement where the pull is applied, the load is lifted 0·012 m.

Find: (*a*) velocity ratio; (*b*) mechanical advantage; (*c*) efficiency.

Data The applied force   = 270 N
Distance moved by force = 0·9 m
Load   = 661·22 × 9·8 = 6480 N

(see p. 21)

Distance moved by load = 0·012 m

(*a*)   Velocity ratio = $\frac{\text{Movement of pull}}{\text{Movement of load}}$

$$= \frac{0·9}{0·012}$$

$$\therefore \underline{VR = 75 \text{ to } 1}$$

(*b*) Mechanical advantage = $\frac{\text{Load}}{\text{Effort}}$

$$= \frac{6480}{270}$$

$$\therefore \underline{MA = 24 \text{ to } 1}$$

(*c*)   Efficiency = $\frac{MA}{VR} = \frac{24}{75}$

$$\therefore \underline{E = 0·32 \text{ or } 32 \text{ per cent}}$$

The Inclined Plane

The inclined plane may be used to raise a load; it is often used for loading heavy machinery when a crane is not available.

Fig. 7.1 shows a load W being moved up the plane by a force F;

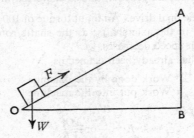

Fig. 7.1.

when it has moved through the distance OA along the plane it has also moved through a vertical distance AB.

$$\text{Velocity ratio} = \frac{\text{Distance OA}}{\text{Distance AB}}$$

$$\text{Mechanical advantage} = \frac{\text{Load } W}{\text{Effort } F}$$

Screw Jack

This is shown in Fig. 7.2. The effort is applied at the end of a bar or lever which moves in a circular path. In one revolution the end of the

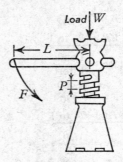

Fig. 7.2.

bar moves a distance $2\pi L$ and the load moves a vertical distance equal to the screw-thread pitch P.

$$\text{Velocity ratio} = \frac{\text{Distance moved by effort}}{\text{Distance moved by load}}$$

$$= \frac{2\pi L}{P}$$

If P is calculated from the **pitch** of the screw thread in metres, L must also be in metres.

$$\text{Mechanical advantage} = \frac{W}{F}$$

$$\text{Efficiency} = \frac{MA}{VR}$$

Example. A screw jack lifts a mass of 10 166 kg, the effort is 445 N, the bar is 0·76 m long and the pitch is 0·0125 m.

Find: (*a*) mechanical advantage; (*b* velocity ratio; (*c*) efficiency.

Data
$$F = 445 \text{ N}$$
$$s_1 = 2\pi L = 2\pi 0 \cdot 76 \text{ m}$$
$$W = 10\,166 \times 9 \cdot 8 = 99\,630 \text{ N}$$
$$s_2 = 0 \cdot 0125 \text{ m}$$

(*a*) Mechanical advantage $= \dfrac{\text{Load}}{\text{Effort}}$

$$= \frac{99\,630}{445} \left(\frac{\text{N}}{\text{N}}\right)$$

$$\therefore \underline{MA = 224 \text{ to } 1}$$

(*b*)   Velocity ratio $= \dfrac{\text{Movement of effort}}{\text{Movement of load}}$

$$= \frac{2 \times 3 \cdot 1416 \times 0 \cdot 76}{0 \cdot 0125} \left(\frac{\text{m}}{\text{m}}\right)$$

$$\therefore \underline{VR = 382 \text{ to } 1}$$

(*c*)   Efficiency $= \dfrac{MA}{VR} = \dfrac{224}{382}$

$$\therefore \underline{E = 0 \cdot 5862 \text{ or } 58 \cdot 62 \text{ per cent}}$$

The Worm and Worm Wheel

The crane and hoist are often operated by worm and worm-wheel gears. These are used because they are not usually **reversible**, and the

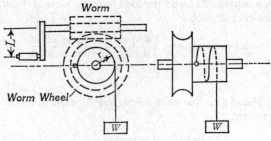

FIG. 7.3.

danger of the load overcoming the operator's effort is eliminated. Here, Fig. 7.3, a **gear ratio** must be considered, and this is the ratio of

$$\frac{\text{Revolutions of worm}}{\text{One revolution of worm wheel}}$$

$$\text{Velocity ratio} = \frac{\text{Distance moved by effort}}{\text{Distance moved by load}}$$

$$= \frac{\text{Circum. of path of handle} \times \text{Gear ratio}}{\text{Circum. of winding drum}}$$

$$= \frac{2\pi L}{2\pi r} \times \text{Gear ratio}$$

$$\therefore VR = \frac{L}{r} \times \text{Gear ratio}$$

$$\text{Mechanical advantage} = \frac{\text{Load}}{\text{Effort}}$$

$$= \frac{W}{F}$$

$$\text{Efficiency} = \frac{MA}{VR}$$

$$= \frac{W}{F} \div \frac{L}{r} \times \text{Gear ratio}$$

$$= \frac{Wr}{FL \times \text{Gear ratio}}$$

Example. The handle operating a crane is 0·38 m long and is connected to a worm with a single lead or start. The worm wheel has 50 teeth and is keyed to a shaft to which is fitted a cable drum, 0·125 m diameter, the rope passing round the drum is 0·025 m diameter. If the efficiency is 40 per cent, what mass will the crane lift when the effort at the handle is 265 N?

Data
$$\text{Effort } F = 265 \text{ N}$$
$$\text{Mass } (m) = \text{to be found (kg)}$$
$$\text{Length of handle } L = 0.38 \text{ m}$$
$$\text{Efficiency } E = 48 \text{ per cent}$$
$$\text{Gear ratio} = 50 \text{ to } 1$$
$$\text{Mean radius of drum } r = \frac{0.125 + 0.025}{2} = 0.075 \text{ m}$$

$$\text{Efficiency } E = \frac{mr}{FL \times \text{Gear Ratio}}$$
$$m = \frac{E \times FL \times \text{Gear ratio}}{r}$$
$$= \frac{48 \times 265 \times 0.38 \times 50}{100 \times 0.075 \times 9.8} \text{ kg}$$
$$\therefore \text{ Mass lifted} = \underline{3287.7 \text{ kg}}$$

Weston Differential Chain Blocks

This type of chain block is used in many garages for lifting engines and other units. The various sizes of block have a lifting capacity

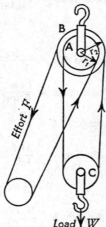

FIG. 7.4.

ranging from 100 kg to 3 tonne. Their efficiency is low, less than 50 per cent; this makes them self-supporting when lifting a load.

The endless chain, see Fig. 7.4, passes round the pulleys or chain wheels A and B and the snatch block pulley C. The pulleys A and B are joined together and rotate as a unit on the spindle.

One revolution of the pulley B reduces the length of chain supporting the load by an amount equal to the circumference of the wheel $B = 2\pi r_2$; at the same time the pulley A increases the length of chain supporting the load by an amount equal to the circumference of pulley $A = 2\pi r_1$.

In one revolution of the pair of pulleys the chain supporting the load is shortened by an amount equal to the difference of their circumferences

$$= 2\pi r_2 - 2\pi r_1$$
$$= 2\pi(r_2 - r_1)$$

Now the load W is lifted by a distance equal to half of this amount

or $$\frac{2(\pi r_2 - r_1)}{2} = \pi(r_2 - r_1)$$

The velocity ratio is the distance moved by the effort when the pair of pulleys rotate one revolution, divided by the distance the load moves.

$$\text{Velocity ratio} = \frac{\text{Circumference of pulley B}}{\text{Distance moved by load}}$$

$$= \frac{2\pi r_2}{\pi(r_2 - r_1)}$$

$$\therefore \text{Velocity ratio } VR = \frac{2r_2}{r_2 - r_1}$$

$$\text{Mechanical advantage} = \frac{\text{Load}}{\text{Effort}}$$

$$\therefore \text{Mechanical advantage } MA = \frac{W}{F}$$

$$\text{Efficiency} = \frac{MA}{VR}$$

$$= \frac{W}{F} \div \frac{2r_2}{r_2 - r_1}$$

$$\therefore \text{Efficiency } E = \frac{W(r_2 - r_1)}{2Fr_2}$$

Hydraulic and Air Power

This form of power is often used for operating units of the motor vehicle and machines in the repair workshop. Typical examples are the operation of brakes, clutches, steering, ignition timing, doors, load tipping gear, lifting jack, hoist and power tools.

This form of power transfer differs from the solid body, like a lever and screw thread, since it can readily change its shape. The **fluid** must be retained in a vessel or container.

Liquids readily change their shape and are virtually not compressible; they can transmit a force but cannot withstand tension. Compressed air, like all **gases**, is compressible and can change its shape.

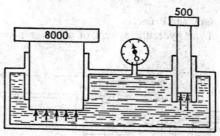

FIG. 7.5.

Pressure within a fluid (liquid or gaseous) is known as the **intensity of pressure** and is considered to be equal on all sides of the vessel containing it. The pressure does, however, vary slightly at different depths of fluid due to its own mass, but when pressure is applied to a fluid it is regarded as equal in all directions.

Fig. 7.5 shows the layout of a hydraulic system with two plungers, one having a diameter four times greater than the other. If friction between the cylinders and plungers is neglected, the force on each plunger is proportional to its cross-sectional area. Force is fluid pressure multiplied by cross-sectional area of cylinder.

Let Fluid pressure = 10 kN/mm²
Cross-sectional area:

$$\text{of small plunger} = 50 \text{ mm}^2$$
$$\text{of large plunger} = 800 \text{ mm}^2$$
$$\text{Force on small plunger} = \text{Fluid pressure} \times \text{Area}$$
$$= 10 \times 50 \left(\frac{\text{kN}}{\text{mm}^2} \times \text{mm}^2 \right)$$
$$= \underline{500 \text{ kN}}$$
$$\text{Force on large plunger} = \text{Fluid pressure} \times \text{Area}$$
$$= 10 \times 800 \left(\frac{\text{kN}}{\text{mm}^2} \times \text{mm}^2 \right)$$
$$= \underline{8000 \text{ kN}}$$

Notice that the diameters, areas and loads are all of the same ratio, 16 : 1.

Fluid pressure comes into many calculations and it can be found by rearranging the formula:

$$\text{Fluid pressure} = \frac{\text{Load or force on plunger}}{\text{Cross-sectional area of plunger}}$$

The Hydraulic Jack and Press

The layout of the hydraulic system of a garage press is shown in Fig. 7.6.

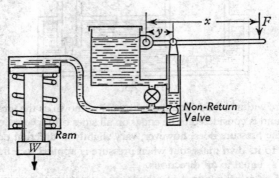

FIG. 7.6.

The plunger which exerts the load or working force is known as the **ram** to distinguish it from the pumping plunger.

$$\text{Mechanical advantage} = \frac{\text{Load}}{\text{Effort}}$$

The load is the force W on the ram and the effort is the force F applied at the end of the lever.

$$\text{Velocity ratio} = \frac{\text{Distance moved by effort}}{\text{Distance moved by ram}}$$

When a fluid is used the displacement of fluid by the plunger equals the displacement of fluid by the ram.

∴ Quantity of fluid

= Cross-sectional area of plunger × Length of stroke
= Cross-sectional area of ram × Distance moved

This data is often required to calculate the number of pumping strokes required to move a ram a certain distance. The plunger of the hand press is operated by a lever; when calculating the hydraulic pressure it is the actual force on the plunger which is required, not the force applied by the operator.

$$\therefore \text{ Hydraulic pressure} = \frac{\text{Force applied to end of lever} \times \text{Leverage}}{\text{Cross-sectional area of plunger}}$$

$$= \frac{\text{Force } F \times \dfrac{x}{y}}{\text{Area of plunger}}$$

The load or force exerted by the ram

$$= \text{Hydraulic pressure} \times \text{Cross-sectional area of ram}$$

Example. The compressed air for operating the brakes on a lorry is stored in a receiver at a pressure of 690 kN/m². The brakes are operated by wheel cylinders 0·125 m diameter.

Find the force exerted by the brake piston-rod when the foot-brake pedal admits 45 per cent of the air pressure to the system and the efficiency is 80 per cent.

$$\text{Air pressure in system} = 0{\cdot}45 \times 690 \text{ kN/m}^2$$

$$= \underline{310{\cdot}5 \text{ kN/m}^2}$$

Force exerted on piston-rod = Air pressure × Area of brake cylinder × Efficiency.

$$\therefore \text{ Force} = 310{\cdot}5 \times \frac{\pi}{4} \times 0{\cdot}125^2 \times 0{\cdot}8 \left(\frac{\text{kN}}{\text{m}^2} \times \text{m}^2\right)$$

$$= \frac{310{\cdot}5 \times 3{\cdot}1416 \times 0{\cdot}125 \times 0{\cdot}125 \times 0{\cdot}8}{4} \text{ kN}$$

$$= \underline{3{\cdot}048 \text{ kN}}$$

Example. A hydraulic garage press is operated by a force of 265 N applied perpendicular to the end of a lever, the lever ratio is 15 to 1. The pumping plunger is 25 mm diameter and its stroke is 50 mm. The ram is 200 mm diameter. Neglecting friction, find: (*a*) load on press; (*b*) the number of pumping strokes required to move the ram 50 mm.

(*a*) Hydraulic pressure in system

$$= \frac{\text{Force on lever} \times \text{Leverage}}{\text{Cross-sectional area of plunger}}$$

$$= \frac{265 \times 15}{\frac{\pi}{4} \times 0.025^2} \text{ N/m}^2$$

$$= \frac{265 \times 15}{0.7854 \times 0.025^2} \text{ N/m}^2$$

Load on press = Hydraulic pressure × Ram area

$$= \frac{265 \times 15}{0.7854 \times 0.025^2} \times 0.7854 \times 0.2 \times 0.2$$

$$\left(\frac{\text{N}}{\text{m}^2} \times \text{m}^2 \right)$$

$$= \frac{265 \times 15 \times 0.2 \times 0.2}{0.025 \times 0.025 \times 1000} \text{ kN}$$

$$= 254.4 \text{ kN}$$

(*b*) This part of the problem is calculated by the displacement of fluid. Number of pumping strokes required

$$= \frac{\text{Vol. of fluid pumped into ram cylinder}}{\text{Vol. of fluid pumped per stroke of plunger}}$$

$$= \frac{\frac{\pi}{4} D^2 \times \text{Distance moved}}{\frac{\pi}{4} d^2 \times \text{Length of stroke}}$$

$$= \frac{\frac{\pi}{4} D^2 \times 50}{\frac{\pi}{4} d^2 \times 50}$$

$$= \frac{D^2}{d^2} = \frac{0.2^2}{0.025^2}$$

$$= \underline{64 \text{ strokes of pump}}$$

Example. A force of 310 N is applied perpendicular to the foot-brake pedal of a car fitted with hydraulic brakes. The pedal leverage is 6 to 1 and the diameter of the master cylinder is 25 mm. The wheel cylinders (4 double acting) are 32 mm diameter, and each wheel cylinder plunger moves 0·8 mm when the brakes are applied. Allowing 25 mm of free pedal movement, find: (*a*) distance moved by the pedal when the brakes are applied; (*b*) force exerted on each brake shoe.

(*a*) To find the pedal movement, the stroke of the master cylinder piston must be known; this is found from the volume of fluid entering the wheel cylinders when the brakes are applied.

Volume of fluid entering wheel cylinders

$$= \text{Area} \times \text{Stroke} \times \text{Number of cylinders}$$

$$= \frac{\pi}{4} \times 32^2 \times 0.8 \times 4 \times 2 \ (\text{mm}^3)$$

This volume is equal to the volume displaced by the master cylinder piston which $= \frac{\pi}{4} \times 25^2 \times \text{Stroke} \ (\text{mm}^3)$.

$$\therefore \frac{\pi}{4} \times 50^2 \times \text{stroke} \ (\text{mm}^3) = \frac{\pi}{4} \times 32^2 \times 0.8 \times 4 \times 2 \ (\text{mm}^3)$$

$$\therefore \text{Stroke of piston (mm)} = \frac{\frac{\pi}{4} \times 32^2 \times 0.8 \times 4 \times 2 \ (\text{mm}^3)}{\frac{\pi}{4} \times 25^2 \qquad (\text{mm}^2)}$$

$$= 10.48 \text{ mm}$$

Pedal movement

$$= (\text{Stroke of piston} \times \text{Pedal leverage}) + \text{Free movement}$$

$$= (10.48 \times 6) + 25$$

$$= \underline{87.88 \text{ mm}}$$

(*b*) To solve this part, the hydraulic pressure must be known, then the force exerted on each brake shoe can be found.

$$\text{Hydraulic pressure} = \frac{\text{Applied force} \times \text{Leverage}}{\text{Area of master cylinder piston}}$$

$$= \frac{310 \times 6}{\frac{\pi}{4} \times 0.025^2} \ \text{N/m}^2$$

$$= 3\ 791\ 000 \text{N/m}^2 \text{ or } 3791 \text{ kN/m}^2$$

Force on brake shoe plunger

$$= \text{Hydraulic pressure} \times \text{Area of wheel cylinder}$$

$$\therefore \text{Force} = 3791 \times \frac{\pi}{4} \times 0.032^2 \text{ kN}$$

$$= 3791 \times 0.7854 \times 0.032 \times 0.032 \text{ kN}$$

$$= \underline{3.048 \text{ kN}}$$

Example. A hydraulic garage jack when lifting the front of a vehicle of a certain mass has an efficiency of 85 per cent. Its velocity ratio is 120 to 1. Find the mass lifted when the applied effort at the handle is 170 N.

This problem not only concerns efficiency but a given velocity ratio, the formula is written down and the unknown value is transposed to the left-hand side.

Data
$$\text{Efficiency } E = 0.85$$
$$\text{Effort } F = 170 \text{ N}$$
$$\text{Mass } (m) = \text{to be found (kg)}$$
$$\text{Velocity ratio } VR = 120 \text{ to } 1$$
$$E = \frac{MA}{VR}$$
$$= \frac{\dfrac{m}{F}}{VR}$$
$$\therefore m = E \times VR \times F$$
$$= \frac{0.85 \times 120 \times 170}{9.8} \text{ kg}$$
$$\therefore \underline{\text{Mass lifted} = 1769.3 \text{ kg or } 1.7693 \text{ tonne}}$$

Example. A hydraulic servo-assisted braking system has a master cylinder of 20 mm diameter and a 140 mm diameter vacuum servo unit

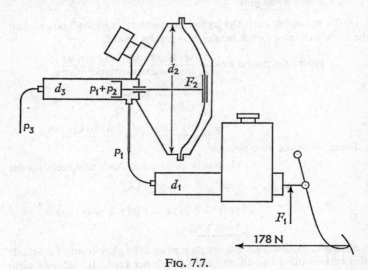

Fig. 7.7.

with slave cylinder of 16 mm diameter. When the brakes are applied by a pedal force of 178 N the effective pedal leverage is 5 to 1 and the air pressure in the vacuum unit is 32·45 kN/m² absolute, see p. 121.

The mechanical efficiency of the system is 90 per cent. Calculate the hydraulic pressure in the brake pipes, see Fig. 7.7.

$$\text{Force } F_1 = 178 \times 5 \text{ N}$$

$$\text{Pressure } p_1 = \frac{178 \times 5}{\frac{\pi}{4}d_1{}^2} \text{ N/m}^2$$

$$= \frac{178 \times 5}{0\cdot7854 \times 0\cdot02^2} \text{ N/m}^2$$

$$= \underline{2\,833\,000 \text{ N/m}^2 \text{ or } 2833 \text{ kN/m}^2}$$

$$\text{Force } F_2 = 68\cdot95 \times \frac{\pi}{4}d_2{}^2 \text{ N}$$

$$= 68\cdot95 \times 0\cdot7854 \times 0\cdot14^2 \text{ N}$$

$$= \underline{1061 \text{ N or } 1\cdot061 \text{ kN}}$$

Hydraulic pressure p_2 produced by vacuum unit.

$$\text{Hydraulic pressure } p_2 = \frac{F_2}{\frac{\pi}{4}d_3{}^2} \text{ kN/m}^2$$

$$= \frac{1\cdot061}{0\cdot7854 \times 0\cdot016^2}$$

$$= \underline{5278 \text{ kN/m}^2}$$

$$\text{Hydraulic pressure } p_3 = p_1 + p_2$$
$$= 2833 + 5278$$
$$= 8111 \text{ kN/m}^2$$
$$\text{Actual pressure} = 8111 \times \text{Efficiency}$$
$$= 8111 \times \frac{90}{100}$$
$$= \underline{7300 \text{ kN/m}^2}$$

The Law of a Machine

The previous work has considered the machine working under one certain condition of load or effort. In practice, we find that both the efficiency and mechanical advantage vary with the load; usually the efficiency increases with an increase of load. Velocity ratio, however, cannot vary unless the construction of the machine is altered.

When a machine is tested the applied efforts and loads are plotted on a graph. The horizontal OX axis is used for the load scale and the vertical OY axis for the applied effort. The plotted results produce a straight line which cuts the OY axis at a point just above the origin, the distance between this point and the origin represents the force of friction when the load on the machine is zero. This straight line, produced by the relationship between the load and effort, can be expressed as an equation, and it is known mathematically as a **linear equation**

$$y = ax + b$$

By substituting y to equal F and x to equal W, the equation is

$$F = aW + b$$

where F = effort

W = load

a = constant, which is the slope of the line

b = constant, the force of friction which must be overcome to operate the machine at zero load.

To find a value for a, two points are selected on the line and lettered k and g as shown in the graph, Fig. 7.8. From g a vertical dotted line

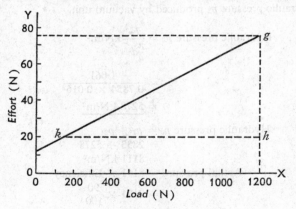

FIG. 7.8.

is drawn to intersect a horizontal dotted line drawn from k at the point h. In Fig. 7.8 the value of $gh = 55$, and $kh = 1050$.

$$\therefore \text{Slope of line} = \frac{gh}{kh} = \frac{55}{1050}$$

$$= 0{\cdot}0524$$

This is the value of constant a.

To find the value of constant *b*, no calculation is necessary. It is the length of the line from 0 to the point of intersection of line *gk* with the OY axis; in this example it is 12.

The law of the machine can now be written:

$$F = aW + b$$
$$= 0.0524W + 12$$

This law may also be found **algebraically**, by putting the values at the two selected points into the equation.

When $W = 150$, $F = 20$
$W = 1200$, $F = 75$

The equations formed are:

$$F = aW + b$$
$$20 = a150 + b \qquad \text{Eq. 1}$$
$$75 = a1200 + b \qquad \text{Eq. 2}$$

To eliminate the value *b*, subtract Eq. 1 from Eq. 2.

$$75 = a1200 + b$$
$$20 = a\,150 + b$$
$$\overline{55 = a1050}$$

$$\therefore a = \frac{55}{1050} \quad \text{or} \quad \underline{0.0524}$$

Substituting this value of *a* in Eq. 2,

$$75 = (0.0524 \times 1200) + b$$
$$\therefore b = 75 - 62.88 = \underline{12.12}$$

This result agrees closely with the graph, but shows that a small error can be made when reading from the graph.

When the law of the machine is known the effort required to raise or apply any load can be calculated, the effort may be expressed in newtons, except where gravitational force is involved, then it will be in kg.

Fig. 7.9 shows a graph for the following calculated and tabulated results of a machine; its velocity ratio is 18:1 and $F = 0.0524W + 12$.

Load in N	100	300	500	700	1000	1200
Effort in N	17.5	28	38.5	49	65	75
Mech. Adv.	5.71	10.71	13.0	14.6	15.4	16
Efficiency	31.7	59.5	72.3	81.2	85.5	89
Friction in N	215	204	193	182	170	150

The frictional losses are calculated from the formula.

$$\text{Frictional loss} = (\text{Effort} \times VR) - \text{Load}$$
$$= (F \times VR) - W$$

Example. From the above results find the effort required to raise a load of 800 N.

$$\text{Effort } F = 0\cdot0524W + 12 \text{ N}$$
$$= (0\cdot0524 \times 800) + 12 \text{ N}$$
$$= \underline{53\cdot92 \text{ N}}$$

Example. The final drive gear of a motor vehicle was tested: input torque was 40 Nm when the output torque was 140 Nm; the input torque was then increased to 120 Nm and the output torque increased to 540 Nm. The effort to load relationship produced a straight-line graph.

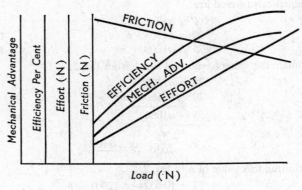

FIG. 7.9.

Find the law of this rear-axle unit and the output torque, when the input torque is 90 Nm; also find the efficiency at all three loads.

Velocity ratio is 5 : 1.

Law of machine $F = aW + b$

Let

F = input torque

W = output torque

a = constant (slope of line)

b = constant (frictional loss)

When $F = 40$, $W = 140$,

$$\therefore 40 = a140 + b \qquad \text{Eq. 1}$$

When $F = 120$, $W = 540$,

$$\therefore 120 = a540 + b \qquad \text{Eq. 2}$$

Subtracting Eq. 1 from Eq. 2 to eliminate b and so find a value for a,

$$120 = a540 + b$$
$$40 = a140 + b$$
$$\overline{80 = a400}$$

$$\therefore a = \frac{80}{400} \quad \text{or} \quad 0\cdot2$$

Substituting this value into Eq. 1,

$$40 = (0\cdot2 \times 140) + b$$
$$\therefore b = 40 - 28 = 12$$

By the law of the rear axle, $F = 0\cdot2W + 12$

Output torque when input torque is 90 Nm:

$$F = 0\cdot2W + 12$$
$$\therefore 0\cdot2W = F - 12$$
$$W = \frac{F - 12}{0\cdot2} = \frac{90 - 12}{0\cdot2} \text{ Nm}$$

$$\therefore \underline{\text{Output torque } W = 390 \text{ Nm}}$$

The efficiency of the rear axle for the three known loads:

$$\text{Efficiency } E = \frac{MA}{VR} = \frac{\dfrac{W}{F}}{5}$$

$$\therefore E = \frac{W}{5F}$$

(a) Input torque 40 Nm, output torque 140 Nm

$$E = \frac{W}{5F} = \frac{140}{5 \times 40}$$
$$= \underline{0\cdot7 \quad \text{or} \quad 70 \text{ per cent}}$$

(b) Input torque 90 Nm, output torque 390 Nm

$$E = \frac{W}{5F} = \frac{390}{5 \times 90}$$
$$= \underline{0\cdot86 \quad \text{or} \quad 86 \text{ per cent}}$$

(c) Input torque 120 Nm, output torque 540 Nm

$$E = \frac{W}{5F} = \frac{540}{5 \times 120}$$
$$= \underline{0\cdot9 \quad \text{or} \quad 90 \text{ per cent}}$$

Exercise 7

1. The effort E, which must be exerted to lift a load W by means of a small crane is given by the equation $E = aW + b$.

If E is 9 N when W is 100 N, and E is 30 N when W is 800 N, determine the values of a and b. $((a)\ 0.03;\ (b)\ 6)$ (E.M.E.U.)

2. A screw jack is operated by a bar pushed through a hole in the spindle. The pitch of the screw is 12 mm. A force of 270 N applied at right angles to the bar, at a radius of 350 mm from the axis of the screw, is found to lift a casting of mass 2033·6 kg which rests upon the top of the jack.

Find the velocity ratio, the mechanical advantage and the mechanical efficiency of the machine under these conditions.

$(183·3;\ 73·8;\ 40·26\ \text{per cent})$ (U.E.I.)

3. A spiral bevel rear-axle unit is arranged for an efficiency test by fixing a pulley 250 mm diameter to the pinion shaft and fastening a load to the rim of a road wheel 450 mm diameter. An effort of 30 N at the rim of the pulley is just sufficient to overcome a downward force of 80 N at the rim of the road wheel.

Find the mechanical efficiency of the rear-axle gears if the gear ratio is 5·25 to 1. $(91·43\ \text{per cent})$ (N.C.T.E.C.)

4. A hydraulic jack has a plunger 19 mm diameter and a ram 57 mm diameter. If the stroke of the plunger is 25 mm, how many strokes will be required to raise the ram 75 mm?

If the efficiency of the jack is 85 per cent, what force at the plunger will be required to lift a mass of 1016·3 kg?

$(27\ \text{strokes};\ 1305\ \text{N})$ (C. and G.)

5. A worm and worm-wheel combination consists of a four-start worm meshing with a worm wheel having 23 teeth. What is the velocity ratio of the combination?

If a twisting moment of 120 Nm on the worm produces a moment of 630 Nm at the worm-wheel shaft, calculate the efficiency of the mechanism. $(5·75\ \text{to}\ 1;\ 91·3\ \text{per cent})$ (C. and G.)

6. A nut, 1·5 mm pitch, is tightened up by a spanner 200 mm long. What is the velocity ratio?

If a force of 110 N applied at the end of the spanner causes the nut to exert a force of 10 680 N, what is the mechanical advantage and the efficiency? $(838;\ 97;\ 11·58\ \text{per cent})$

7. A hydraulic jack has a plunger 25 mm diameter by 100 mm stroke and a ram 100 mm diameter. If a force of 265 N is applied to the handle, whose leverage is 15 to 1, find: (*a*) mass lifted by the jack if the efficiency is 85 per cent; (*b*) number of pumping strokes to raise the ram 150 mm.

((*a*) 5470 kg; (*b*) 24 strokes)

8. Define the terms 'velocity ratio', 'mechanical advantage' and 'efficiency' as applied to a machine.

In a lifting machine, velocity ratio 30, an effort of 10 N is required to raise a load of 35 N and an effort of 25 N to raise 260 N. Calculate the probable effort required to raise a load of 165 N and the efficiency under this load.   (18·66 N; 29·4 per cent)   (I.M.I.)

9. The following data were obtained in a test on a crane. Plot the graph and from your graph find the load required for an effort of 40 N.

Load in N	28	56	84	112	140	168
Effort in N	14·2	26·6	38·1	50	59·1	72

(87 N)   (U.L.C.I.)

10. A lifting appliance was tested and the following results were obtained:

Load in N	14	28	42	56	70	84
Effort in N	14·5	20·5	26	32	38·5	44·5

The velocity ratio of the machine was 3.

Draw graphs of the effort, mechanical advantage and efficiency of the machine on a load base and find the law of the machine.

((*a*) 0·4285; (*b*) 8·5)   (I.M.I.)

11. Define the terms 'mechanical advantage', 'velocity ratio' and 'efficiency' as applied to a machine. Find the relationship between them.

A wheel and axle have diameters 375 mm and 75 mm respectively, and it is necessary to apply a force of 20 N to lift a load of 70 N.

Find: (1) the work done by the effort in raising the load 3 m; (2) work done against friction; (3) efficiency of the machine.

((1) 300 J; (2) 90 J; (3) 70 per cent)   (I.M.I.)

12. A pulley block, velocity ratio 30, supports a working platform of mass 100 kg. Determine the vertical effort to be applied to the hauling chain by a man of mass 70 kg standing on the platform, just sufficient to raise himself and the platform if the efficiency of the tackle for the given load system is 35 per cent.   (148 N)   (I.M.I.)

13. A cranked lever has its unequal arms at right angles. The short lever is 70 mm long and presses at right angles on a piston 38 mm diameter operating in a cylinder full of oil. The other lever is 185 mm long and a force of 3560 N is applied at right angles to its end. Calculate, in kN/m² the oil pressure produced in the cylinder.

$$(8294 \text{ kN/m}^2) \quad \text{(U.E.I.)}$$

14. What is the difference between 'work' and 'power'? If the average pressure on a piston 75 mm diameter is 385 kN/m², calculate the power developed in the cylinder in one stroke if the stroke is 100 mm long and the piston takes 0·01 s to travel that distance.

$$(17·02 \text{ kW}) \quad \text{(U.E.I.)}$$

15. A garage crane has a chain drum 250 mm diameter and the drum shaft carries a gear wheel having 48 teeth. This wheel is in mesh with a pinion having 12 teeth, which is on the driving shaft. The winding handle is 400 mm long and the pull in the chain is 2480 N. Calculate the force required on the winding handle.　　　　(195 N)　(U.E.I.)

16. Give an outline sketch and describe a Weston differential chain block. If the chain wheel has 20 and 19 teeth, and the pitch of the links is 25 mm, how much will the load be raised by turning the chain wheel 40 times?　　　　　　　　　(500 mm)　(E.M.E.U.)

17. A driver exerts a tangential force of 35 N with each hand on the rim of a 250 mm steering wheel. If the steering arm under these conditions exerts a torque of 130 Nm and moves through 12 degrees for one revolution of the steering wheel, determine: (i) velocity ratio; (ii) mechanical advantage; (iii) efficiency of the steering gear.

$$\text{((i) 30; (ii) 14·86; (iii) 49·53 per cent)} \quad \text{(N.C.T.E.C.)}$$

Properties of Gases

Matter exists as a **solid**, a **liquid** and a **gas**. A gas is usually invisible, but it can be compressed and expanded. A quantity of gas, however small, can expand and completely fill an empty space. Examples of gases are:

> **Air, exhaust gases; acetylene** and **oxygen** (used in welding); **coal gas; nitrogen; hydrogen.**

Various substances can take the form of **vapour** which is not a so-called 'perfect' gas but a stage in the change from a liquid to a gaseous state. Although a gas is usually invisible, we can often see a vapour because it consists of fine particles of liquid carried in the air. Examples of vapour are:

> Petrol vapour from the carburettor; atomized Diesel fuel oil; condensing steam leaving a radiator.

Certain laws have been discovered which apply closely to almost all gases, and these laws are explained later in this chapter.

Pressure of Gases

Gases exert a pressure on all bodies with which they are in contact, and this pressure can be measured by means of a **pressure gauge** which registers a zero reading when open to **atmospheric pressure** (pressure of the atmosphere). Atmospheric pressure is usually taken as **101·3 kN/m²** at sea-level.

Atmospheric Pressure

Atmospheric pressure is the pressure exerted by the mass of gas or air which covers the earth's surface. This pressure is reduced as the distance from the earth's surface increases, which is one reason why aircraft engines are supercharged when designed to fly at high altitudes.

A simple method to determine atmospheric pressure or air pressure is to fill with mercury a glass tube, about 1 metre long with one end closed and having a cross-sectional area of 100 mm². When the open end of the tube is inverted into a bowl of mercury the column of mercury in the tube falls to about 760 mm, see Fig. 8.1.

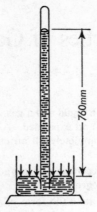

760mm

FIG. 8·1.

The space in the tube above the mercury is a vacuum, and the pressure of air on the exposed surface of the mercury supports the column. Therefore air pressure is supporting the mass of mercury in the tube.

Then, Volume of mercury = Area × Length
$$= 100 \times 760 \text{ mm}^3$$
$$= 100 \times 760 \times 10^{-9} \text{ m}^3$$
$$= 76 \times 10^{-6} \text{ m}^3$$

Mass of 76×10^{-6} m³ of water $= 76 \times 10^{-6} \times 1000$ kg
(since mass of 1 litre of water is 1 kg, the mass of 1 m³ of water is 1000 kg)
$$= 76 \times 10^{-3} \text{ kg}$$

Mass of mercury = mass of water × relative density of mercury
$$= 76 \times 10^{-3} \times 13 \cdot 6 \text{ kg}$$

Force exerted on cross-sectional area of 100 mm²
$$= 76 \times 10^{-3} \times 13 \cdot 6 \times 9 \cdot 8 \text{ N}$$

∴ Force on 1 mm² $= \dfrac{76 \times 10^{-3} \times 13 \cdot 6 \times 9 \cdot 8 \text{ N}}{100}$

∴ Atmospheric pressure $= 0 \cdot 101\ 292\ 8$ N/mm²
$$= 101\ 292 \cdot 8 \text{ N/m}^2$$
$$= 101 \cdot 2928 \text{ kN/m}^2$$
$$= 101 \cdot 3 \text{ (approx.) when the column}$$
of mercury is 760 mm high.

The principle of the **barometer** is based on the foregoing and, although the height of the mercury column in the barometer may vary with the weather conditions, the normal height will be 760 mm of mercury, usually written **760 mmHg.** Hg is the chemical symbol given to mercury.

The Water Gauge

When low pressures have to be determined the **water gauge** is often used. Taking the relative density of Hg as 13·6, the height of water equivalent to 760 mmHg is:

$$\text{Height of water} = \text{Height of Hg} \times \text{relative density of Hg}$$
$$= 760 \times 13·6 \text{ mm}$$
$$= 10\,340 \text{ mm or } 10·34 \text{ m}$$

This is the height of a column of water supported by atmospheric pressure.

Therefore, a pressure measured by a water gauge is indicated by a much greater rise in water level than if mercury were used in the gauge.

The reading shown on most types of pressure gauge, called **gauge pressure,** is not the true pressure of the gas but is the difference between atmospheric pressure and the pressure of the gas under measurement. The true pressure of a gas, called **absolute pressure,** is therefore:

$$\text{Absolute pressure} = \text{Gauge pressure} + \text{Atmospheric pressure}$$

In all calculations concerning gases we use absolute pressures.

Example. The reading on an engine compression gauge is 690 kN/m². Express this reading as absolute pressure in kN/m².

$$\text{Absolute pressure} = \text{Gauge pressure} + \text{Atmospheric pressure}$$
$$= 690 + 101·3 \text{ kN/m}^2$$
$$= \underline{791·3 \text{ kN/m}^2}$$

High Pressures

For high pressures, a unit of pressure called the **atmosphere** is used. This unit is taken as the pressure of the atmosphere (atmospheric pressure), i.e. 101·3 kN/m². Therefore, a pressure of 10 atmospheres equals 101·3 multiplied by 10, i.e. 1013 kN/m². Atmospheres are used to indicate the 'breaking' pressures of fuel-injector nozzles; these pressures vary from 120 to 180 atmospheres.

An alternative unit, the **bar** may also be used. It may be expressed as 1 bar = 10^5 N/m² or 100 000 N/m², and 1 bar is approximately equal to one atmosphere, so the fuel injector nozzle pressure may 'break' between 125 and 175 bars.

Vacuum Measurement

A perfect **vacuum** exists when an enclosed space is quite empty, i.e. contains no material and therefore has no pressure. A perfect vacuum cannot be obtained in practice.

To measure the amount of vacuum, a gauge graduated in **millimetres of mercury** is usually used. Twenty-five millimetres of mercury is equivalent to about 3·35 kN/m² *below* atmospheric pressure. For a perfect vacuum the gauge reading would be 760 mm, but at atmospheric pressure the vacuum-gauge reading is zero.

The vacuum gauge is used to measure the amount of partial vacuum or **depression** in the induction manifold of an engine, typical values at idling speeds are:

Four-cylinder engines .	.	450–500 mmHg
Six-cylinder engines .	.	475–525 mmHg
Eight-cylinder engines	.	500–550 mmHg

The foregoing measurements are correct only when the altitude is between sea-level and 300 m, and for every 300 m above this height the reading is reduced by about 25 mm.

The depression inside the induction manifold of an engine will vary with both engine speed and throttle opening. The vacuum is at its maximum when the throttle is closed quickly; a typical figure is 600 mmHg. During open-road cruising the vacuum reading is about 250 mmHg. During hard pulling on full throttle the vacuum reading is at its lowest, about 50 mmHg.

Engine 'tune-up' service equipment is usually fitted with a vacuum gauge and, with skilful use, this gauge can determine engine faults, thus enabling adjustments to be carried out with accuracy.

Thermodynamic Temperature (the kelvin)

In calculations dealing with gases it is necessary to use the SI unit of temperature, the **kelvin (K)**.

Equal volumes of all gases expand or contract by equal amounts for the same rise or fall of temperature when the pressure is constant. The amount of this expansion or contraction has been found by experiment to be $\frac{1}{273}$ part of the volume of the gas for every Celsius degree change of temperature above or below 0°C.

From the foregoing, if the volume at 0°C = 1 m³, then

$$\text{the volume at } 1°C = (1 + \tfrac{1}{273}) \text{ m}^3,$$
$$\text{the volume at } -1°C = (1 - \tfrac{1}{273}) = \tfrac{272}{273} \text{ m}^3,$$
$$\text{and the volume at } -273°C = 1 - \tfrac{273}{273} = 0$$

This temperature of $-273°$ represents the absolute zero of temperature, at which a gas theoretically has no volume. To obtain kelvins, we add 273° to the normal Celsius temperature; the minus sign is omitted because the figure is the temperature above absolute zero.

Example. The cooling water temperature of an engine is 95°C. Express this value in kelvins.

$$\text{Thermodynamic temperature} = \text{Normal temperature } °C + 273 \text{ K}$$
$$= 95 + 273 \text{ K}$$
$$= \underline{368 \text{ K}}$$

Example. In a certain high-speed c.i. engine the air temperature at the end of compression is 430°C. Express this figure in kelvins.

$$\text{Thermodynamic temperature} = \text{Normal temperature } °C + 273 \text{ K}$$
$$= 430 + 273 \text{ K}$$
$$= \underline{703 \text{ K}}$$

The application of absolute pressure and thermodynamic temperature is shown later in this chapter.

Compression Ratios

In the motor-vehicle engine the fuel–air mixture (gas) is compressed, ignited and burnt in the combustion chamber and the cylinder. The gases thus formed expand and force the piston along the cylinder to do useful work. In this section we are concerned with the **compression ratio** or the measure of the amount of compression of the mixture. The compression ratio is one of the most important factors on which the power and efficiency of an engine depends.

To calculate the compression ratio of an engine we must have values for the following (see Fig. 8.2):

(a) The diameter of the cylinder bore or simply **bore**.
(b) The length of the **stroke** or the distance moved by the piston between t.d.c. and b.d.c.
(c) The **clearance** or combustion chamber volume or the volume above the piston when it is at t.d.c.

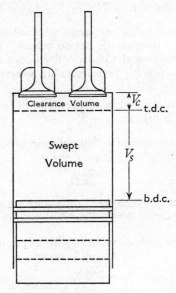

Fig. 8.2.

We can express these values by means of a formula:

$$\text{CR} = \frac{V_s + V_c}{V_c}$$

where CR = the compression ratio
V_s = the piston swept volume
V_c = the clearance volume

The clearance volume of some engines can be found by having one piston at t.d.c. position (firing stroke) and filling the combustion chamber with oil from a measuring cylinder or flask.

In many examination problems the clearance volume *either* is given or it may have to be calculated.

Example. The bore and stroke of an engine are 75 mm and 112 mm respectively. If the volume of the combustion chamber is 65 550 mm³, calculate the compression ratio.

$$CR = \frac{V_s + V_c}{V_c}$$

Now

$$V_s = \text{area of bore} \times \text{length of stroke}$$

$$= \frac{\pi}{4} \times 75^2 \times 112 \text{ mm}^3 = 494\,900 \text{ mm}^3$$

$$\therefore CR = \frac{494\,900 + 65\,550}{65\,550} = \underline{8\cdot55 \text{ to } 1}$$

Example. A petrol engine has a cylinder bore of 95 mm and a stroke of 120 mm. If the compression ratio is 9 to 1, calculate the volume of the combustion space (clearance volume).   (C. and G.)

$$CR = \frac{V_s + V_c}{V_c}$$

Now

$$V_s = \frac{\pi}{4} \times 95^2 \times 120 = 851\,000 \text{ mm}^3$$

Thus

$$9 = \frac{851\,000 + V_c}{V_c}$$

Transposing

$$9V_c = 851\,000 + V_c$$

$$9V_c - V_c = 851\,000 \text{ mm}^3$$

$$8V_c = 851\,000 \text{ mm}^3$$

$$\therefore V_c = \frac{851\,000 \text{ mm}^3}{8} = \underline{106\,375 \text{ mm}^3}$$

Example. The bore and stroke of an engine are 75 mm and 108 mm respectively. To increase the compression ratio, 1·52 mm is machined off the mating surface of the cylinder head. If the original value of the compression ratio was 7·5 to 1, calculate the new compression ratio.

In Fig. 8.2, S = the length of the stroke,

C = the height of the clearance volume.

If we assume that the shape of the clearance volume is cylindrical and of the same diameter as the cylinder (see dotted line, Fig. 8.2),

then

$$CR = \frac{S \times \text{Area} + C \times \text{Area}}{C \times \text{Area}}$$

$$= \frac{\text{Area } (S + C)}{\text{Area} \times C} = \frac{S + C}{C}$$

The area cancels out of the equation because it is a constant.
The original CR = 7·5 to 1.

$$\therefore 7\cdot5 = \frac{S + C}{C}; \ S = 108 \text{ mm}$$

$$\therefore 7\cdot5 = \frac{108 + C}{C}$$

$$\therefore 7\cdot5C - C = 108$$

$$C = \frac{108}{6\cdot5} = 16\cdot62 \text{ mm}$$

When 1·52 mm is removed from the cylinder-head face the new value of

$$C = 16\cdot62 - 1\cdot52 \text{ mm}$$

$$= 15\cdot1 \text{ mm}$$

$$\therefore \text{ new CR} = \frac{108 + 15\cdot1}{15\cdot1} = \underline{8\cdot13 \text{ to } 1}$$

Connection between the Volume, the Pressure and the Temperature of a Gas

Changes in the **volume** of a gas can be produced:
(a) By a change in **pressure** (abs.).
(b) By a change in **temperature** (K).
(c) By changes in both the pressure and the temperature at the same time.

Note. Pressure *must* be **absolute** and temperature K.

We can study the changes which take place in the volume, the pressure and the temperature of a gas in three distinct stages:

(1) The temperature is kept constant, but the pressure is varied.
(2) The temperature is varied, but the pressure or the volume is kept constant.

(3) The temperature, the volume and the pressure are varied simultaneously.

We take each stage in turn.

(1) Pressure varied, temperature constant. Let us imagine the following apparatus (see Fig. 8.3), a cylinder fitted with a pressure gauge and a movable piston assumed to be frictionless. The cylinder is closed at one end so that it contains a quantity of gas maintained at a constant temperature. If we move the piston up the cylinder the volume of gas V_1 decreases and the pressure gauge shows that the pressure p_1 increases

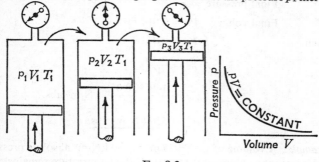

FIG 8.3.

in inverse ratio. That is, when the volume is halved the pressure is doubled, and when the volume is decreased to one-third of its original value the pressure is trebled and so on. Whether the piston is moved up or down the cylinder the volume of gas is always inversely proportional to its pressure; whatever the volume and pressure may be, their product is always the same.

If p_1 and V_1 denote the pressure and the volume of a gas at one stage, p_2, V_2 and p_3, V_3 the corresponding values of the same gas at other stages, then $p_1V_1 = p_2V_2 = p_3V_3$ and so on. This relationship is known as **Boyle's Law,** and it states:

At constant temperature, the product of the absolute pressure and volume of a gas remains constant.

The pressure must be **absolute.**

This law can be expressed as follows:

$$pV = \text{a constant}$$

Example. Air was compressed in a cylinder so that the temperature remained constant. The initial volume was 0·055 m³ and the pressure then was 140 kN/m² absolute. If the final volume was 0·014 m³, what was then the pressure?

Since the temperature remains constant, the change must follow Boyle's Law.

Data   Initial pressure $p_1 = 140$ kN/m² abs.

Initial volume $V_1 = 0·055$ m³

Final pressure $p_2 = ?$

Final volume $V_2 = 0·014$ m³

Then
$$p_1 V_1 = p_2 V_2$$
$$\therefore p_2 = \frac{p_1 V_1}{V_2}$$
$$= \frac{140 \times 0·055}{0·014} \text{ kN/m² abs.}$$
$$= \underline{550 \text{ kN/m² abs.}}$$

Example. A volume of gas 0·055 m³ at 550 kN/m² absolute pressure expands until the volume is 0·142 m³. If the temperature remains constant, what will be the final pressure?

Data   Initial pressure $p_1 = 550$ kN/m² abs.

Initial volume $V_1 = 0·055$ m³

Final pressure $p_2 = ?$

Final volume $V_2 = 0·142$ m³

Then
$$p_1 V_1 = p_2 V_2$$
$$\therefore p_2 = \frac{p_1 V_1}{V_2}$$
$$= \frac{550 \times 0·055}{0·142} \text{ kN/m² abs.}$$
$$= \underline{213 \text{ kN/m² abs.}}$$

(2) Temperature varied, volume or pressure kept constant. Using the same apparatus as for the first stage, with the addition of a thermometer (see Fig. 8.4 (*a*)), the temperature T_1 is increased by a known amount and this new temperature is denoted by T_2. Now, either of two things must happen:

(a) If a constant volume is maintained by preventing the piston from moving, then the pressure will rise and the new pressure is denoted by p_2, see Fig. 8.4 (*b*).

(b) If a constant pressure is maintained by allowing the piston to move down (see Fig. 8.4 (*c*)), then the volume will increase and the new volume is denoted by V_2.

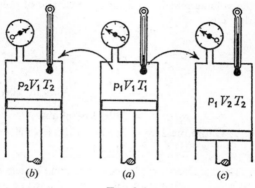

(*b*)   (*a*)   (*c*)

FIG. 8.4.

If p_1, V_1 and T_1 are the initial values of the pressure, the volume and the temperature, and P_2, V_2 and T_2 are the final values of the pressure, the volume and the temperature, then:

$$\frac{V_1}{V_2} = \frac{T_1}{T_2} \quad \text{or} \quad \frac{p_1}{p_2} = \frac{T_1}{T_2}$$

This relationship is known as **Charles' Law**, and it can be stated:

At constant pressure, the volume of a gas increases by equal amounts for equal rises of temperature.

Also at constant volume, the pressure of a gas increases by equal amounts for equal rises of temperature.

Temperature must be in K and pressure must be in absolute units.

Example. Motor-vehicle tyres have burst when exposed to considerable heat from the sun. The air inside the tyre has been heated, but it has been unable to increase in volume, the pressure has therefore increased until the tyre has burst.

Example. The pressure gauge shows that the air pressure in a tyre is 248 kN/m² at a temperature of 45°C. If the temperature drops to 18°C and the volume remains constant, what is the gauge pressure at the lower temperature?

Data Initial pressure $= p_1 = 248 + 101 \cdot 3 = 349 \cdot 3$ kN/m² abs.
Final pressure $= p_2 = ?$
Initial temperature $= T_1 = 45 + 273 = 318$ K
Final temperature $= T_2 = 18 + 273 = 291$ K

Because the volume remains constant, the change of pressure must follow Charles' Law.

Then
$$\frac{p_1}{p_2} = \frac{T_1}{T_2}$$
$$\therefore \ p_2 = \frac{p_1 T_2}{T_1}$$
$$= \frac{349 \cdot 3 \times 291}{318} \text{ kN/m}^2 \text{ abs.}$$
$$= 319 \cdot 7 \text{ kN/m}^2 \text{ abs.}$$
$$\therefore \text{ Gauge pressure} = 319 \cdot 7 - 101 \cdot 3 \text{ kN/m}^2$$
$$= \underline{218 \cdot 4 \text{ kN/m}^2}$$

Example. The air reservoir of a power braking system is pumped up rapidly to a gauge pressure of 830 kN/m², the temperature of the air being 40°C. Shortly afterwards the temperature has fallen to 19°C.

Assuming that no air has left or entered the reservoir during the interval, calculate the gauge pressure at the lower temperature.

Data Initial pressure $= p_1 = 830 + 101 \cdot 3 = 931 \cdot 3$ kN/m² abs.
Final pressure $= p_2 = ?$
Initial temperature $= T_1 = 40 + 273 = 313$ K
Final temperature $= T_2 = 19 + 273 = 292$ K

Because the volume remains constant, the change of pressure must follow Charles' Law.

Then
$$\frac{p_1}{p_2} = \frac{T_1}{T_2}$$
$$\therefore \ p_2 = \frac{p_1 T_2}{T_1}$$
$$= \frac{931 \cdot 3 \times 292}{313} = 868 \cdot 8 \text{ kN/m}^2 \text{ abs.}$$
$$\therefore \text{ Gauge pressure} = 868 \cdot 8 - 101 \cdot 3 \text{ kN/m}^2$$
$$= \underline{767 \cdot 5 \text{ kN/m}^2}$$

(3) Variation in volume, pressure and temperature simultaneously. In practice it is usual to find that the pressure, volume and temperature of a gas all change at the same time. Therefore, in order to solve the problems involved in these changes, the laws of Boyle and Charles must be combined, so that

$$\frac{p_1 V_1}{T_1} = \frac{p_2 V_2}{T_2}$$

where

Initial pressure $= p_1$

Final pressure $= p_2$

Initial volume $= V_1$

Final volume $= V_2$

Initial temperature $= T_1$

Final temperature $= T_2$

The temperature must be in K and pressure *must* be *absolute* in every instance.

The change is assumed to take place in two steps which we denote by (*a*) and (*b*).

(*a*) A change of pressure from p_1 to p_2 at a constant temperature T_1. Since the temperature has not yet changed, the final volume V_2 will not be reached. The volume V_1 will, however, change to an intermediate value which we denote by V. Then, from Boyle's law, $p_1 V_1 = p_2 V$; therefore the state of the gas is now p_2; V; T_1.

(*b*) A change of temperature from T_1 to T_2 at a constant pressure p_2 follows Charles' law and results in the following:

The volume changes from V to V_2 and completes the total change of state of the gas to p_2, V_2, T_2.

We can now express the steps (*a*) and (*b*) each as a formula:

(*a*)
$$p_1 V_1 = p_2 V$$
$$\therefore V = \frac{p_1 V_1}{p_2}$$

(*b*) We know already from Charles' law that $\frac{V_1}{V_2} = \frac{T_1}{T_2}$ and by transposing we get $\frac{V_1}{T_1} = \frac{V_2}{T_2}$.

When V_1 changes to V in the intermediate stage we get $\dfrac{V}{T_1} = \dfrac{V_2}{T_2}$, which we can call Eq. 1. But from (a) $V = \dfrac{p_1 V_1}{p_2}$ and, if we substitute this $\dfrac{p_1 V_1}{p_2}$ in place of V in Eq. 1, we have:

$$\frac{p_1 V_1}{p_2} \div T_1 = \frac{V_2}{T_2} \text{ or } \frac{p_1 V_1}{p_2 T_1} = \frac{V_2}{T_2}$$

and, by transposing, we have $\dfrac{p_1 V_1}{T_1} = \dfrac{p_2 V_2}{T_2}$, which is the law of Boyle and Charles combined.

The combined laws find expression in the operation of the c.i. engine. The piston compresses the air inside the cylinder (change in pressure and volume). This increases the temperature of the air to about 550°C (change in temperature). When the fuel oil is sprayed into the combustion chamber the prevailing high air temperature ignites the oil and causes the required expansion.

Example. In a certain c.i. engine whose compression ratio is 15 to 1, pressure at the beginning of compression is 100 kN/m² abs., and at the end of compression 3500 kN/m² abs. If the temperature of the air is 27°C at the start of compression, what will be the temperature of the air at the end of compression stroke?

Data	$p_1 = 100 \text{ kN/m}^2$ abs.
	$p_2 = 3500 \text{ kN/m}^2$ abs.
	$\dfrac{V_1}{V_2} = \dfrac{15}{1}$
	$T_1 = 27 + 273 = 300 \text{ K}$
	$T_2 = ?$
Now	$\dfrac{p_1 V_1}{T_1} = \dfrac{p_2 V_2}{T_2}$

$$\therefore T_2 = \frac{p_2 V_2 T_1}{p_1 V_1}$$

$$= \frac{3500 \times 300 \times 1}{100 \times 15} = 700 \text{ K}$$

$\therefore$ Final temperature $= 700 - 273 = \underline{427°C}$

Example. In a certain engine cylinder the volume of gas is 0·0024 m³ at 120 kN/m² abs. and 27°C. What will be the volume when the pressure and the temperature are increased to 840 kN/m² abs. and 77°C?

Data
$$p_1 = 120 \text{ kN/m}^2 \text{ abs.}$$
$$p_2 = 840 \text{ kN/m}^2 \text{ abs.}$$
$$V_1 = 0\cdot0024 \text{ m}^3$$
$$V_2 = ?$$
$$T_1 = 27 + 273 = 300 \text{ K}$$
$$T_2 = 77 + 273 = 350 \text{ K}$$

Now
$$\frac{p_1 V_1}{T_1} = \frac{p_2 V_2}{T_2}$$
$$\therefore V_2 = \frac{p_1 V_1 T_2}{p_2 T_1} = \frac{120 \times 0\cdot0024 \times 350}{840 \times 300} \text{ m}^3$$
$$= \underline{0\cdot0004 \text{ m}^3}$$

Standard Temperature and Pressure (s.t.p.)

It is often necessary for comparison and other reasons to know the volume of gas at a definite temperature and pressure. The values chosen are 0°C and 101·3 kN/m². These values are called **standard temperature and pressure (s.t.p.)**. To calculate the volume of gas at s.t.p. we use Boyle's and Charles' Laws.

Example. An oxygen cylinder contains 0·6m³ of gas, and the pressure of the gas is 811·2 kN/m² abs. at a temperature of 21°C. Reduce the volume of gas to s.t.p.

Data
$$p_1 = 811\cdot2 \text{ kN/m}^2 \text{ abs.}$$
$$V_1 = 0\cdot6 \text{ m}^3$$
$$T_1 = 273 + 21 = 294 \text{ K}$$
$$p_2 = 101\cdot3 \text{ kN/m}^2 \text{ abs.}$$
$$V_2 = ?$$
$$T_2 = 273 \text{ K}$$
$$\frac{p_1 V_1}{T_1} = \frac{p_2 V_2}{T_2}$$
$$\therefore V_2 = \frac{811\cdot2 \times 0\cdot6 \times 273}{101\cdot3 \times 294} = \underline{4\cdot45 \text{ m}^3}$$

Specific Heat of Gases

The specific heat of a gas is the quantity of heat required to give 1 degree rise in temperature to 1 kg of gas.

When dealing with the heating of gases there are two extreme conditions:

(a) heating at **constant volume**;

(b) heating at **constant pressure**.

When the gas is heated at constant volume all the heat is used to produce a rise of temperature and therefore an increased pressure. For example, tyres have failed when subjected to high temperatures because the volume of air in the tyre remains almost constant, but the pressure increases with high temperatures so that the tyres burst.

The symbol used for the specific heat of a gas at constant volume is c_v and its value for dry air is 0.7076 kJ/kg K.

When a gas is heated at constant pressure, then the volume increases and work is done by the expanding gas on its surroundings; this is called the **external work** done. For example, in theory the Diesel engine relies on expansion at constant pressure. The air heated by the burning fuel expands at constant pressure and so does work on the piston.

The symbol used for specific heat at constant pressure is c_p, and its value for dry air is 0.9965 kJ/kg K.

In practice, the heating of gases is generally between the foregoing extremes and the heating is neither at constant volume nor at constant pressure. We shall use the values for specific heat later in this chapter.

Expansion and Compression of Gases

The operation of the internal-combustion engine depends on the expansion and compression of a mixture of gases; in this section we consider the various types of expansion and compression which occur.

There are again two extreme conditions:

(a) **isothermal** expansion and compression;

(b) **adiabatic** expansion and compression.

In isothermal expansion and compression the volume of a gas changes without a change of temperature occurring; any heat due to the expansion or compression is immediately absorbed by the surroundings. The change therefore follows Boyle's law, i.e. $pV =$ a constant. Generally speaking, however, we are not concerned with isothermal changes in calculations for internal-combustion engines.

In adiabatic expansion and compression when the volume of a gas changes there is no transfer of heat either way between the gas and any external substance. The change then follows the law

$$pV^\gamma = \text{a constant}$$

where γ (gamma) $= c_p \div c_v = 0.9965 \div 0.7076 = 1.4$ for dry air.

In practice, neither isothermal nor adiabatic changes are possible, as there is always some transfer of heat either way between the gas and any external substance. But the expansion of gases in the high-speed modern engines is fairly close to adiabatic, since there is little time for any interchange of heat between the gas and the cylinder walls. The type of change which does occur follows a law between $pV = $ a constant and $pV^\gamma = $ a constant. This law is generally stated as $pV^n = $ a constant. The value of n depends on the type of gas, but its value lies between 1 and γ; a typical figure is 1.25. The value of γ for dry air has already been given as 1.4.

By experiment, it has also been found that

$$T_1 V_1^{\gamma-1} = T_2 V_2^{\gamma-1} \quad \text{and} \quad \frac{T_1^\gamma}{p_1^{\gamma-1}} = \frac{T_2^\gamma}{p_2^{\gamma-1}}$$

Worked examples showing the application of the foregoing equations are given later in this chapter.

We are now in a position to apply some of the terms used earlier in this section.

Constant-volume and Constant-pressure Engine Cycles

The petrol engine generally uses the Otto or constant-volume cycle of operations:

(1) adiabatic compression of the mixture;
(2) constant volume heating of the mixture, hence the term 'constant volume' used for this cycle;
(3) adiabatic expansion of the mixture;
(4) constant volume cooling of the mixture.

The diesel or constant pressure cycle is:

(1) adiabatic compression;
(2) constant pressure heating, hence the term 'constant pressure' used for this cycle;
(3) adiabatic expansion;
(4) constant volume cooling.

The practical c.i. engine works on a 'mixed' cycle, since the expansion pressure does not remain constant during the first part of the expansion stroke. But we generally use the term constant pressure for the c.i. engine cycle and the term constant volume for the Otto cycle.

The following worked examples show the application of the equations given earlier in this section.

Example. At the commencement of compression a cylinder contains 0·000 375 m³ of gas at a pressure of 100 kN/m² absolute, and temperature 110°C. Compression takes place according to the law $pV^{1·27} =$ constant. Calculate the pressure and temperature when the volume of the gas is 0·000 075 m³. If the pressure is raised to 3792 kN/m² absolute by combustion at constant volume, what will be the temperature of the gas?   (C. and G.)

Data

$p_1 = 100$ kN/m² abs.
$p_2 = ?$
$V_1 = 0·000\ 375$ m³
$V_2 = 0·000\ 075$ m³
$T_1 = 110°C,\ 383$ K
$T_2 = ?$

Now $p_1 V_1^{1·27} = p_2 V_2^{1·27}$

thus $100 \times 0·000\ 375^{1·27} = p_2 \times 0·000\ 075^{1·27}$

$$\therefore p_2 = 100 \times \left(\frac{0·000\ 375}{0·000\ 075}\right)^{1·27} \text{kN/m² abs.}$$

$$= 772·1 \text{ kN/m² abs.}$$

Then $\dfrac{p_1 V_1}{T_1} = \dfrac{p_2 V_2}{T_2}$

$$\frac{100 \times 0·000\ 375}{383} = \frac{772·1 \times 0·000\ 075}{T_2}$$

$$\therefore T_2 = \frac{772·1 \times 0·000\ 075 \times 383}{100 \times 0·000\ 375} \text{ K}$$

$$= 591·4 - 273 = 318·4 \text{ °C}$$

From the foregoing working we have

$T^2 = 591·4$ K
$T_3 = ?$
$p_3 = 3792$ kN/m² abs.
$p_2 = 772·1$ kN/m² abs.

Since the gas is heated at constant volume all the heat passes into the gas.

Thus
$$\frac{T_2}{T_3} = \frac{p_2}{p_3}$$

$$\frac{591 \cdot 4}{T_3} = \frac{772 \cdot 1}{3792}$$

$$\therefore T_3 = \frac{591 \cdot 4 \times 3792}{772 \cdot 1} \text{ K}$$

$$= 2904 \text{ K}$$

$$= 2904 - 273°C$$

$$= \underline{2631°C}$$

Example. A certain c.i. engine has a compression ratio of 16 to 1.

(*a*) Calculate the air temperature at maximum compression, starting from cold, when air enters the engine at 20°C. The initial pressure is 96·5 kN/m² abs.

(*b*) Calculate the pressure at the end of compression stroke. (Take $\gamma = 1 \cdot 4$.)

Data
$$T_1 = 20°C = 293 \text{ K}$$
$$T_2 = ?$$
$$V_1 = 16$$
$$V_2 = \frac{1}{16}$$
$$\gamma = 1 \cdot 4$$

(*a*) Using the formula $T_1 \cdot V_1{}^{\gamma-1} = T_2 \cdot V_2{}^{\gamma-1}$,

$$293 V_1{}^{0 \cdot 4} = T_2 \left(\frac{V_1}{16}\right)^{0 \cdot 4} \qquad (\gamma - 1 = 0 \cdot 4)$$

Dividing each side by $V_1{}^{0 \cdot 4}$, we get

$$293 = \frac{T_2}{16^{0 \cdot 4}}$$

$$\therefore T_2 = 293 \times 16^{0 \cdot 4} \text{ K}$$

$$= 888 \cdot 2 \text{ K}$$

$$= \underline{615 \cdot 2°C}$$

(b) Using the formula $\dfrac{T_1^\gamma}{p_1^{\gamma-1}} = \dfrac{T_2^\gamma}{p_2^{\gamma-1}}$, then

$$\frac{293^{1\cdot4}}{96\cdot5^{0\cdot4}} = \frac{888\cdot2^{1\cdot4}}{p_2^{0\cdot4}}$$

$$\therefore p_2^{0\cdot4} = \frac{888\cdot2^{1\cdot4} \times 96\cdot5^{0\cdot4}}{293^{1\cdot4}}$$

Using logs we get

$$0\cdot4 \log p_2 = (2\cdot9485 \times 1\cdot4) + (1\cdot9845 \times 0\cdot4) - (2\cdot4669 \times 1\cdot4)$$

$$0\cdot4 \log p_2 = 1\cdot468\,04$$

$$\log p_2 = 1\cdot468\,04 \div 0\cdot4 = 3\cdot67$$

$$\therefore p_2 = 4677 \text{ kN/m}^2 \text{ abs.}$$

$$= \underline{4575\cdot6 \text{ kN/m}^2}$$

Example. In a certain c.i. engine, air is compressed according to the law $pV^{1\cdot35} = $ constant.

The initial pressure is 96·5 kN/m² abs. and the compression ratio is 14 to 1. Calculate the pressure at the end of the compression stroke.

Data	$p_1 = 96\cdot5 \text{ kN/m}^2 \text{ abs.}$
	$p_2 = ?$
	$V_1 = 14$
	$V_2 = \dfrac{1}{14}$

Then

$$p_1 V_1^{1\cdot35} = p_2 V_2^{1\cdot35}$$

$$96\cdot5 \times V_1^{1\cdot35} = p_2 \times \left(\frac{1}{14}\right)^{1\cdot35}$$

$$\therefore p_2 = 96\cdot5 \times 14^{1\cdot35}$$

(we have divided each side by $V_1^{1\cdot35}$)

$$= \underline{3402 \text{ kN/m}^2 \text{ abs.}}$$

Temperature/Pressure Curves for Boiling Point of Water

Modern motor-vehicle engines have pressurized water-cooling systems. There are several advantages in this system:

(1) a small loss of coolant and reduction in the formation of sludge and scale;

(2) the temperature of the boiling point of the coolant is not unduly lowered at high altitudes;

(3) the pressure raises the boiling point and thus improves the thermal efficiency of the engine:

A laboratory experiment to determine the relationship between boiling-point temperature and pressure is as follows:

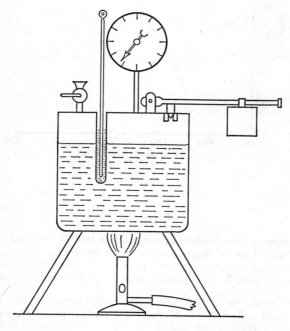

Fig. 8.5.

Fig. 8.5 shows a boiler partly filled with water and a thermometer in the 'pocket'. Heat is applied to the boiler, and when steam issues from the filling valve it is closed; the thermometer should now record 100°C and the pressure gauge 0 kN/m² (101·3 kN/m² abs.). As further

heat is applied the temperature and pressure readings should be recorded
and plotted to give a graph as shown in Fig. 8.6.

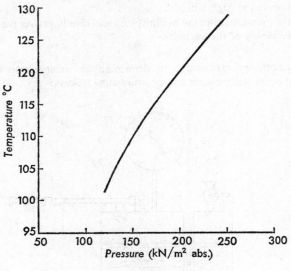

Fig. 8.6.

Exercise 8

1. A four-cylinder engine has a cylinder bore of 60 mm and a stroke
of 95 mm. What is the total capacity of the engine and what must
be the volume of the combustion chamber in order to give a 6 to 1
compression ratio?   (1 075 000 mm³; 53 740 mm²)   (C. and G.)

2. An engine has a bore of 60 mm and a stroke of 95 mm, the
compression ratio is 4·75 to 1. Assuming that the piston crown is flat,
find the increase in length between the gudgeon-pin centre line and the
piston crown which would be necessary to increase the compression
ratio to 5 to 1?   (1·58 mm)   (C. and G.)

3. An engine has a 75 mm bore and 75 mm stroke, the compression
ratio is 5·6 to 1. To increase this 1·27 mm of metal is removed from the
cylinder head joint face. Calculate the new compression ratio.

(5·988)   (C. and G.)

4. The pressure in a tyre is checked and found to be 172 kN/m² by tyre gauge at a temperature of 16°C. After running for some time the temperature rises to 48°C. Assuming the volume of air in the tyre to be constant, calculate its pressure. (202·3 kN/m²) (C. and G.)

5. The air reservoir of a power-braking system is pumped up rapidly to a gauge pressure of 690 kN/m², the temperature of the air being 33°C (306 K). Shortly afterwards the temperature has fallen to 15°C (288 K). Assuming that no air has entered or left the reservoir during the interval, calculate the gauge pressure at the lower temperature.

(643·5 kN/m²) (C. and G.)

6. In a certain engine the volume of the gas is 0·002 13 m³ at 180 kN/m² and 37°C. What will the volume become when the pressure and temperature are increased to 910 kN/m² and 87°C?

(Pressures are given as absolute.)

(0·000 489 4 m³ or 489 400 mm³)

7. In a certain c.i. engine whose compression ratio is 16 to 1, the pressure at the beginning of compression is 103 kN/m² abs., and at the end of compression 3792 kN/m² abs. If the air temperature is then 43°C, what will be the temperature of the air at the end of the compression stroke? (454°C)

8. Write down the equation connecting the pressure, temperature and volume of a gas, stating clearly the meaning of each term.

If the compression ratio in an engine is 7 to 1, what will be the compression pressure if the fuel–air mixture is drawn in at 96·5 kN/m² abs. and temperature 13°C, the temperature at the end of compression is 149°C? (895·2 kN/m² gauge) (E.M.E.U.)

9. The bore and stroke of an engine are 75 mm and 114 mm respectively. The volume of the combustion chamber is 110 600 mm³. Calculate the compression ratio. (5·55) (C. and G.)

10. The combustion chamber of an o.h.v. engine is hemispherical, the radius being equal to that of the bore radius. The bore and stroke are 80 mm and 140 mm respectively. Assuming that the piston just reaches the hemisphere, calculate the swept volume of the cylinder and the compression ratio. (0·000 704 m³; 6·25) (C. and G.)

11. The volume of air in a tyre is 0·012 72 m³ when the pressure-gauge reading is 193 kN/m² and the temperature is 18°C. If the temperature of the air rises to 72°C while the volume increases to 0·013 27 m³, what will be the new pressure-gauge reading? (233·3 kN/m²) (N.C.T.E.C.)

12. An engine has a bore and stroke of 65 mm by 106 mm and a compression ratio of 6·5. The area of the combustion chamber space in the plane of the gasket is 6000 mm². How much thicker will the gasket have to be in order to make the compression ratio 5·5?

$$(2·37 \text{ mm}) \quad (\text{C. and G.})$$

13. A certain engine has a bore of 100 mm and the volume of the combustion space (clearance volume) is equal to that of a hemisphere of diameter equal to the bore. Calculate the stroke of the piston if the compression ratio, based on a full stroke volume, is 4·75 to 1.

$$(125 \text{ mm}) \quad (\text{C. and G.})$$

14. (*a*) What do you understand by kelvin and Absolute Pressure? (*b*) At the commencement of compression a cylinder contains 0·000 49 m³ of gas at a pressure of 96·5 kN/m² abs. and temperature 100°C. At the end of compression the volume is 0·000 098 m³ and the pressure 724 kN/m² abs. What will be the temperature at the end of compression? $\qquad (286·7°\text{C}) \quad (\text{C. and G.})$

15. An air receiver having a volume of 0·000 065 m³ has air pumped into it until the pressure rises to 586 kN/m² on the gauge, the temperature of the air being 90°C. When the temperature of the air has fallen to 18°C, what then will be the pressure-gauge reading?

$$(449·7 \text{ kN/m}^2) \quad (\text{U.E.I.})$$

16. Calculate the adiabatic compression pressure for an engine whose compression ratio is 6·8 to 1 when

$$p_2 = p_1\left(\frac{V_1}{V_2}\right)^{1·4}, \quad p_1 = 101·3 \text{ kN/m}^2 \text{ abs.}$$

$$(1381·7 \text{ kN/m}^2)$$

17. A volume of 0·28 m³ of air at a pressure of 96·5 kN/m² abs. and a temperature of 22°C is compressed to a volume of 0·07 m³, the temperature rising to 140°C. Calculate the new pressure of the air.

$$(540·5 \text{ kN/m}^2 \text{ abs.}) \quad (\text{U.E.I.})$$

18. An engine cylinder is 85 mm bore and the stroke of the piston is 100 mm while the clearance volume is 92 000 mm³. If the temperature and pressure at the commencement of the compression stroke are 27°C and 90 kN/m² absolute respectively, calculate the temperature at the end of the compression stroke if the pressure has risen to 1070 kN/m² absolute. $\qquad (226°\text{C}) \quad (\text{U.E.I.})$

19. The piston of an engine sweeps a volume of 475 000 mm³ and the clearance volume at the top of the stroke is 96 000 mm³. Calculate the compression ratio. At the end of the suction stroke the cylinder is full of mixture at a pressure of 3·5 kN/m² below atmospheric. Assuming no loss of volume, and the temperature to remain constant, calculate the pressure at the end of the compression stroke.

How could the clearance volume of a cylinder be measured?

$$(5·947; 480·3 \text{ kN/m}^2) \quad (\text{U.E.I.})$$

20. (*a*) The compression ratio of an engine is 7·5 to 1. If air enters the cylinder at a pressure of 96·5 kN/m² abs. and temperature 15°C, what is the pressure at the end of compression if the compression is according to Boyle's Law?

(*b*) Determine the compression ratio in a Diesel-type engine in which the temperature of the air in the cylinder is raised by compression from 15°C to 550°C, the pressure rising at the same time from 100 kN/m² abs. to 3400 kN/m² abs. ((*a*) 622·3 kN/m²; (*b*) 11·89) (E.M.E.U.)

21. (*a*) Describe with the aid of sketches an experiment to show that the absolute pressure of a gas varies inversely as its volume when the temperature of the gas remains constant.

(*b*) What is the relationship between the absolute pressure, thermodynamic temperature and the volume of a gas?

(*c*) Calculate the temperature at the end of the compression stroke of an engine having a compression ratio of 13 to 1 if the initial volume is 0·000 64 m³, the initial pressure is 110 kN/m² abs., the initial temperature 65°C and the final pressure 3310 kN/m² abs.

(782·1 K or 509·1°C) (C.and G.)

9 Liquids

Pressure in a Liquid

Liquids such as hydraulic brake and jack fluids, damper (shock-absorber) fluids and special fluids for vehicle suspension systems are in general use. In the following section some of the principles relating to the pressure of liquids are examined.

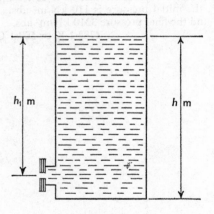

FIG. 9.1.

(1) **The pressure of a liquid is constant throughout when applied to the inside of a hydraulic system or liquids transmit pressure equally in all directions.**

This principle is the most important when considering the pressure of a liquid as far as automobile engineering is concerned, because all the hydraulic systems of vehicles and equipment operate on the principle of equal fluid pressure. Also, if a pressure is exerted on the surface or some section of the fluid, then a corresponding increase in pressure occurs on all sides and surfaces of the system containing the fluid. The examples given in Chapter 7, pp. 107–13, show the application of fluid pressure to various hydraulic systems.

(2) **The pressure exerted by a liquid depends entirely on the head of liquid.**

The **head** of a liquid is the vertical height of the liquid measured from a given base to the surface of the liquid, see Fig. 9.1, where h represents the head of a liquid. The height of a liquid above a given base is entirely responsible for the pressure exerted on that base.

The following examples show the value of the pressure, in kN/m², of a mass of water having a cross-sectional area of 1 m² and a height of 1 m.

Let h = height of the mass of water = 1 m

$$\text{Volume of water} = \text{Height} \times \text{Area of base}$$

$$= h \times 1 \text{ m}^3$$

$$\text{Mass of water} = h \times 1 \times 1000 \text{ kg}$$

$$= h\,1000 \text{ kg}$$

$$\therefore \text{Force on base} = h\,1000 \times 9{\cdot}8 \text{ N}$$

$$= h \times 9{\cdot}8 \text{ kN}$$

Since the area of the base = 1 m³, then:

$$\text{Pressure on base} = \frac{\text{Force}}{\text{Area}}$$

$$= \underline{9{\cdot}8\,h \text{ kN/m}^2}$$

Thus the pressure, in kN/m², of a mass of water is 9·8 kN/m², multiplied by the height of the mass in metres. This value is used in the following examples.

Example. A rectangular water tank 3·5 m long, 3 m wide and 1·8 m deep, is filled with water. Calculate: (a) the pressure on the base of the tank, in kN/m²; (b) the total force exerted by the water on the base of the tank, in newtons.

Pressure on the base depends on the head of water, which is 1·8 m.

$$\text{Pressure on base} = 9·8 \times 1·8$$
$$= \underline{17·64 \text{ kN/m}^2}$$
$$\text{Total force on base} = \text{Pressure} \times \text{Area}$$
$$= 17·64 \times 3·5 \times 3$$
$$= \underline{185·2 \text{ kN}}$$

If we have to consider other liquids besides water, the pressure exerted at any depth can be calculated provided we know the relative density of the liquid.

Example. A petrol storage tank 5 m × 4 m × 3 m deep is filled with petrol of relative density 0·72. Calculate: (a) the pressure on the base of the tank, in kN/m²; (b) the total force on the base of the tank, in kN.

$$\text{Pressure on base} = 9·8 \times \text{relative density} \times h$$
$$= 9·8 \times 0·72 \times 3$$
$$= \underline{21·17 \text{ kN/m}^2}$$
$$\text{Total force on base} = \text{Pressure} \times \text{Area}$$
$$= 21·17 \times 5 \times 4 \text{ kN}$$
$$= \underline{423·4 \text{ kN}}$$

Flow of Liquids

A simple example of the flow of a liquid is a jet of water discharging through a sharp-edged **orifice** (circular hole) from a tank containing a constant head of water, Fig. 9.1. The potential energy of the water at the surface is changed into kinetic energy at the orifice. After the jet of water has passed the orifice, its cross-sectional area contracts at a short distance from the orifice. This effect is called the **vena contracta** or contracted vein; the water reaches its maximum velocity at this point.

To obtain the quantity of water discharged in a given time we must consider both the contraction and the velocity of the water. For a sharp-edged orifice the cross-sectional area of the contracted vein is about 0·64 of the cross-sectional area of the orifice. This value has been determined by experiment and is called the **coefficient of contraction** (*C*).

The velocity of the water is determined as follows, Fig. 9.1. The level of water in the tank is h_1 m above the centre of the orifice, and the theoretical velocity of the jet of water is about equal to that of a body falling freely through the height h m, i.e., $\sqrt{2gh_1}$ m/s. The actual velocity, however, has been found to be about 0·97 of the theoretical velocity $\sqrt{2gh_1}$ m/s, and this number is called the **coefficient of velocity** (*C_v*). The product of the coefficient of contraction *C* and **the coefficient of velocity** C_v is known as the coefficient of discharge. Since

$$C = 0\cdot64 \quad \text{and} \quad C_v = 0\cdot97$$

then

$$C_a = 0\cdot64 \times 0\cdot97 = 0\cdot62$$

The determination of the coefficient of discharge C_a is now shown. The value of the coefficient of discharge is obtained by experiment. The actual discharge of water from the tank is collected in a calibrated vessel of known mass; the value of the mass of the vessel and water are taken and the mass of water is determined by subtraction.

The theoretical discharge of water is given by the theoretical velocity × area of orifice *A*, thus:

Theoretical discharge $= \sqrt{2gh_1} \times A$

The coefficient of discharge C_a is given by:

$$C_a = \frac{\text{Actual discharge}}{\text{Theoretical discharge}}$$

Quantity of water discharged through orifice

The quantity of water discharged can be calculated by using the following formula:

Let $\quad Q$ = quantity of water discharged, in m³/s

$\qquad C_a$ = coefficient of discharge

$\quad \sqrt{2gh_1}$ = velocity of body falling freely through the distance *h*, in m/s

$\qquad A$ = area of orifice, in m²

then $\qquad Q = C_a\sqrt{2gh_1} \times A$ m³/s

Example. Water is discharged through a sharp-edged orifice 0·0125 m diameter under a constant head of 1·2 m; the coefficient of discharge is 0·62.

Calculate the quantity of water discharged per minute, in litres.

$$Q = C_d \sqrt{2gh_1} \times A, \text{ m}^3/\text{s}$$

$$A = \frac{\pi \times (0.0125)^2}{4} = 0.000\ 122\ 8 \text{ m}^2$$

Then $Q = 0.62 \times \sqrt{2 \times 9.8 \times 1.2} \times 0.000\ 122\ 8 \text{ m}^3/\text{s}$

$\quad = 0.62 \times \sqrt{2 \times 9.8 \times 1.2} \times 0.000\ 122\ 8 \times 60 \text{ m}^3/\text{min}$

$\quad = 0.022\ 14 \text{ m}^3/\text{min}$

Now 1 m³ of water contains 1000 litres

$$\therefore Q \text{ litres/min} = 0.022\ 14 \times 1000$$

$$= \underline{22.14 \text{ litres/min}}$$

Example. An orifice 0·025 m diameter discharges 89 litres of water per min under a head of 1·2 m. Calculate the coefficient of discharge of the orifice. The acceleration due to gravity may be taken as 9·8 m/s².

(U.L.C.I.)

Area of orifice $A = \frac{\pi}{4} \times 0.025^2 = 0.000\ 490\ 9 \text{ m}^2$

Theoretical velocity of flow $= \sqrt{2gh_1}$

$$= \sqrt{2 \times 9.8 \times 1.2}$$

$$= 4.849 \text{ m/s}$$

Theoretical discharge $=$ Area $\times$ Velocity

$$= 0.000\ 490\ 9 \times 4.849 \times 60 \text{ m}^3/\text{min}$$

$$= 0.1429 \text{ m}^3/\text{min}$$

Actual discharge $= 89 \div 1000$

$$= 0.089 \text{ m}^3/\text{min}$$

$$\therefore \text{Coefficient of discharge} = \frac{\text{Actual discharge}}{\text{Theoretical discharge}}$$

$$= \frac{0.089}{0.1429}$$

$$= \underline{0.6232}$$

Rate of Flow of Oil through a Gear-type Pump

The rate of flow or discharge rate of an oil pump can be calculated from the following formula:

$$\text{Rate of discharge} = ALNRne \text{ litres/min}$$

where A = area of space between two adjacent teeth, m²

L = length of teeth, m

N = pump-shaft speed, rev/min

R = number of teeth in each gear wheel

n = number of gear wheels in pump

e = efficiency of pump, per cent

Example. In a gear-type oil pump containing two gear wheels, each wheel has 12 teeth, the area between two teeth is 0·045 16 m², length of teeth 0·025 m, pump-shaft speed 1000 rev/min and efficiency of the pump is 65 per cent.

Determine the oil discharge from the pump in litres per minute

Discharge rate = 2 × 12 × 0·045 16 × 0·025 × 1000 × 0·65 litres/min

= 17·61 litres/min

The Principle of Archimedes

The Principle of Archimedes can be defined:

When a body is immersed in a liquid the upward force exerted by the liquid on the body is equal to the mass of the liquid displaced.

The principle can be illustrated by means of a simple experiment, see Fig. 9.2.

Experiment

(1) Obtain a mild steel block about 75 mm × 50 mm × 25 mm and by using a spring balance determine its mass.

(2) Lower the block, still suspended by the spring balance, into a beaker containing water until the block is fully covered.

(3) Take the reading on the spring balance. It will be seen that the mass now recorded is less than before.

The block appears to have lost mass, but why? The difference between its true mass and its mass in water is the mass of water the block displaces.

Archimedes' principle enables us to find the mass of a definite **volume** of a liquid:

A solid (non-soluble) whose volume is known is weighed in the liquid. The apparent loss of mass of the solid is equal to the mass of the liquid displaced, but the volume of the liquid is equal to the known volume of the solid. Knowing the mass and volume of the displaced liquid, the density and relative density of the solid can both be calculated. See Part 1 Chapter 5, pp. 61 and 62.

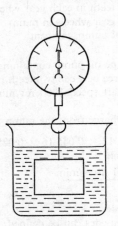

Fig. 9.2.

Example. A block of mild steel has a volume of 0·000 098 m³. When the block is weighed in water its mass is 0·64 kg. Determine the density and relative density of the steel.

$$\text{Mass of water displaced} = 0.000\ 098 \times 1000 = 0.098 \text{ kg}$$

$$\text{Density} = \frac{\text{Mass}}{\text{Volume}}$$

$$\text{Density of steel} = \frac{0.64 + 0.098}{0.000\ 098} = \underline{7532 \text{ kg/m}^3}$$

$$\text{Relative density} = \frac{\text{Density}}{1000}$$

$$\text{Relative density of steel} = \frac{7532}{1000} = \underline{7.532}$$

The foregoing method is used only when the volume of the solid can be accurately determined.

The relative density of irregular-shaped solids, whose volume cannot be accurately obtained, is also determined by using the simple experiment illustrated in Fig. 9.2. An example is given in the following section, where a method of determining the relative density of liquids is also given.

Determination of Relative Density

(1) **Solids.** When the mass of the solid in both air and water is obtained we proceed:

$$\text{Relative density} = \frac{\text{Mass of body in air}}{\text{Mass in air} - \text{Mass in water}}$$

Example. A block of metal has a mass of 51 kg in air and 44 kg in water. Calculate the relative density of the metal.

$$\text{Relative density} = \frac{51}{51 - 44}$$

$$= \frac{51}{7} = \underline{7.3}$$

(2) **Liquids.** (*a*) By use of a special bottle, called a relative density bottle, whose mass and internal capacity are known.

(1) The bottle, full of liquid, is weighed.
(2) The mass of the empty bottle is subtracted from the mass of the bottle full of liquid.

The mass of the known volume is thus obtained.

Example. A relative density bottle has a mass of 45 g empty. It is filled with petrol and then has a mass of 82·5 g. If the capacity of the bottle is 52 millilitres, determine the relative density of the petrol.

$$\text{Mass of petrol} = 82.5 - 45$$

$$= 37.5 \text{ g}$$

$$\therefore \text{Relative density} = \frac{37.5}{52}$$

$$= \underline{0.72}$$

Liquids

Note. The mass in g of 1 cm³ of any solid or 1 millilitre of any liquid represents the relative density of that solid or liquid.

(*b*) By means of an hydrometer with which all motor-vehicle students should be familiar.

In liquids of different densities, different fractions of the volume of the float are immersed. Because the upthrust on the float is equal to the mass of liquid displaced by the float, any differences in the relative density of the liquids under test are shown by the graduations marked on the float. The relative density is given by a direct reading on the float of the hydrometer.

The Principle of the Venturi

The principle of the venturi giving a pressure reduction or partial vacuum at the 'throat' can be illustrated by means of an experiment.

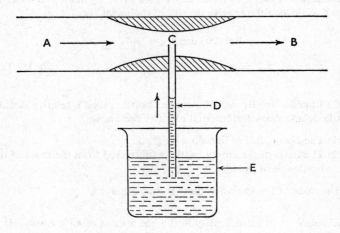

FIG. 9.3.

Experiment

Fig. 9.3 shows a horizontal glass venturi AB with the constriction or 'throat' at C. A small-bore diameter short glass tube D is connected at one end to about the centre of the throat, and the other end dips in a glass beaker E containing coloured water. The end A of the venturi is connected by means of a rubber hose to a water tap, and the other end is arranged to discharge to waste.

When the tap is turned on, after a short time water will flow steadily through the venturi. At the same time the coloured water in the beaker E will pass up the tube D and join the water already flowing in the venturi. This can be explained by the following:

Because the water in the venturi is flowing steadily, equal quantities of water must pass from A to B in the same time. Neglecting friction, the sum of the pressure energy and kinetic energy of a given quantity of the water flowing must remain constant. Because of the throat, the velocity of the water must be greater at C than at A or B; thus the kinetic energy must also be greater at C than at A or B. Since the pressure at B is atmospheric, the pressure at C must be less than atmospheric, i.e. a partial vacuum exists at C, and it follows that atmospheric pressure acting on the surface of the coloured water in the beaker E causes this water to flow up the tube D.

A similar effect can be obtained by substituting coloured petrol for the water in the beaker E and then:

(1) pass air under pressure through the venturi; or
(2) connect one end of the venturi to the induction pipe of a running engine.

A practical application of this principle can be found in the carburettor of a petrol engine. Air passing through the venturi (choke tube) of the carburettor causes a reduction of pressure (partial vacuum) at the throat of the choke tube, and atmospheric pressure acting on the surface of the petrol in the float chamber causes petrol to flow from the jet outlet.

To solve problems which concern the flow of a liquid or a gas Bernoulli's law is used, which states that if there is no loss due to friction then Pressure energy/kg + Kinetic energy/kg + Potential energy/kg = a constant. For air or gas potential energy is ignored so the law may be written:

$$\frac{p_1}{w} + \frac{v_1^2}{2} = \frac{p_2}{w} + \frac{v_2^2}{2}$$

Example. The gas velocity through the venturi of a carburettor is 60 m/s. Calculate the reduction in pressure at the throat of the venturi (density of air 1·28 kg/m³).

Let p_2 = pressure in venturi, v_2 = air velocity in venturi, w = mass of air, 1·28 kg/m³. Since we are only interested in the venturi, then:

$$\frac{p_2}{w} = \frac{v_2^2}{2} = 0$$

$$p_2 = \frac{-v_2^2}{2} w$$

$$= \frac{-60^2 \times 1\cdot28}{2} \text{ N/m}^2$$

$$= -2304 \text{ N/m}^2 \text{ or } -2\cdot304 \text{ kN/m}^2$$

Exercise 9

1. Explain the meaning of the term 'coefficient of discharge of an orifice'. An orifice 22 mm diameter discharges 68 litres of water per min. under a head of 1·2 m. Calculate the coefficient of discharge of the orifice. The acceleration due to gravity may be taken as 9·8 m/s².
(0·62) (U.L.C.I.)

2. Determine the diameter, in mm, of a circular orifice in the bottom of a tank in order that it may pass 45 480 litres of water an hour, when a constant head of 1·8 m is maintained in the tank. Take the coefficient of discharge as 0·62. (66 mm) (U.E.I.)

3. A four-stroke engine has a cubic capacity of 0·002 164 m³. Calculate: (*a*) the mean gas velocity in m/s, through the carburettor venturi, which is 0·025 m in diameter, when the engine is developing its maximum torque at 2000 rev/min; (*b*) the depression at the venturi, in kN/m², at the above conditions, given that the density of the air flowing is 1·28 kN/m³. ((*a*) 73·47 m/s; (*b*) 3·454 kN/m²) (I.M.I.)

10   Fuels

The basis of all fuels is the elements **carbon** and **hydrogen**, which unite with oxygen in the air, producing heat.

Liquid fuels used for motor-vehicle engines may be classified as: **volatile**, those which vaporize at normal temperatures; and **non-volatile**, those which do not vaporize at normal temperatures.

Volatile types of fuel are petrol, benzole, alcohol and kerosene; these are used in engines which have spark ignition.

Non-volatile fuels are fuel oil and gas oil; these are used in compression-ignition engines.

All of these fuels contain hydrogen and carbon (hydrocarbons), but the alcohols also contain oxygen.

Elements are substances which cannot be broken up into other substances. They consist of extremely minute and indivisible particles known as **atoms**. The atoms of any one element are all exactly alike, they have the same mass and are the smallest particle of that element which can take part in a chemical change. Common **non-metallic** elements are the gases hydrogen, oxygen and nitrogen, and the solid, carbon. Common **metallic** elements are lead, tin, copper, aluminium and iron.

A **compound** is composed of several elements which combine in definite proportions and are held together by chemical force. The appearance and properties of a compound do not resemble the elements of which it is composed. Water is a compound composed of hydrogen and oxygen.

A **mixture** is composed of various elements or compounds which retain their own characteristics and properties. For example, oxygen, when mixed with nitrogen in the air, supports combustion in the same way as oxygen does when not mixed. The gases used for oxy-acetylene welding are a mixture as they leave the blow-pipe; after combustion, compounds of water and carbon dioxide are formed.

A **molecule** is the smallest particle of a substance which can exist in a free state. It is built up from one or more atoms. For example, one molecule of water consists of two atoms of hydrogen and one atom of oxygen. The closeness of the molecules to each other determines whether the substance is a gas, liquid or solid; the molecules in a solid are closer together than those of a liquid and much closer than those of a gas. The molecules of a liquid, and particularly of a gas, have considerable movement, and this is increased by heat. The molecules of gas are small when compared with the space between them.

The **atomic mass** of an element is a number expressing the ratio of the mass of an atom of the element to the mass of an atom of hydrogen. The atomic mass of an atom of hydrogen is unity (one).

The **molecular mass** of a substance is a number expressing the ratio of the mass of a molecule of the substance to the mass of an atom of hydrogen. If the number and type of atoms in a molecule are known the molecular mass can be found by adding the atomic masses.

Chemical Symbols and Formulae

Many chemical symbols are derived from Latin names of elements, for example the Latin name for copper is *cuprum* and the symbol for copper is Cu.

Element or Compound	Symbol	Atomic Mass	Molecular Mass
Hydrogen . .	H	1	2
Carbon . .	C	12	12
Nitrogen .	N	14	28
Oxygen . .	O	16	32
Sulphur . .	S	32	32
Carbon monoxide .	CO	..	28
Carbon dioxide .	CO_2	..	44
Steam or water .	H_2O	..	18
Sulphur dioxide .	SO_2	..	64
Methane . .	CH_4	..	16

Hydrogen has the symbol H. One molecule of hydrogen contains two atoms so it is written H_2, the **suffix** 2 meaning it contains 2 atoms. Since the atom of hydrogen has an atomic mass of 1, the molecular mass of hydrogen is 2. Also $2H_2$ means 2 molecules of hydrogen, each consisting of 2 atoms; the mass would be $2 \times 2 = 4$. Similarly, H_2O (the formula for water) means 2 atoms of hydrogen united with 1 atom of oxygen. The molecular mass of

$$H_2O = (1 \times 2) + (16 \times 1) = 18$$

since the atomic mass of oxygen is 16. Similarly the formula for octane C_8H_{18} means that 8 carbon atoms are united with 18 hydrogen atoms.

$$\therefore \text{ Molecular mass of } C_8H_{18} = (12 \times 8) + (1 \times 18)$$
$$= 114$$

Similarly, the formula for benzene is C_6H_6,

$$\therefore \text{ Molecular mass of } C_6H_6 = (12 \times 6) + (1 \times 6)$$
$$= 78$$

Fuels

The volatile fuels distilled from crude petroleum consist mainly of fractions which boil between the temperatures of 55° and 200° C. During the process of distillation, fractions at certain ranges of temperature are collected and condensed. Fuel known as '**cracked**' petrol is produced by subjecting the crude oil to high temperature and pressure.

Fuel **fractions** belong chemically to three series:

paraffins	C_nH_{2n+2}
naphthenes	C_nH_{2n}
aromatics	C_nH_{2n-6}

The formula C_nH_{2n+2} means that, if the molecule contains 8 atoms of carbon, the value of n is 8, so the molecule would have $(2 \times 8) + 2$ atoms $= 18$ of hydrogen. So

$$C_nH_{2n+2} = C_8H_{18}$$

The series are subdivided as shown in the table, which also gives other data.

Fuel	Symbol	Relative Density	Boiling point, °C	Latent heat of evaporation, kJ/kg	Air/fuel ratio by mass	L.C.V., kJ/kg
Paraffin Series						
Hexane .	C_6H_{14}	0·663	68	363	15·2	
Heptane .	C_7H_{16}	0·691	98	310	15·1	
Octane .	C_8H_{18}	0·709	124	298	15·05	45 120
Nonane .	C_9H_{20}	0·723	150	...	15	45 820
Decane .	$C_{10}H_{22}$	0·735	172	251	15	
Undecane .	$C_{11}H_{24}$	0·746	195	...	...	
Naphthene Series						
Cyclohexane	C_6H_{12}	0·780	81	363	14·7	
Hexahydro-toluene .	C_7H_{14}	0·770	100	321	14·7	43 940 44 060
Hexahydro-xylene .	C_8H_{16}	0·756	118	310	14·7	
Aromatic Series						
Benzene .	C_6H_6	0·884	80	400	13·2	
Toluene .	C_7H_8	0·870	110	351	13·4	43 030 44 770
Xylene .	C_8H_{10}	0·862	140	338	13·6	
Alcohols						
Ethyl alcohol .	C_2H_6O	0·806	78	923	8·95	23 260
Methyl alcohol .	CH_4O	0·800	65	1191	6·44	27 450

Properties of Fuels

Flash point is the temperature at which sufficient inflammable vapour is given off by the fuel to cause a momentary flash when a flame is brought near to its surface.

Fire point is the temperature at which oil gives off enough vapour to burn continuously; it is about 10°C higher than the flash point.

Boiling point is the temperature at which the fuel boils; it varies for different fuels over a wide range of temperature and is some measure of the volatility.

Volatility is a measure of the rapidity of evaporation of a fuel and the amount of pre-heating required to bring about the change from liquid to gas. The pre-heating is closely related to the latent heat value. Most fuels have some fractions which are highly volatile; these give the engine an 'easy start' in cold weather. When the latent heat values are high, as in the alcohol and benzole fuels, difficult cold starting of engines may be experienced; this is increased further by long, cold induction passages where condensation can readily occur. Engines are often started by ether in very cold climates.

Calorific value of a fuel is the amount of heat liberated by a unit quantity of fuel when completely burnt. Fuels containing hydrogen have a lower and higher calorific value (**L.C.V. and H.C.V.**). The lower value is used when calculating the thermal efficiency of an engine, since the water formed from the hydrogen exists as steam in the gases, and does not give up its latent heat until it has left the combustion chamber, and passed into the exhaust system.

Octane number or value of a fuel is its tendency to detonate. **Iso-octane** has a high anti-knock property and is given an arbitrary value of 100. **Heptane**, which detonates easily, is given the value of 0. The octane value of any fuel is determined by testing it in a 'standard test engine', the results, especially when detonation occurs, are noted, then the same results are produced with a fuel mixture of iso-octane and heptane; the percentage of iso-octane in the fuel mixture is the octane number of the tested fuel. For example, if the mixture contains 93 per cent iso-octane and 7 per cent heptane the octane value is 93.

Anti-detonators are substances added to fuel to delay the rate of burning and suppress detonation. The usual additive is about 0·04 per cent of **tetra-ethyl-lead**, to which is added a small quantity of **ethyl bromide**. This encourages the lead to leave the engine as lead bromide vapour, and so reduces the corrosive and fouling effect of the lead deposit on the valves and sparking plugs. Another method of suppressing detonation is to use a mixture of petrol, benzol and alcohol as a fuel.

Other properties possessed by fuels are relative density, latent heat of evaporation and viscosity; these have been dealt with elsewhere.

Petrol has a composition of about 85 per cent carbon and 15 per cent hydrogen. The hydrogen content of a fuel is the primary cause of detonation; it is noticeable in commercial grades of petrol, which contain a high percentage of the paraffin series. Fuels containing a high percentage of aromatic series are less liable to detonate; they have a higher latent heat value and can be satisfactorily used in engines with a high compression ratio.

Kerosene is a fuel which is not used for motor-vehicle engines, but for agricultural machinery engines and tractors. Its distillation temperature is between 150° and 290°C, and it is therefore less volatile than petrol at atmospheric pressure. Engines using this type of fuel are often started on petrol; this heats a device used for vaporizing the kerosene.

Benzol is a fuel distillation of coal tar, a by-product of coal in the production of gas. It is a mixture of the aromatic series, mainly benzene, C_6H_6, which distils between 80° and 120°C. Benzol is a suitable fuel for engines with a high compression ratio, as its tendency to detonate is less than petrol.

Fuels from Vegetation

Methyl alcohol and ethyl alcohol, with chemical formulae CH_4O and C_2H_6O respectively, are manufactured from vegetable matter and both contain oxygen. Both fuels are highly volatile. Their calorific values are much lower than the hydrocarbon fuels, and for complete combustion an air-fuel ratio of about 9 to 1 is used. Their high latent heat value prevents detonation at all compression pressures below 1380 kN/m^2, and to obtain sufficient heat for complete and efficient combustion a compression ratio of between 10 and 14 to 1 is required.

Non-volatile Fuels

These are the fuel and gas oils; there are many grades, varying from the light fuel and gas oils, used for motor-vehicle type engines, to the heavy grades used for industrial boilers and marine engines. Their viscosity at 15°C varies from 55 to 750 Redwood seconds, and their relative density is between 0·75 and 0·9. The chemical composition of a fuel suitable for a road-vehicle engine is about C 87 per cent, H 11 per cent, O 1 per cent and S 1 per cent. The **sulphur content** should be low, as it forms sulphuric acid during combustion; this acid has a corrosive action on the engine cylinder walls.

Congealing point is the temperature at which paraffin wax commences to settle and restrict the flow of fuel oil; fuel-oil filters are often fitted close to the hot engine for this reason.

Flash point of all fuel oils is high, and the risk of fire is remote.

Cetane number is the percentage by volume of cetane in a mixture of cetane, $C_{16}H_{34}$, and alpha-methyl-naphthalene, $C_{11}H_{10}$, which has the same ignition quality as a particular fuel tested. **Ignition quality** is determined by running a 'standard test engine' under specified conditions and measuring with an indicator the number of crank-angle degrees between the start of injection and the start of rapid pressure rise. Fuels showing the smallest delay angle give easy starting, smooth quiet running and minimum combustion shock. These fuels are rated at a cetane number of 60 or more; fuels showing a long delay angle have a poor ignition quality and are rated at a cetane number of 30.

Fuel Oil Dopes and Additives

The cetane number of a fuel may be raised by the addition of a small amount, usually less than 5 per cent, of amyl nitrate or ethyl nitrate; this tends to reduce the ignition temperature and therefore lowers the maximum combustion pressure.

Properties of Elements and Compounds

Carbon, C, exists in many forms, differing in physical properties, colour, density, melting point and crystalline form. Such types, known as allotropic forms of carbon, include diamond, graphite, charcoal, gas carbon and soot, which is powdered carbon formed by decomposition of hydrocarbon gases.

Hydrogen, H, is a colourless, odourless, tasteless gas which is lighter than air, will burn, but does not support combustion.

Oxygen, O, is a colourless, odourless, tasteless gas which is heavier than air, does not burn, but supports combustion.

Nitrogen, N, is a colourless, odourless, tasteless gas which does not support combustion or burn. When heated, it combines with metals to form nitrides (nitriding of crankshafts) and at a very high temperature it combines with oxygen to form a compound, nitric oxide.

Carbon monoxide, CO, is colourless, practically odourless and an extremely poisonous gas. It is slightly lighter than air and burns but does not support combustion.

Carbon dioxide, CO_2, is colourless and odourless; it has a faint acid taste and does not support combustion. It is heavier than air, and its industrial uses are for refrigerators and fire extinguishers.

A chemical equation may be regarded as a summarized statement of a chemical reaction. Actually it has a more precise meaning, since, by using the atomic mass of the elements concerned, it is possible to calculate the mass of substances taking part, as their mass does not change when reaction occurs. Chemical equations of combustion are made up on one side by the elements, compounds and air taking part in the combustion and on the other side by the products of combustion. These are expressed in terms of their volumes since, from **Avogadro's law**, equal volumes of all gases at the same temperature and pressure contain the same number of molecules, that is, volumes are proportional to number of molecules.

This theory of Avogadro is now applied to steam:

A laboratory experiment can show that two volumes of hydrogen require one volume of oxygen for complete combustion and that the product is two volumes of steam. The apparatus consists of a U-tube which has one limb closed at the end; this end is fitted in a heating chamber. The tube is filled with mercury to displace all the air from the closed limb. Then two volumes of hydrogen and one volume of oxygen are introduced into the closed limb of the tube. The heating chamber raises the temperature of the gases to 130°C. Some of the mercury is then removed until its level is the same in both limbs; this ensures that the oxygen and hydrogen are at atmospheric pressure. The volume of gas is measured and an electric spark is passed into the chamber to ignite the gas, which burns rapidly to form steam, and this occupies exactly the same volume as the hydrogen and oxygen. It may therefore be stated that two volumes of hydrogen combine with one volume of oxygen to give two volumes of steam, when their pressures and temperature remain constant.

∴ 2 molecules of hydrogen combine with 1 molecule of oxygen to form 2 molecules of steam.

∴ 1 molecule of hydrogen combines with 0·5 molecule of oxygen to form 1 molecule of steam.

The hydrogen and oxygen molecule both contain two atoms.

∴ 2 atoms of hydrogen combine with 1 atom of oxygen to form 1 molecule of steam.

The equation is $H_2 + O = H_2O$

It is not usual to write 0·5 molecule as was done for the oxygen; the more usual equation for the chemical change is:

2 molecules of hydrogen combine with 1 molecule of oxygen to form 2 molecules of steam or water.

Then the equation is

$$2H_2 + O_2 = 2H_2O$$

Fig. 10.1 shows three separate and equal volumes containing hydrogen and oxygen atoms. These equal three volumes of mixed atoms, which, when combined, form a volume exactly twice the size of one of the original volumes.

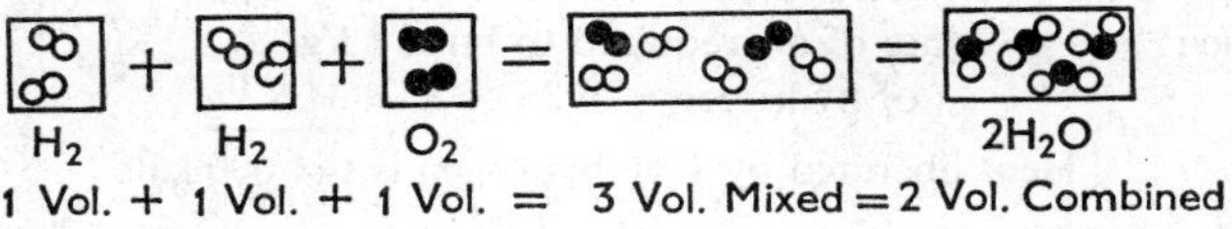

$$H_2 + H_2 + O_2 = \quad = 2H_2O$$

1 Vol. + 1 Vol. + 1 Vol. = 3 Vol. Mixed = 2 Vol. Combined

FIG. 10.1.

Combustion Calculations

Air contains 23 per cent of oxygen by **mass**. This means that 1 kg of air contains 0·23 kg of oxygen.

If 1 kg of air contains 0·23 kg of oxygen, then 1 kg of oxygen will be contained in

$$\frac{1}{0·23} \text{ kg of air} = \underline{4·35 \text{ kg of air}}$$

Air contains 77 per cent of nitrogen by mass.

If 1 kg of air contains 0·77 kg of nitrogen, then 1 kg of nitrogen will be contained in

$$\frac{1}{0·77} \text{ kg of air} = \underline{1·3 \text{ kg of air}}$$

By **volume**, the air contains 21 per cent oxygen and 79 per cent nitrogen.

Air Required to Burn Hydrogen

The mass of air required to burn completely 1 kg of hydrogen to water is calculated from the equation

$$2H_2 + O_2 = 2H_2O$$

It is usual practice and convenient always to consider 1 kg of fuel.

From the equation,

$$2 \times \text{Molecular mass of hydrogen} + \text{Molecular mass of oxygen} = 2(2 + 16)$$
$$(2 \times 2) + 32 = 36$$

As the units are kilogrammes, then

$$4 \text{ kg H} + 32 \text{ kg O} = 36 \text{ kg } H_2O$$

Dividing throughout by 4 to bring the mass of hydrogen to 1 kg, which is required,

$$1 \text{ kg H combines with 8 kg O to form 9 kg } H_2O.$$

Since 1 kg of oxygen is contained in 4·35 kg air,

then   8 kg of oxygen are contained in 4·35 × 8 kg air.

Then   Mass of air required to burn 1 kg
of hydrogen = 4·35 × 8 = <u>34·8 kg</u>

Heat liberated by 1 kg hydrogen is 144 600 kJ

Air Required for Complete Combustion of Carbon

The equation for the burning of carbon to carbon dioxide is:

$$C + O_2 = CO_2$$

Molecular mass of carbon + molecular mass of oxygen:

$$12 + 32 = 44$$

Then   12 kg C + 32 kg O = 44 kg CO_2

∴ 1 kg C + $\frac{32}{12}$ kg O = $\frac{44}{12}$ kg CO_2

1 kg C + 2·66 kg O = 3·66 kg CO_2

Since   1 kg O is contained in 4·35 kg air,

then   2·66 kg O is contained in 4·35 × 2·66 kg air.

Mass of air required = <u>11·6 kg</u>

Heat liberated by 1 kg carbon burning to carbon dioxide
is 33 830 kJ

Air Required to Burn Carbon to Carbon Monoxide

The equation for incomplete combustion, or burning carbon to carbon monoxide, is:

$$2C + O_2 = 2CO$$

Molecular mass of carbon + molecular mass of oxygen:

$$(2 \times 12) + 32 = 2(12 + 16)$$

Then   24 kg C + 32 kg O = 56 kg CO

∴ 1 kg C + $\frac{32}{24}$ kg O = $\frac{56}{24}$ kg CO

1 kg C + 1·33 kg O = 2·33 kg CO

Since   1 kg O is contained in 4·35 kg air,

then   1·33 kg O is contained in 4·35 × 1·33 kg air.

Mass of air required = <u>5·8 kg</u>

Heat liberated by 1 kg carbon burning to carbon monoxide
is 10 230 kJ

Air Required to Burn Carbon Monoxide to Carbon Dioxide

The equation for burning carbon monoxide to carbon dioxide is:

$$2CO + O_2 = 2CO_2$$

Molecular mass of carbon monoxide + Molecular mass of oxygen:

$$(2 \times 28) + 32 = 2(12 + 32)$$

Then $\qquad$ 56 kg CO + 32 kg O $\quad = 88$ kg CO_2

$\therefore$ 1 kg CO + $\frac{32}{56}$ kg O $\quad = \frac{88}{56}$ kg CO_2

1 kg CO + 0·571 kg O = 1·571 CO_2

Since $\qquad$ 1 kg O is contained in 4·35 kg air,

then $\qquad$ 0·571 kg O is contained in 4·35 $\times$ 0·571 kg air.

Mass of air required = <u>2·52 kg</u>

Heat liberated by 1 kg carbon monoxide burning to carbon dioxide
is 10 120 kJ

The quantity of heat liberated by burning completely 1 kg of carbon is always constant; it may be burnt direct to CO_2 or first to CO and then to CO_2.

Air Required to Burn Sulphur

The equation for burning sulphur to sulphur dioxide is:

$$S + O_2 = SO_2$$

Molecular mass of sulphur + molecular mass of oxygen:

$$32 + 32 = 64$$

Then $\qquad$ 32 kg S + 32 kg O = 64 kg SO_2

$\therefore$ 1 kg S + 1 kg O = 2 kg SO_2

Since $\qquad$ 1 kg O is contained in 4·35 kg air,

Mass of air required = <u>4·35 kg</u>

Heat liberated by 1 kg of sulphur burning to sulphur dioxide
is 9304 kJ

Air Required to Burn a Fuel

The following data should be memorized to make calculations easier:

> 1 kg hydrogen requires 8 kg oxygen.
> 1 kg carbon requires $\frac{8}{3}$ or 2·66 kg oxygen.
> 1 kg sulphur requires 1 kg oxygen.
> 1 kg oxygen is contained in 4·35 kg air.

Example. A certain petrol consists of 84 per cent carbon and 16 per cent hydrogen by mass. What mass of air is required for complete combustion?

$$\text{O required to burn 1 kg C} = 2 \cdot 66 \text{ kg}$$
$$\therefore \text{ O required to burn } 0 \cdot 84 \text{ kg C} = 0 \cdot 84 \times 2 \cdot 66 \text{ kg}$$
$$\text{O required to burn 1 kg H} = 8 \text{ kg}$$
$$\therefore \text{ O required to burn } 0 \cdot 16 \text{ kg H} = 0 \cdot 16 \times 8 \text{ kg}$$
$$\therefore \text{ Oxygen required} = (0 \cdot 84 \times 2 \cdot 66) + (0 \cdot 16 \times 8) \text{ kg}$$
$$\therefore \text{ Air required} = [(0 \cdot 84 \times 2 \cdot 66) + (0 \cdot 16 \times 8)] \times 4 \cdot 35 \text{ kg}$$
$$= (2 \cdot 23 + 1 \cdot 28)4 \cdot 35 \text{ kg}$$
$$= \underline{15 \cdot 268 \text{ kg}}$$

The air–fuel ratio by mass is 15·268 to 1

Example. A fuel oil contains, by mass, 87 per cent carbon, 11 per cent hydrogen, 1 per cent sulphur and 1 per cent oxygen. What mass of air is required for complete combustion?

$$\text{O required for carbon} = 0 \cdot 87 \times 2 \cdot 66 = 2 \cdot 314$$
$$\text{O required for hydrogen} = 0 \cdot 11 \times 8 = 0 \cdot 88$$
$$\text{O required for sulphur} = 0 \cdot 01 \times 1 = 0 \cdot 01$$
$$\overline{3 \cdot 204 \text{ kg}}$$

The fuel oil supplies 0·01 kg of oxygen per kg of fuel.

Then, actual mass of oxygen required from the air

$$= 3 \cdot 204 - 0 \cdot 01 = \underline{3 \cdot 194 \text{ kg}}$$
$$\text{Mass of air required} = \underline{3 \cdot 194 \times 4 \cdot 35 \text{ kg}}$$
$$= \underline{13 \cdot 894 \text{ kg}}$$

The air–fuel ratio by mass is 13·894 to 1

Example. What mass of air is required to burn completely 1 kg of benzole C_6H_6?

The molecular mass of benzole, C_6H_6, is:

$$(12 \times 6) + (1 \times 6) = 72 + 6 = 78.$$
$$\text{The percentage of carbon by mass} = \tfrac{72}{78} \times 100$$
$$= 92$$
$$\text{The percentage of hydrogen by mass} = \tfrac{6}{78} \times 100$$
$$= 8$$
$$\text{O required for carbon} = 0 \cdot 92 \times 2 \cdot 66 = 2 \cdot 45 \text{ kg}$$
$$\text{O required for hydrogen} = 0 \cdot 08 \times 8 = 0 \cdot 64 \text{ kg}$$
$$\overline{3 \cdot 09 \text{ kg}}$$

Air required $= 3.09 \times 4.35$ kg

$= \underline{13.4 \text{ kg}}$

The air–fuel ratio by mass is 13.4 to 1

Example. What mass of air is required to burn completely 1 kg of ethyl alcohol, H_2C_6O?

Molecular mass of $C_2H_6O = (12 \times 2) + (1 \times 6) + (16 \times 1)$

$= 24 + 6 + 16 = 46$

Percentage of carbon by mass $= \frac{24}{46} \times 100 = 52$

,, ,, hydrogen ,, ,, $= \frac{6}{46} \times 100 = 13$

,, ,, oxygen ,, ,, $= \frac{16}{46} \times 100 = 35$

O required for carbon $= 0.52 \times 2.66 = 1.383$ kg

O ,, ,, hydrogen $= 0.13 \times 8 = \underline{1.04 \text{ kg}}$

$\underline{2.423 \text{ kg}}$

The fuel supplies 0.35 kg of oxygen per kg of fuel, so the actual amount of oxygen required from the air

$= 2.423 - 0.35$ kg $= \underline{2.073 \text{ kg}}$

Air required $= 2.073 \times 4.35$ kg

$= \underline{9 \text{ kg}}$

The air–fuel ratio by mass is 9 to 1

Determination of calorific value by calculation, when the composition of a fuel is known. This method is not so accurate as burning fuel in a calorimeter, so the answers are only approximate.

Example. To find the H.C.V. and L.C.V. of hexane C_6H_{14}. This fuel contains 84 per cent carbon and 16 per cent hydrogen.

Heat liberated by 1 kg C $= 33\,830$ kJ

$\therefore$,, ,, ,, 0.84 kg C $= 33\,830 \times 0.84$ kJ

$= \underline{28\,417 \text{ kJ}}$

Heat liberated by 1 kg H $= 144\,600$ kJ

$\therefore$,, ,, ,, 0.16 kg H $= 144\,600 \times 0.16$ kJ

$= \underline{23\,136 \text{ kJ}}$

$\therefore$ H.C.V. of hexane $= 28\,417 + 23\,136$ kJ/kg

$= \underline{51\,553 \text{ kJ/kg}}$

To find the L.C.V., the latent heat of steam produced by the combination of hydrogen and oxygen must be known, and subtracted from the H.C.V.

Oxygen required for combustion of the hydrogen

$$= 8 \times 0 \cdot 16 \text{ kg} = \underline{1 \cdot 28 \text{ kg}}$$

The steam formed by combustion is the mass of hydrogen and the mass of the oxygen, which combines with the hydrogen.

$$\therefore \text{Mass of } H_2O = 0 \cdot 16 \text{ kg H} + 1 \cdot 28 \text{ kg O}$$
$$= \underline{1 \cdot 44 \text{ kg}}$$

The latent heat of the steam produced

$$= \text{Mass of steam} \times \text{Latent heat of steam}$$
$$= 1 \cdot 44 \times 2256 \text{ kJ}$$
$$= \underline{3248 \cdot 64 \text{ kJ}}$$
$$\therefore \text{L.C.V.} = \text{H.C.V.} - \text{Latent heat of steam}$$
$$= 51\,553 - 3248 \cdot 64$$
$$= \underline{48\,304 \cdot 36 \text{ kJ/kg}}$$

Exercise 10

1. What is the approximate calorific value of petrol and the ratio of air to fuel for its correct combustion?

How should the ratio be modified to obtain (*a*) greatest possible economy, and (*b*) greatest possible power?

What other effects would be produced by these alterations?

(47 000 kJ/kg; 17 to 1; 12 to 1)   (C. and G.)

2. Correct combustion of the fuel in a petrol engine produces water vapour, carbon dioxide and nitrogen at the exhaust pipe. Explain how these products are formed.

What changes will be produced by (*a*) a slightly rich mixture? (*b*) a slightly weak mixture?   (C. and G.)

3. An engine consumes 6·8 kg of air per minute. What mass of oxygen does this quantity of air contain?

If this mass of oxygen were to combine with the correct quantity of hydrogen, how much water (H_2O) would be produced?

(1·564 kg O; 1·7595 kg H_2O)

4. What engine design factors determine the octane rating of a fuel specified for use in a particular engine?

What is understood by the statement that a certain fuel has an octane rating of 97?   (C. and G.)

5. The use of high-octane fuel is usually associated with high-efficiency engines. Explain the reason for this.

What is the effect of using 101-octane fuel in an engine which is designed to run on a 94-octane fuel? (C. and G.)

6. Petrol used in a motor-car engine consists of 83·5 per cent carbon and 16·5 per cent hydrogen by mass. Assume the combustion is chemically correct and that the engine consumes 0·3048 litres per minute (relative density of petrol 0·725). Calculate: (*a*) air–fuel ratio by mass; (*b*) mass of air consumed per minute. (15·403 to 1; 8·38 kg)

7. What are the chief reasons which have led to the use of 'anti-knock' or high-octane fuel? (C. and G.)

8. What are the principal chemical elements contained in an average petrol? What is the ratio of air to petrol for its complete combustion, and what are the products of that combustion?

(Carbon and Hydrogen; 15 to 1) (C. and G.)

9. Explain what is meant by the following terms used in connection with fuels for internal-combustion engines: (*a*) volatility; (*b*) detonation; (*c*) calorific value. (U.E.I.)

10. State the ratio of petrol to air by mass to give the following results when used in a modern internal-combustion engine: (*a*) perfect combustion; (*b*) maximum power; (*c*) maximum economy as expressed in litres per indicated power.

Describe a method of testing the mixture strength. (C. and G.)

11. A four-stroke four-cylinder oil engine uses 9 kg of fuel per hour when running at 1000 rev/min. Calculate: (*a*) the mass of fuel injected per cycle; (*b*) the volume injected per cycle assuming the oil has a mass of 8304×10^{-6} kg/mm².

((*a*) 0·000 075 kg; 0·009 031 mm³) (E.M.E.U.)

12. It is generally accepted that a slightly weak mixture is needed for maximum thermal efficiency in the running of a petrol engine and that a rich mixture is needed for maximum power. Give the reasons for the above statement. (C. and G.)

13. (*a*) State the two main elements contained in petrol and give the average proportion of air to petrol for: (1) normal running; (2) starting from cold.

(*b*) What gases are contained in the exhaust? (U.L.C.I.)

14. The exhaust gases from a petrol engine have a temperature of 450°C and a specific heat capacity value at constant pressure of 1·004 89. If there are 18 kg of exhaust gases formed per kilogramme of fuel consumed, what heat is carried away in them if the air enters the carburettor at a temperature of 35°C? If the heating value of the petrol is 45 000 kJ/kg, what percentage of the heat supply is lost to the exhaust?

(7506 kJ; 16·68 per cent)

15. A benzole mixture contains 30 per cent by mass benzole C_6H_6 and 70 per cent by mass petrol C_6H_{18}. What air–fuel ratio by mass is required for chemically correct combustion? (14·56 to 1)

16. A high-compression motor-cycle engine was rebuilt to burn methyl alcohol CH_4O instead of benzole C_6H_6.

What is the air–fuel ratio by mass for each of these fuels?

If the choke tube size of the carburettor is not altered, by what percentage must the fuel supply be increased?

(6·514 to 1; 13·4 to 1; 105·7 per cent)

17. An engine uses 15 kg of fuel per hour, each kg of which develops 45 000 kJ. If the efficiency of the engine is 30 per cent, what is the power? (56·25 kW) (E.M.E.U.)

18. Give an explanation of the phenomenon of detonation in a spark-ignition engine. (C. and G.)

19. What is meant by the brake thermal efficiency of an engine? Describe how you would carry out the test to determine brake thermal efficiency. Enumerate the equipment required and the readings that should be taken. What must be known about the fuel before calculations can be completed? (C. and G.)

20. A motor-car engine burns 9 litres of fuel in an hour, the fuel giving out 47 000 kJ/kg. If 36 per cent of the heat in the fuel is lost in the exhaust gases, calculate the number of joules of work lost in this way per second. (Relative density of petrol 0·78.)

(3290 J) (U.E.I.)

21. An engine uses 0·3 kg of fuel per hour, L.C.V. 43 400 kJ/kg, per kilowatt developed. What is its thermal efficiency?

(27·64 per cent) (E.M.E.U.)

22. What is meant by the flash point of a diesel fuel? How is flash point determined and of what value is the information? (I.M.I.)

Engine Testing

The testing of motor-vehicle engines is usually carried out on a special test bed; some tests can, however, take place in the chassis using special equipment. On the test bed the tests vary in type and length of time; some tests may only take ten minutes, while others last for many weeks.

Tests carried out in Technical Colleges are to illustrate, and often prove, the theories and characteristics of the i.c. engine. They can be simple or extensive according to the stage of study the student has reached.

The engine manufacturer and research engineer conduct many tests when an engine is being developed; these are scientific, occupy a long time and require special equipment.

When in production, the manufacturer tests the engines as they leave the assembly line. The test might be a **motoring test,** that is, driving the engine with an electric motor, or running the engine under its **own power** on a test bed for several hours. The speed and power are slowly increased, with frequent checks on fuel consumption and temperature until a satisfactory standard is reached. At this stage a 10 per cent **overload test** is given for a short time.

The vehicle repairer and transport engineer who overhaul and recondition engines test their engines and compare the results with the manufacturers' specification. Transport engineers often carry out tests to see what modifications they can make to reduce operating costs of vehicles doing a special type of work.

The oil companies and manufacturers of pistons, bearings, carburettors and other components carry out special tests to study and develop their own products.

Standard Tests for Technical Colleges

1. **Brake** power (P_b) and torque test, at full load conditions and varying engine speed.

2. **Indicated** power (P_i), brake power and mechanical efficiency test.

3. **Morse** test to determine P_i.

4. **Fuel consumption** and torque test at constant speed.

5. The **effect of ignition timing** on power and fuel consumption at constant engine speed.

6. **Air consumption and volumetric efficiency** test at varying engine speed.

7. The **effect of the air–fuel ratio** on the mean effective pressure at constant speed.

8. The **exhaust gas analysis** for varying mixture strengths at constant engine speed.

9. The **effect of cooling-water temperature** on power output at constant speed.

Test Procedure

Before testing, the plant and equipment must be carefully checked, then the engine is started and adjusted to steady working conditions. Readings or observations should be taken simultaneously, and recorded on the report sheet so that the progress of the test can be seen.

Writing up the report. This should be set out as follows:

Title

Date

Object

The reason for carrying out the experiment and whether it is to prove some theory.

Apparatus

Specification of engine and equipment. A clear description of the apparatus used, illustrated by simple diagrams and photos.

Procedure

An account of things done before and during the experiment.

Results

A record of all data, including the readings taken before and during the experiment. The results should appear in a tabulated form.

The formula used for the calculations and one specimen of each type of calculation should be shown.

Graphs drawn to show the results must be clearly marked with title, date and scales used.

Conclusions

An account of any incident or event during the experiment. Suggestions why the experimental and theoretical results do not agree (do not always blame the equipment).

Hints on Writing the Report

Always write in the **past** tense, i.e. something that has been done, and make no personal references. For example: 'weights' **were** placed on the carrier; readings **were** observed at two-minute intervals; the engine speed **was** increased; the temperature **was** constant.

Brake Power Tests

Hydraulic and electric dynamometers are used for the testing of motor-vehicle engines. In Part I the hydraulic dynamometer was described and its operation explained. The electric dynamometer has basically a similar theory for the measurement of torque; it has, however, a wider application. This dynamometer can measure the output torque when driven by the engine, and also measure the input torque when it is used as an electric motor to drive or rotate the engine. This second feature enables the engine to be started by the motor. The 'motoring' test, if carried out when the engine is cold, gives a measure of the load which would be put on the starter motor when the engine is in the vehicle. Further tests can be carried out at various engine temperatures, including extreme starting conditions and with different grades of lubricating oil. Motoring the engine at its normal working temperature enables the **friction** and **pumping 'losses'** to be determined. For the pumping losses, the engine can be relieved of its effective compression by removing the sparking plugs or injectors, the remaining losses are frictional.

Calculation of Brake Power and Torque

The torque is the product of the force on the torque arm and its perpendicular distance from the shaft centre.

Let F (newtons) be the force, and L metres the length of arm, then the torque $T = FL$(Nm).

Then   brake power $(P_b) = T \times$ Angle in radians
$$= T \times 2\pi \times \text{rev/s}$$
$$= FL2\pi \times \text{rev/s}$$

As the watt (W) is a small unit, the i.c. engine may be rated in kilowatts (kW) (1000 W = 1 kW) as an alternative unit of power, the kW is used extensively in this chapter.

Since brake power $(P_b) = FL\,2\pi$ rev/s and the speed of rotation is usually recorded as rev/min, then these rev/min must be divided by 60:

$$\text{brake power } (P_b) = FL2\pi\,\frac{\text{rev/min}}{60}$$

If the constant terms $\frac{L2\pi}{60}$ are extracted from the formula to give a constant $\frac{1}{K_c}$ then:

$$\text{brake power } (P_b) = \frac{F\,\text{rev/min}}{K_c}$$

Use of Constants in Engine Testing

On p. 183, Part 1, the term K_c appeared in the formula used with the Heenan and Froude dynamometer. The method of calculating K_c and other constants used during engine testing is shown in the following example.

Example. A four-cylinder, four-stroke engine has a piston area of 0.008 m^2 and stroke of 0.125 m, and it is tested against a dynamometer with a torque arm length of 0.4475 m, P_b is given by $FK_{c1}\,\dfrac{\text{rev/min}}{60}$; torque in Nm by FK_{c2} and b.m.e.p. in kN/m^2 by FK_{c3}, where F = brake load in N and K_{c1}, K_{c2} and K_{c3} are constants depending on the given dimensions. Find the values of K_{c1}, K_{c2} and K_{c3}.

To find K_{c1}.

$$\text{brake power } (P_b) = F \times 0.4775 \times 2\pi \times \frac{\text{rev/min}}{60}$$
$$= F \times 3 \times \frac{\text{rev/min}}{60}$$
$$= F\frac{\text{rev/min}}{20}$$
$$\therefore K_{c1} = 20.$$

To find K_{c2}.

$$\text{Torque} = F \times 0.4775 \text{ Nm} = F\,0.4775 \text{ Nm}$$
$$\therefore K_{c2} = 0.4775$$

To find K_{c3}.

$$\text{brake power} = \frac{\eta\,pLA\,\text{rev/min}}{60}\frac{\text{n}}{2} \quad \text{where } \eta\,p = \text{b.m.e.p.}$$
$$= \frac{\eta\,p \times 0.125 \times 0.008 \times \text{rev/min} \times 4}{60}\frac{}{2}$$
$$= \frac{\eta\,p \times \text{rev/min}}{30\,000}$$

Now brake power $= \dfrac{F \text{ rev/min}}{20} = \dfrac{\eta\, p \text{ rev/min}}{30\,000}$

$$\therefore \eta p = \frac{F \times 30\,000}{20} = F\,1500$$

$$\therefore K_{c_3} = \underline{1500}$$

The Brake Power Test

This test is carried out at full load and different engine speeds. After the petrol engine is 'warmed up' the load is increased and the throttle opened wide, the ignition timing is adjusted to give maximum torque at the lowest speed at which the engine will run smoothly. For the next test the load on the dynamometer is reduced to allow the engine speed to increase, the ignition timing is again adjusted for maximum torque and the various readings are recorded. Tests are repeated at intervals of 200/400 rev/min until the maximum engine speed is reached. We see that the torque-arm load is reduced after the first few tests; this reading is proportional to torque.

The results should be recorded on a sheet and graph as shown in Fig. 11.1.

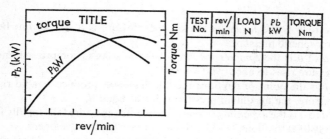

FIG. 11.1.

Indicated Power (P_i)

The **indicated** power is the actual power produced in the engine cylinder. Burning fuel in the cylinder produces the mechanical energy; this is measured and compared with the power available at the flywheel, known as P_b; the power 'lost' can thus be determined.

The **indicator diagram** is a recording of the pressure and rate of pressure change in the cylinder at all points during the cycle. It also gives a record of the combustion process and pressure rise, which will show any fault in the timing of the ignition or valves.

The **diagram** is produced by an instrument or **indicator**. The areas of the diagram represent the work done *by* the gas and the work done *on* the gas. Fig. 11.2 shows a typical diagram of a petrol engine at **full** load; the dotted line represents **half** load.

The **OY axis** is the **pressure** scale, and all vertical measurements represent pressure in the engine cylinder.

The **OX axis** is the **piston movement** scale; its length is proportional to the length of the piston travel or stroke.

The four strokes of the cycle are represented on the diagram, Fig. 11.2.

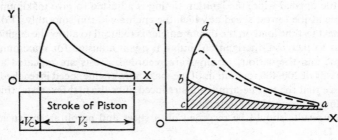

FIG. 11.2.

c to *a* is the *induction* stroke; the pressure is a few kN/m² below atmospheric pressure.

a to *b* is the *compression* stroke; the mixture is compressed and its pressure rises to about 900 kN/m².

b is the point of ignition; the burning gases produce a rapid rise in pressure, the maximum pressure being at point *d*.

d to *a* is the *expansion* or *power* stroke; the pressure falls rapidly from 2000/4000 to about 275 kN/m² when the exhaust valve opens.

a to *c* is the *exhaust* stroke and the pressure is a few kN/m² above atmospheric pressure.

During the compression stroke the work done *on* the gases will be represented by the shaded area *abc*. After ignition, work is done by the expanding gases; this is represented by the area *acbda*. The net work done during this revolution of the engine is equal to the work done by the expanding gases, less the work done on the gases. This net work is the difference of the two areas or the area *abd*.

A small area along the line *ac* represents the induction and exhaust stroke. The pressure difference between the two lines is so small that it appears on the normal diagram as a straight, thick line; its area is so small that for normal calculations it is neglected.

Fig. 11.3 shows the **actual** indicator diagram of the **compression-ignition** engine. The top of the diagram is nearly flat; this is because the fuel is injected at such a rate that the pressure of the burning gases remains nearly constant, hence its name, **constant pressure** type of engine cycle, which distinguishes it from the **constant volume** cycle of the petrol engine. The dotted line represents the expansion line when the fuel is injected for a shorter time for half or medium power output.

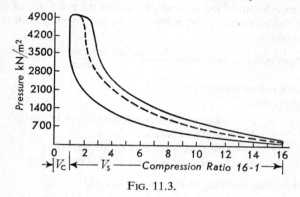

FIG. 11.3.

Fig. 11.4 shows the **theoretical** or ideal diagram; the positions *a*, *b* and *c* are different points at which the fuel is cut off. The period *oa* is for light load, *ob* for medium load and *oc* for full load running condi-

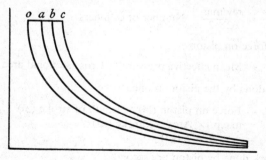

FIG. 11.4.

tions. We see that the ideal condition is not quite achieved in actual practice.

The method of finding the **area** of an indicator diagram by Simpson's rule has been explained in Part 1. The area is then divided by the length of the base line and the average or **mean height** is found. This height is then multiplied by the scale or **spring rate** to give the average or mean pressure existing on the piston during the length of its stroke.

The **planimeter** is an instrument which quickly and accurately measures the diagram. The gauge points on the instrument are adjusted to the base length of the diagram, and when the boundary of the diagram is traced round by the pointer on the instrument a reading on its scale is noted.

$$\text{Mean effective pressure} = \frac{\text{Instrument reading} \times \text{Spring rate}}{\text{Constant}}.$$

Calculation of Indicated Power
Symbols used:

$p = $ Mean effective pressure (m.e.p.), kN/m^2
$L = $ Length of piston stroke, m
$A = $ Cross-sectional area of piston, m^2
$S = $ Number of working strokes per second

S for engines working on the **two-stroke** cycle

$$= \frac{\text{rev/min}}{60} \times \text{Number of cylinders}$$

S for engines working on the **four-stroke** cycle

$$= \frac{\text{rev/min}}{62 \times 2} \times \text{Number of cylinders}$$

Total force on piston

$$= \text{Mean effective pressure} \times \text{Cross-sectional area of piston}$$

Work done by the piston in one stroke

$$= \text{Force on piston (N)} \times \text{length of stroke (m)}$$
$$= \text{m.e.p.} \times \text{Area} \times \text{Stroke (kJ)}$$
$$= p \times A \times L \text{ (kJ)}$$

$\therefore$ Work done by piston per second

$$= pAL \times \text{Number of working strokes } (S)$$
$$= pLAS \text{ (kJ)}$$

$\therefore$ Indicated power $(P_i) = pLAS$

This mean effective pressure is known as the **indicated mean effective pressure** or **i.m.e.p.** When it is based on the brake power it is known as **brake mean effective pressure, b.m.e.p.**

From this, the i.m.e.p. $\times$ Mechanical efficiency $=$ b.m.e.p.

Example. A four-cylinder four-stroke engine with 100 mm bore and 100 mm stroke develops its maximum power at 3600 rev/min. At this speed the i.m.e.p. is 760 kN/m² and mechanical efficiency is 85 per cent.

Find: (*a*) Indicated power; (*b*) b.m.e.p.

$$Data \qquad p = 760 \text{ kN/m}^2$$
$$L = 0\cdot10 \text{ m}$$
$$A = \frac{\pi}{4} \times 0\cdot010^2 \text{ m}^2$$
$$S = \frac{3600 \times 4}{60 \times 2} = 120$$

$$\text{Indicated power} = pLAS$$
$$= \frac{760 \times 0\cdot1 \times 3\cdot1416 \times 0\cdot1 \times 0\cdot1 \times 120}{4} \text{ kW}$$
$$\therefore P_i = \underline{71\cdot63 \text{ kW}}$$
$$\text{b.m.e.p.} = \text{i.m.e.p.} \times \text{mechanical efficiency}$$
$$= 760 \times 0\cdot85 \text{ kN/m}^2$$
$$\therefore \text{b.m.e.p.} = \underline{646 \text{ kN/m}^2}$$

Example. A six-cylinder, four-stroke engine of bore 60 mm and stroke 85 mm develops a brake power of 24 kW at 2200 rev/min. Calculate the brake mean effective pressure (b.m.e.p.) at this speed.

Let ηp denote b.m.e.p.

$$Data \qquad P_b = 24 \text{ kW}$$
$$L = 85 \text{ mm or } 0\cdot085 \text{ m}$$
$$A = \frac{\pi}{4} \times 60^2 \text{ mm}^2 \text{ or } 0\cdot06^2 \text{ m}^2$$
$$S = \frac{2200 \times 6}{2 \times 60} = 110$$
$$\eta p = ?$$
$$P_b = \eta pLAS$$
$$24 = \eta p \times 0\cdot085 \times \frac{\pi}{4} \times 0\cdot06^2 \times 110$$
$$\eta p = \frac{24}{0\cdot085 \times 0\cdot7854 \times 0\cdot06^2 \times 110} \text{ kN/m}^2$$
$$= \underline{907\cdot4 \text{ kN/m}^2}$$

The Indicator

Indicators of the piston type are successfully used on the steam, gas and slow-speed oil engines; they are not, however, suitable for the high-speed motor-vehicle engine. The high engine speed produces inertia forces in the moving parts of the indicator and reduces the accuracy of the diagram. The time allowed for the production of a diagram is so short that the diagram has to be small, and this also tends to make it inaccurate. The size of the instrument, the method of fitting and the layout of the operating mechanism are also a disadvantage.

To overcome these difficulties, two indicators have been produced, the **Farnboro Electrical Indicator** and the **Cathode-ray Indicator**. Both instruments are now past their developmental stage and in continuous use in industry and laboratory. Most Technical Colleges are equipped with these indicators, as they form an important part of the students' advanced study of the i.c. engine.

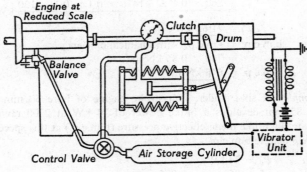

Fig. 11.5.

The Farnboro Indicator

Fig. 11.5 shows a diagrammatic layout of this instrument. Special black paper is securely fitted on the drum. This drum is driven by the engine at exactly crankshaft or camshaft speed, so the diagram is on the **crank angle base** and not **piston displacement**. Fig. 11.6 shows a typical diagram paper, which is about 178 mm high and 330 mm long in actual size. The diagram is a series of small holes pierced through the paper by an electric H.T. spark, jumping from the spark point to the drum; this is an electrical circuit like the coil ignition system.

A balanced disc-valve unit is fitted into the cylinder head, the valve is held on its seat, in the closed position relative to the combustion chamber, by air or nitrogen at high pressure from the storage cylinder.

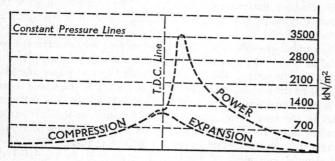

FIG. 11.6.

When the pressure in the engine cylinder exceeds the air pressure the disc valve lifts off its seat on the engine side and seats on a second seating on the air line side; the movement of the valve is about 0·5 mm. This disc valve will not return to its original position until the combustion chamber pressure falls below the air line pressure. The disc valve is mounted on an insulated spindle so that when seated it completes the low-tension circuit, but when it lifts off either seat the circuit is broken and the H.T. is produced. Two sparks occur in every engine cycle, one as the cylinder pressure rises and one as it falls. The air pressure from the storage cylinder is controlled so as to increase gradually the pressure in the valve unit. Thus, in a short period of time, hundreds of perforations appear on the indicator paper, outlining the pressure variation in the cylinder over the complete cycle. When completed, the drum is declutched and the diagram paper is removed and examined by placing it over an illuminated ground-glass screen. The diagram is replotted on a piston displacement basis and the m.e.p. is found in kN/m^2.

Cathode-ray Indicator

This precision **electronic indicator** operates at any engine speed and it has special timing devices to overcome the problem of inertia forces. Fig. 11.7 shows a diagrammatic layout of this indicator. The pressure unit screws into the cylinder head and contains a water-cooled pressure-sensitive element, which is in contact with the diaphragm formed on the screwed end of the unit. Any change in gas pressure in the combustion chamber immediately varies the pressure on the diaphragm which changes the electrical resistance. The water cooling of this resistance prevents any change which temperature might have on its characteristic.

The **cathode-ray tube** has a fluorescent surface on the screen to give an 'after glow'; the complete diagram traced by the 'spot' is thus retained on the screen. This diagram is traced on thin paper or photographed by the camera, which is hinged to the top of the screen frame.

Vertical movement of the spot is controlled by the YY deflecting plates in the tube. Any change of gas pressure in the combustion chamber varies the value of the resistance in the pressure unit; this changes the voltage applied to the YY deflecting plates.

Horizontal movement of the spot is controlled by changing the voltage applied to the XX plates in the tube. This movement can be arranged to change at a rate to represent piston movement or crank angle.

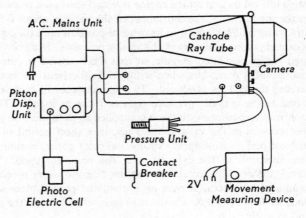

Fig. 11.7.

The combined varying voltages on the XX and YY plates move the spot, which traces out the diagram on the screen.

This indicator is extremely useful to demonstrate the effects on combustion and rate of pressure rise when changes are made to ignition timing, mixture strength and change of load; pre-ignition and pinking produce remarkable diagrams.

The description of these indicators has been brief, but the student can become better acquainted with their operation by using them and reading the manufacturers' manuals.

Morse Test

This is one method of obtaining the indicated power (P_i), mechanical efficiency and friction-pumping losses of an engine.

(1) The test consists of measuring the (P_b) of the engine when coupled to a dynamometer with all cylinders working, at a certain speed and under load.

(2) One cylinder is then deprived of its power by cutting off the ignition or fuel to that cylinder. As the engine speed falls, so the dynamometer load must be reduced, until the engine speed returns to its original figure. The P_b is again measured, but is found to be lower.

(3) This reduction in P_b is approximately the P_i of the idle cylinder, because the working cylinders have to overcome the friction-pumping losses of the idle cylinder as well as their own; thus the reduction in P_b must be the P_i of the idle cylinder.

To **calculate** the P_i and **friction** power (P_f) of a four-cylinder engine, five tests are made, one with all cylinders working, the others with each of the cylinders cut out in turn.

Let $A = P_b$ when all cylinders are working

Let $B = P_b$ when one cylinder is not working

Then $A - B = P_i$ of the idle cylinder

∴ P_i of all the cylinders

$$= (A - B_1) + (A - B_2) + (A - B_3) + (A - B_4)$$

∴ $P_i = (A \times 4) - (B_1 + B_2 + B_3 + B_4)$

Also:

$$\text{Friction power} = P_i - P_b$$

$$\text{Mechanical efficiency} = \frac{P_b}{P_i} \times 100$$

Note. Friction power is the term used for all losses of power in the engine: friction, pumping, fan, dynamo and water pump.

The Morse test is repeated at various engine speeds; the results are then plotted on a graph as shown in Fig. 11.8.

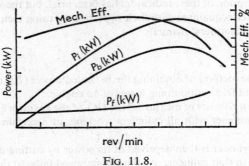

FIG. 11.8.

Example. A Morse test on an engine gave the following results:

P_b	All cylinders working	100 kW
P_b	No. 1 cylinder cut out	69 kW
P_b	No. 2 " " "	71 kW
P_b	No. 3 " " "	68·5 kW
P_b	No. 4 " " "	71·5 kW

Find: (a) P_i; (b) P_f; (c) mechanical efficiency.

(a)
$$P_i = (A \times 4) - (B_1 + B_2 + B_3 + B_4)$$
$$= (100 \times 4) - (69 + 71 + 68·5 + 71·5)$$
$$= 400 - 280$$
$$\therefore \underline{P_i = 120 \text{ kW}}$$

(b)
$$P_f = P_i - P_b$$
$$= 120 - 100$$
$$\therefore \underline{P_f = 20 \text{ kW}}$$

(c)
$$\text{Mechanical efficiency} = \frac{P_b}{P_i} \times 100$$
$$= \frac{100}{120} \times 100$$
$$\therefore \underline{\text{M.E.} = 83 \text{ per cent}}$$

Fuel Consumption

The fuel consumed by a motor-vehicle engine accounts for the largest part of the vehicle operating costs. A motorist or fleet engineer is always watching the km per litre of his vehicle, but the designer of the engine is interested in the quantity of fuel consumed per hour for each kilowatt developed. From this data the **thermal efficiency** of the engine is calculated; thermal efficiency is the percentage of heat energy in the fuel converted into useful work.

When the fuel consumed is measured by *volume* the consumption units are litres/kW hour; if the fuel is measured by *mass* the consumption units are kg/kW hour. The first units are used for most of the standard routine tests, but the second units are more accurate, since they take into consideration the relative density of the fuel.

Fuel consumption tests for the engine on a test bed are easily carried out by using an accurate fuel-measuring tank and a stop watch. To ensure accuracy the time taken for a specified quantity of fuel to be consumed should not be less than *two minutes*.

A simple method of measuring the fuel consumed is shown in Fig. 11.9 (*a*). The test tank is fitted with hook gauges, and if the calibration between them is 100 ml and 200 ml litre, then a third volume can be arranged by using the quantity of fuel between the top and bottom hook gauges. These three volumes are useful for testing at light load, half-load and full load running conditions.

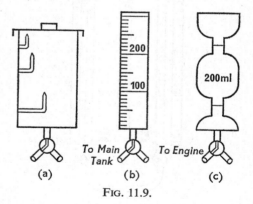

FIG. 11.9.

Fig. 11.9 (*b*) shows a measuring device made from a calibrated glass measuring cylinder. The volume of fuel used for the test can be varied to suit the engine's requirements.

Fig. 11.9 (*c*) shows a more accurate form of measuring glass, shaped so that the fuel falls fast at the points of calibration, where the timing starts and finishes.

Another accurate form of measurement is the **flow-meter**, which indicates the rate of fuel flow to the engine, in litres per hour. Fig. 11.10 shows the diagrammatic layout of the meter. The jets A and B can be changed to give different ranges of flow, and the scales are also changed to suit the size of jet.

The petrol is maintained at a constant level in the float chamber and rises in the indicating glass tubes to the same level when no fuel is flowing. When fuel flows, the level in the glass tube drops, since the pressure or 'head' cannot be maintained; at the maximum rate of flow for a jet no 'head' of fuel is visible in the tube. One jet or both jets may be used. The scales are not linear, since the quantity of fuel flowing in unit time

$$= K_e \sqrt{2gh}$$

Where K_e is coefficient of discharge;
h is height of fuel above the jet.

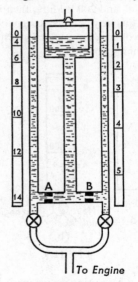

FIG. 11.10.

This instrument is a useful guide when running adjustments are made to the carburettor; the direct reading immediately indicates any change made in the fuel consumed.

Calculations

Graduated glass measuring cylinders are usually calibrated in millilitres (ml) or litres.

To convert millilitres (ml) or litres (l) to mass (kg)
$$1000 \text{ ml} = 1 \text{ litre}$$

since 1 litre of water has a mass of 1 kg.

∴ 1 litre of fuel has a mass of $1 \times$ relative density of fuel (kg)

∴ x litres of fuel has a mass of:

$x \times$ relative density of fuel (kg)

The quantity of fuel consumed is measured in litres per brake power (kW) per hour, or kg per brake power (kW) per hour.

Fuel consumption l/kW h

$$= \frac{\text{Volume of fuel in litres} \times 60 \times 60}{\text{Time taken to consume fuel (s)} \times \text{kW}}$$

Fuel consumption kg/kW h

$$= \frac{\text{Mass of fuel in kg} \times 60 \times 60}{\text{Time taken to consume fuel (s)} \times \text{kW}}$$

Fuel consumption when using a flow-meter:

Fuel consumption l/kW h

$$= \frac{\text{Litres of fuel per hour}}{\text{kW}}$$

Fuel consumption kg/bkW h

$$= \frac{\text{Litres of fuel per hour} \times \text{relative density}}{\text{kW}}$$

Graphs of Fuel Consumption

The graph, Fig. 11.11 (*a*), is plotted from experimental results of an engine tested at **full load** and **variable speed.** We see that the most

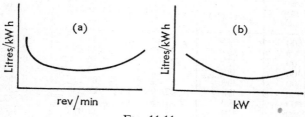

Fig. 11.11.

economical speed range is between 35 and 75 per cent of full speed. Above or below those speeds the fuel consumption increases.

The graph, Fig. 11.11 (*b*), is plotted from experimental results of an engine tested at **constant speed** and **variable load**. When the engine is idling at light load or at full load the fuel consumption is high.

A vehicle driven hard at high speed has a low km/l.

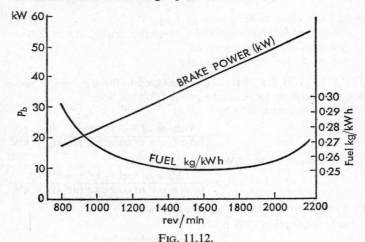

FIG. 11.12.

Example. A six-cylinder oil engine was tested for max. P_b and fuel consumption. The relative density of the fuel oil was 0·855 and constant K_c for the brake 16·66 or $\frac{50}{3}$. Plot a graph of the results.

The graph, Fig. 11.12, represents the results shown in the following table:

rev/min	F Load (N)	P_b(kW)	Fuel, time for 0·25 l (s)	kg/kW h
800	365	17·46	147·5	0·2988
1000	367	21·93	128·8	0·2724
1200	372	26·64	110	0·2625
1400	385	32·22	92	0·2595
1600	390	37·44	80	0·2568
1800	398	42·89	69·5	0·2582
2000	400	47·96	61·2	0·2622
2200	410	54·16	51·0	0·2786

Volumetric Efficiency and Air Consumption

The **volumetric efficiency** of an i.c. engine may be defined as:

$$\frac{\text{Volume of air or mixture entering cylinder}}{\text{Volume swept by piston}}$$

at standard temperature and pressure (s.t.p.).

There is, however, another opinion about this definition which considers that the denominator of the ratio should be the volume swept by the piston *after* the inlet valve or port is closed.

The volume of air entering the cylinder of any unsupercharged engine is less than the swept volume and depends on:

1. The pressure, temperature and proportional volume of the residual gases left in the cylinder when the inlet valve opens. The proportional volume decreases as the compression ratio increases.
2. Efficiency of the induction and exhaust system.
3. Engine speed, which determines the time that the inlet valve remains open.
4. Valve timing and number of cylinders, also layout of induction passages and number of cylinders fed by one carburettor.

The maximum torque of any engine is determined by the mass of fuel and air entering the cylinder per cycle, and the efficiency with which it is burnt. As the period of time for the induction stroke decreases, the volumetric efficiency also decreases, and a reduced mass of fuel and air enters the cylinder per cycle; thus the work done per cycle will also be less. As the engine approaches its maximum speed, the work done per cycle falls at such a rate that the power of the engine also falls; it has then passed its 'peak' or maximum power. At high engine speeds the induction system gets hotter, the ingoing mixture is heated and expands, resulting in a reduction in mass of the fresh charge.

Measurement of Air Consumed

The volume and mass of air consumed by an engine can be measured by various types of meter or by analysis of the exhaust gases.

A simple type of meter is shown in Fig. 11.13. A box or tank is mounted above the engine for convenience and coupled to the induction by a length of tube. Opposite to the outlet is the inlet, where air passes through a knife-edged orifice plate; the area of its hole is made to suit the capacity of the engine. The volume of the box depends on engine capacity and number of cylinders, since its function is to damp out induction pulsations in the air as it passes through the orifice. A **manometer** is fitted to measure the drop in air pressure across the orifice; the pressure drop should be small, or the engine performance will be altered. The gauge is designed to measure the pressure in *mm of*

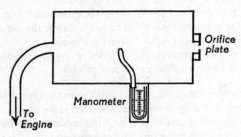

FIG. 11.13.

water. To obtain an accurate result, curved, inclined or differential manometers may be used. It is sometimes necessary to fit a balance pipe between the float chamber of the carburettor and the air pipe to prevent petrol flooding at high engine speeds.

Air consumption is measured in m³/s and is given by the formula:

$$Q = C_d A \sqrt{\frac{2hRT_a}{13 \cdot 6 p_a}}$$

Symbols:

Q = Volume of air (m³/s)

C_d = Coefficient of discharge of the orifice plate (0·64 for knife-edged)

A = Area of orifice (m²)

R = Gas constant (286·7 J/kgK)

h = Manometer reading (mm of water)

T_a = Atmospheric temperature (K)

p_a = Atmospheric pressure (mmHg)

13·6 = Relative density of mercury

The equation can be simplified for any engine test.

When the area A is known, the value of $C_d A$ can be calculated and given the constant K_c.

The values which are constant can be calculated:

$$\frac{2R}{13 \cdot 6} = \frac{2 \times 286 \cdot 7}{13 \cdot 6} = 42 \cdot 16$$

Then
$$Q = C_d A \sqrt{\frac{2hRT_a}{13 \cdot 6 p_a}}$$
$$= K_c \sqrt{\frac{42 \cdot 16 \times hT_a}{p_a}}$$

The *volume* of air entering the engine per minute is $Q \times 60$ m³.

The *mass* of air entering the engine is calculated at s.t.p. The mass of 1 m³ of air at s.t.p. is 1·29 kg. But the air temperature, when testing an engine, is seldom at 0°C, so the mass of 1 m³ of air must be calculated at the temperature of the test.

Mass of 1 m³ of air at any temperature and pressure

$$= 1 \cdot 29 \times \frac{273}{\substack{\text{Atmospheric temp.} \\ \text{K}}} \times \frac{760}{\substack{\text{Atmospheric pressure} \\ \text{(mmHg)}}}$$

or
$$1 \cdot 29 \times \text{Correction factor}$$

$$\text{Volumetric efficiency} = \frac{\text{Volume of air consumed/min}}{\text{Swept volume of engine} \times \dfrac{\text{rev/min}}{2}}$$

If the engine operates on the two-stroke cycle the rev/min are *not* divided by 2.

$$\text{Air–fuel ratio} = \frac{\text{Mass of air consumed/min}}{\text{Mass of fuel consumed/min}}$$

A graph, plotted from the results of a volumetric efficiency test, is similar to the graph shown in Fig. 11.14. We see that, at one point, the efficiency drops suddenly, this is probably due to valve bounce.

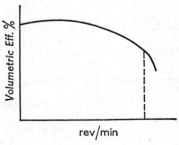

FIG. 11.14.

Example. A six-cylinder four-stroke petrol engine of 63·5 mm bore and 100 mm stroke, running at 2000 rev/min, develops 17·904 kW and consumes 0·1 litre of petrol in 41·25 s (relative density of petrol used 0·731). The air-box orifice was 38 mm diameter and the water-gauge reading showed a pressure difference of 61 mm. Atmospheric temperature was 20°C and the pressure 760 mmHg.

Find: (*a*) fuel consumption kg/kW h; (*b*) volumetric efficiency; (*c*) air–fuel ratio.

$$(a) \quad \text{Fuel consumed kg/min} = \frac{0·1 \times \text{relative density} \times 60}{\text{Time (s)}}$$

$$= \frac{0·1 \times 0·731 \times 60}{41·25} \text{ kg}$$

$$\therefore \text{ Fuel consumed in 1 min} = \underline{0·1063 \text{ kg}}$$

$$\text{Fuel consumption} = \frac{\text{Fuel consumed/hour}}{\text{kW}}$$

$$= \frac{0·1063 \times 60}{17·904} \text{ kg/kW h}$$

$$\therefore \text{ Fuel consumption} = \underline{0·356 \text{ kg/kW h}}$$

(*b*) *Volumetric efficiency.* The swept volume of the engine is calculated:

Swept volume

$$= \text{Area of cylinder} \times \text{Length of stroke} \times \text{Number of cylinders}$$

$$= \frac{\pi}{4} d^2 ln \text{ m}^3$$

$$= \frac{3·1416 \times 0·0635 \times 0·0635 \times 4 \times 6}{4} \text{ m}^3$$

$$= \underline{0·001 \ 901 \text{ m}^3}$$

Theoretical volume of air consumed per minute

$$= \text{Engine capacity} \times \frac{\text{rev/min}}{2} \text{ m}^3$$

$$= 0·001 \ 901 \times \frac{2000}{2} \text{ m}^3$$

$$= \underline{1·901 \text{ m}^3}$$

Actual volume of air consumed:

$$Q = K_c \sqrt{\frac{42 \cdot 16 h T_a}{p_a}} \text{ m}^3/\text{s}$$

The value of $K_c = 0 \cdot 64 \times \dfrac{\pi d^2}{4} \text{ m}^2$

$$= \frac{0 \cdot 64 \times 3 \cdot 1416 \times 0 \cdot 038 \times 0 \cdot 038}{4} \text{ m}^2$$

$$= \underline{0 \cdot 000\ 725\ 7 \text{ m}^2}$$

$$\therefore Q = 0 \cdot 000\ 725\ 7 \sqrt{\frac{42 \cdot 16 \times 0 \cdot 061 \times 293}{0 \cdot 76}} \text{ m}^3/\text{s}$$

$$= 0 \cdot 0228 \text{ m}^3/\text{s}$$

$$= 0 \cdot 0228 \times 60 \text{ m}^3/\text{min}$$

$$= \underline{1 \cdot 368 \text{ m}^3/\text{min}}$$

Volumetric efficiency $= \dfrac{\text{Actual volume of air consumed/min}}{\text{Theoretical volume of air consumed/min}}$

$$= \frac{1 \cdot 368}{1 \cdot 901}$$

$$= \underline{0 \cdot 7196 \text{ or } 71 \cdot 96 \text{ per cent}}$$

The volumetric efficiency can also be calculated from the engine capacity after the inlet valve has closed. If the valve closes 40° after b.d.c., the piston has travelled 13 mm up the cylinder on the compression stroke, so the theoretical air consumption is:

$$1 \cdot 901 \times \left(\frac{100 - 13}{100}\right) \text{ m}^3/\text{min} = 1 \cdot 901 \times 0 \cdot 87 \text{ m}^3/\text{min}$$

$$\therefore \text{ Volumetric efficiency} = \frac{1 \cdot 368}{1 \cdot 901 \times 0 \cdot 87}$$

$$= \underline{0 \cdot 8271 \text{ or } 82 \cdot 71 \text{ per cent}}$$

The volumetric efficiency is thus increased by 10 per cent by using this assumption.

(c) *Air–fuel ratio*.

Mass of air consumed per minute

$$= \text{Volume of air} \times 1 \cdot 29 \times \text{Correction factor}$$

$$= 1 \cdot 368 \times 1 \cdot 29 \times \frac{273}{293} \times \frac{760}{760} \text{ kg/min}$$

$$= \underline{1 \cdot 644 \text{ kg/min}}$$

$$\text{Air–fuel ratio} = \frac{\text{Mass of air consumed per min}}{\text{Mass of fuel consumed per min}}$$

$$= \frac{1 \cdot 644}{0 \cdot 1063} = \underline{15 \cdot 47 \text{ to } 1}$$

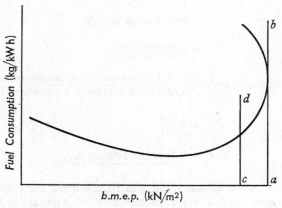

Fig. 11.15.

Volumetric Efficiency by Calculation

The volumetric efficiency of a petrol engine at the chemically correct air–fuel ratio may be calculated from a **torque–consumption loop.**

To carry out this test at any given engine speed the throttle valve must be fully open and the engine speed maintained constant by adjustment to the dynamometer, to ensure that the air consumption does not change.

The mixture strength is varied over the widest possible range, from very weak to very rich, and at each mixture setting the ignition timing is adjusted to give maximum torque at the determined engine speed.

A table of results containing brake load and fuel consumption is required; from these b.m.e.p. (kN/m²) and fuel consumption (kg/kW h) can be calculated. A graph is drawn, the OY axis representing fuel consumption and the OX axis b.m.e.p., see Fig. 11.15.

The results are plotted and a vertical tangent **ab** to the curve of the loop indicates the fuel consumption at which maximum b.m.e.p. is produced. This fuel consumption is, however, not at the chemically correct air–fuel ratio and research engineers have ascertained by experiment that the chemically correct ratio occurs when the b.m.e.p. is about 96 per cent of its maximum value.

A second vertical line **cd** is now drawn on the graph at a point representing 96 per cent of the maximum b.m.e.p.; this line passes through the loop and indicates the fuel consumption required.

Mass of air consumed per minute = Mass of fuel consumed per minute × Chemically correct air–fuel ratio.

This mass is converted to a volume:

$$\text{Volumetric efficiency} = \frac{\text{Calculated volume of air consumed/min}}{\text{Theoretical volume of air consumed/min}}$$

The theoretical volume is calculated from the engine capacity, but a more realistic answer is obtained if the closing position of the inlet valve is considered, as in the previous section, p. 195.

Air–Fuel Ratio and Power Output

The power output of a petrol engine at any given speed depends on many factors, such as air–fuel ratio, temperature, compression ratio, turbulence, volumetric efficiency and the timing of the valves and ignition. Assuming that all factors are ideal, an engine on a test bed can produce interesting results by varying the air–fuel ratio. An air–fuel ratio which produces maximum power does not give maximum thermal efficiency. The engine manufacturer designs his engine to give maximum power for acceleration and high speed and maximum thermal efficiency when the engine load is light. These characteristics are obtained by carburation, ignition timing and the rate at which the flame spreads during the combustion period.

Fig. 11.16 is a graph showing the different rates of flame speed. This flame speed rapidly increases when the mixture is heated and compressed in the engine cylinder. When the flame rate is maximum the pressure rise and m.e.p. are also maximum, but the air–fuel ratio is 20 per cent richer than the ideal mixture ratio (shown as a dotted line, Fig. 11.16) which satisfies the chemical equations of combustion.

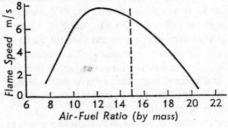

Fig. 11.16.

This richer mixture is heavier, contains more joules of heat and has a higher latent heat content, which assists the mass of fuel and oxygen entering the cylinder. The richer mixture enables all the oxygen available in the cylinder to be burnt completely, and thus produces maximum power.

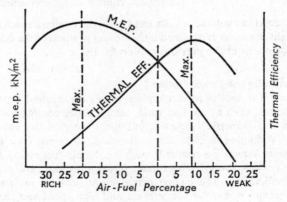

Fig. 11.17.

The weaker mixtures are slower burning and this results in a lower m.e.p.; to counteract this, the ignition timing is advanced so that the maximum pressure occurs at about t.d.c. The m.e.p., however, still remains lower, due to the reduced mass of fuel. When the air–fuel ratio is about 10 per cent weaker the thermal efficiency is maximum because all the fuel available in the cylinder is burnt completely, see Fig. 11.17.

Heat Balance

This is an account of where the heat energy goes after it appears in the combustion chamber. The quantity of heat supplied to the engine is the product of the mass of fuel and its calorific value. The engine must be working steadily and at constant temperature before the heat-balance test can start.

Heat to Power

$$\text{Heat to } P_b = \text{kW kJ/s}$$

Heat to cooling water.

Heat passing into the cooling water

= Mass of water × Change in temperature × specific heat capacity (4·187) kJ/s

To determine the mass of water flowing through the engine it can be collected in a tank and measured or passed through a flow-meter. The temperature must be recorded at points close to where the water enters and leaves the engine.

Heat to exhaust. This heat can be measured by passing the exhaust gases through a calorimeter; a water spray removes or extracts the heat from the gases, and the heat given up to the water is calculated from the mass of water multiplied by its temperature rise and a constant (4·187).

Heat to radiation is assumed to be that quantity of heat which cannot be accounted for in the heat-balance calculation, so it is added to the exhaust heat, which also radiates direct to the air.

$$\begin{matrix} \text{Total heat} \\ \text{supplied} \end{matrix} = \begin{bmatrix} \text{Heat to} \\ \text{power} \end{bmatrix} + \begin{bmatrix} \text{Heat to cooling} \\ \text{water} \end{bmatrix} + \begin{bmatrix} \text{Heat to exhaust} \\ \text{and radiation} \end{bmatrix}$$

The heat-balance ratios vary as the engine load changes; a typical result is shown in Fig. 11.18.

Example. A petrol engine developing 29·84 kW consumes petrol at the rate of 0·15 kg/min; its calorific value is 47 000 kJ/kg. Cooling water circulates at the rate of 8·4 kg/min; the inlet temperature is 18°C and the outlet temperature is 85°C. Determine the heat balance for this engine.

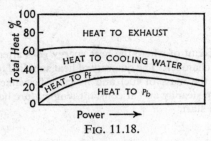

Fig. 11.18.

Total heat supplied = Mass of fuel × L.C.V.

$$= \frac{0.15 \times 47\,000}{60} \text{ kJ/s}$$

$$= \underline{117.5 \text{ kJ/s}}$$

Heat to P_b = kW kJ/s

$$= \underline{29.84 \text{ kJ/s}}$$

Heat to cooling water = Rate of flow × Temp. rise × Constant

$$= \frac{8.4}{60} \times (85 - 18) \times 4.187 \text{ kJ/s}$$

$$= \underline{39.28 \text{ kJ/s}}$$

Heat to exhaust and radiation

$$= \text{Total heat supplied} - \text{Heat to } P_b + \text{Heat to water}$$
$$= 117.5 - (29.84 + 39.28) \text{ kJ/s}$$
$$= 117.5 - 69.12 \text{ kJ/s}$$
$$= \underline{48.38 \text{ kJ/s}}$$

Balance

$$\text{Total heat } 117.5 \text{ kJ/s} = \underline{100 \text{ per cent}}$$

$$\text{Heat to } P_b = \frac{29.84}{117.5}$$

$$= \underline{0.2541 \text{ or } 25.41 \text{ per cent}}$$

$$\text{Heat to cooling water} = \frac{39\cdot28}{117\cdot5}$$

$$= \underline{0\cdot3343 \text{ or } 33\cdot43 \text{ per cent}}$$

$$\text{Heat to exhaust and radiation} = \frac{48\cdot38}{117\cdot5}$$

$$= \underline{0\cdot4116 \text{ or } 41\cdot16}$$

Cooling Water Temperature and Power Output

The modern motor-vehicle engine is fitted with thermostatic controls to ensure rapid warming up and to control engine temperature. When the cooling-water temperature is just below boiling point the engine efficiency is maximum. The heat also reduces **precipitation** of the fuel and improves its distribution in the induction passages. Precipitation is the tendency of the fuel particles not to remain in suspension and so fall to the bottom of the induction passages, hence the manifold drain. A hot engine also reduces fuel consumption and cylinder-bore wear. Rapid 'warming up' of the engine enables it to produce its maximum power in the shortest possible time, and also lowers the viscosity of the lubricating oil, which reduces the piston friction and raises the mechanical efficiency of the engine.

When the cooling water temperature is raised from 20°C to about 90°C a power increase of about 10 per cent is obtained. Most of this gain comes from the reduction of piston friction; this is why the manufacturers consider piston design, piston thrust pressures and piston speed as very important. The gain in power is partly offset by losses due to a reduced mass of mixture or air entering the hot engine; the mean effective pressure decreases by about 3 per cent. The net result is a gain in power and efficiency for the hot running engine of about 5–8 per cent.

Recent oil-engine practice is to operate the engine at a high temperature, use a low-viscosity lubricating oil and gain the maximum power by reducing frictional losses to a minimum. The air intake is arranged so that cold air from outside the bonnet is fed to the engine. This arrangement ensures the maximum mass of oxygen, and the increase in power is about 15 per cent.

Willan's Line

This is a graphical method of determining the power at which the brake thermal efficiency of an engine is maximum. A graph is plotted as shown in Fig. 11.19 (a).

The fuel consumed per minute or hour is plotted along the OY axis and P_b on the OX axis.

If the thermal efficiency of an engine were 100 per cent the fuel consumption would be proportional to the power output and the curve would be a straight line passing through the origin. This condition is not possible, as fuel is used to overcome friction and produce heat which appears in the cooling water and exhaust gases. Fuel used for this is represented on the graph by the distance O*m* along the OY axis.

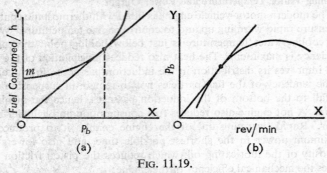

FIG. 11.19.

To determine the P_b at which the thermal efficiency is maximum, a **tangent** is drawn to the curve, passing through the origin and touching the curve. The point of **tangency** gives the P_b at maximum brake thermal efficiency.

Maximum thermal efficiency is calculated from the P_b and fuel consumption at this point and is:

$$\frac{\text{kW expressed as heat units}}{\text{Total heat units}}$$

Example. A c.i. engine on test consumes 0·25 kg of fuel per kW per hour. If the calorific value of the fuel is 45 000 kJ/kg, that is the brake thermal efficiency (b.t.e.)?

$$\begin{aligned} \text{b.t.e.} &= \frac{1 \text{ kW expressed as heat units per s}}{\text{Heat units supplied per s as fuel}} \\ &= \frac{1}{\dfrac{0 \cdot 25}{60 \times 60} \times 45\,000} \\ &= \frac{1 \times 60 \times 60}{0 \cdot 25 \times 45\,000} \\ &= 0 \cdot 32 \text{ or } 32 \text{ per cent} \end{aligned}$$

Maximum b.m.e.p.

This may be found graphically from the power curve of an engine. The graph is drawn (see Fig. 11.19 (b)) with P_b represented on the OY axis and rev/min along the OX axis. A tangent is drawn to pass through the origin and touch the curve; the point of tangency indicates the point of maximum b.m.e.p. This is also the point of maximum torque.

Exhaust-gas Analysis

The composition of the exhaust gases leaving an i.c. engine is a reliable indication of the air–fuel ratio and also shows if the mixing of the fuel and air is efficient. When the fuel burns it mixes with the air to form carbon monoxide, carbon dioxide, water vapour and traces of other gases; the nitrogen in the air is an inert gas, so takes no part in normal combustion. Fig. 11.20 shows a graph constructed from tests on a petrol engine running at constant speed, maximum load and variable mixture strengths.

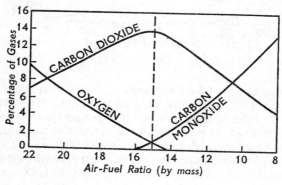

FIG. 11.20.

At the chemically correct air–fuel ratio of 15 to 1 the carbon dioxide CO_2, content was maximum, with only small traces of oxygen, O, and carbon monoxide, CO. This indicates that the carbon in the fuel was burnt completely to CO_2, and all its heat was liberated. When the mixture was weak less carbon entered the engine, so less CO_2 was present in the same volume of exhaust gases; some oxygen was also present, but this was excess and not required for combustion. When the mixture was rich more carbon entered the engine with the same volume of air. Thus, with insufficient oxygen, only a proportion of the carbon burnt completely to CO_2, the remainder burnt to CO and, in doing this, only part of its heat was liberated.

The air–fuel ratio of the petrol engine remains nearly constant over the working-speed range. This is not so with the compression-ignition engine; its air–fuel ratio varies considerably. Fig. 11.21 shows the graph of the exhaust gases of the oil engine. The engine always admits

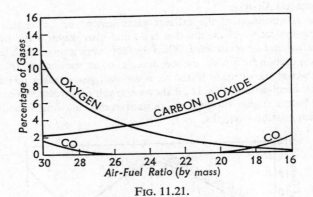

Fig. 11.21.

a maximum charge of fresh air during each induction stroke; this is necessary to obtain the required compression pressure. When the engine is idling the exhaust gases contain a high percentage of oxygen; this gradually falls as the load on the engine increases, so that when maximum load is reached only a trace is present. The CO_2 content increases as the load on the engine increases; this is due to the increased quantity of fuel injected. When the air–fuel ratio is about 16 to 1, CO appears in the exhaust gases, which indicates that the smoke limit has been reached, and that no oxygen is available to complete the combustion.

Methods of Analysis

Two different methods can be used to analyse the exhaust gases of an engine; absorption of the gases by chemicals, or by measuring their thermal conductivity with a galvanometer.

When the **absorption method** is used a volume of the gases, usually 1×10^5 mm³, is contained in an **eudiometer or measuring** cylinder. These gases are brought into contact with a solution of caustic potash, which absorbs the CO_2 gas; the quantity absorbed is indicated by the reduced volume of gas in the eudiometer. The remaining gases are then brought into contact with a solution of pyrogallic acid, which absorbs the O; the quantity absorbed is indicated by the change in volume. The remaining gases are then brought into contact with a solution of cuprous chloride, which absorbs the CO gas; the quantity absorbed is calculated by the change in volume of the gases in the eudiometer. The remaining volume is nitrogen.

The **electrical method of** analysis had for its basic principle the effect of temperature on an electrical circuit. The thermal conductivity of the gases is balanced against the thermal conductivity of air. Hydrogen conducts heat seven times faster than air, carbon dioxide conducts heat half as fast as air, while oxygen and nitrogen are about equal to air. Hydrogen and carbon dioxide are the important gases, and their **combined** thermal conductivity varies with the air–fuel ratio supplied to the engine. The two heated filaments of the electrical circuit are placed in the gas and air cells; heat is conducted away from the filament in the air cell at **constant rate**, but the filament in the gas cell is cooled by the exhaust gas, and heat is therefore conducted away from the filament at a rate depending on the proportions of carbon dioxide and hydrogen in the gas. As the temperatures of the filaments vary, so do their resistances; this unbalances the electrical bridge circuit and deflects the needle of the galvanometer, whose scale is graduated as **mixture strength** or air–petrol ratio.

Exercise 11

1. An engine on test develops a maximum torque of 136 Nm at a speed of 2000 rev/min, and a maximum power of 43·17 kW at 3600 rev/min.

Calculate the P_b at maximum torque, and the percentage of maximum torque developed at maximum power.

(28·47 kW; 84·2 per cent) (C. and G.)

2. An oil engine is tested and found to overcome a resistance of 860 N, with a brake arm of 0·5 m radius, when running at 1650 rev/min. Find the torque and P_b. (430 Nm; 74·29 bkW)

3. An engine running at 2800 rev/min overcomes a load of 245 N at a radius of 0·4 m. Calculate the P_b of the engine.

(28·74 kW) (N.C.T.E.C.)

4. Determine the P_i of a four-cylinder four-stroke cycle engine, of cylinder diameter 0·06 m, stroke 0·088 m, speed 3200 rev/min, m.e.p. 600 kN/m². (15·928 kW) (E.M.E.U.)

5. A six-cylinder four-stroke oil engine running at 1500 rev/min was tested with an indicator for P_i; the heights of the ordinates of the indicator diagram, measured in mm, were as follows: $h_1 = 30·5$, $h_2 = 26·7$, $h_3 = 20·8$, $h_4 = 16·4$, $h_5 = 14$, $h_6 = 11·2$, $h_7 = 8·3$, $h_8 = 5·7$, $h_9 = 3·8$ and $h_{10} = 2·3$, the indicator spring rate, 1380 kN/m².

If the bore and stroke of the engine were 100 mm and 150 mm, find: (a) indicated mean effective pressure; (b) indicated power.

((a) 760 kN/m²; (b) 67·16 kW)

6. A certain six-cylinder engine is known to have a total swept volume of 0·00 147 5 m³ and a stroke/bore ratio of 1·4. If it develops 23·87 kW at 2200 rev/min, calculate the b.m.e.p. of the engine under these conditions. (882 kN/m²) (C. and G.)

7. A certain four-cylinder is normally capable of developing a maximum of 29·84 kW. If the sparking plug fails on one cylinder, make a reasonable estimate of the maximum P_b that would be delivered by the engine running on three cylinders. (20·142 kW) (C. and G.)

8. Draw an indicator diagram for a four-stroke engine and state the approximate pressures at the principal parts of the cycle. What is the use of such a diagram? (U.L.C.I.)

9. A six-cylinder engine is to develop 29·84 kW at 2500 rev/min, at which speed the b.m.e.p. is expected to be 827 kN/m².

If the ratio of stroke to bore is to be 1·4, determine the bore and stroke of the engine. (64 mm; 89·6 mm) (C. and G.)

10. A single-cylinder four-stroke motor-cycle engine with bore and stroke of 88·9 mm is coupled to a hydraulic dynamometer. When running at 4800 rev/min the mechanical efficiency is 91 per cent. The brake load is 160 N and constant $K_c = 2$.

Find: (a) brake power; (b) indicated power; (c) brake mean effective pressure. ((a) 25·6 kW; (b) 28·132 kW; (c) 1160 kN/m²)

11. Describe some form of engine indicator suitable for a high-speed engine. What method is there of determining the P_i of an engine without the use of an indicator? (C. and G.)

12. A six-cylinder two-stroke oil engine develops 93·996 kW at 2000 rev/min. The engine bore is 85 mm and stroke 120 mm. Maximum torque of 475 Nm is produced at 1500 rev/min. Fuel consumption at maximum torque is 0·3 kg/kW h, the relative density of the fuel is 0·848.

Find: (*a*) b.m.e.p. at maximum torque; (*b*) b.m.e.p. at maximum power; (*c*) P_b at maximum torque; (*d*) litres of fuel consumed per min at maximum torque.

((*a*) 730·7 kN/m²; (*b*) 690·2 kN/m²; (*c*) 74·61 kW; (*d*) 0·3986 litres/min)

13. What characteristics are required of a dynamometer suitable for testing high-speed automobile engines? Describe the operation of one such dynamometer and explain how the power delivered by the engine is measured. (C. and G.)

14. A petrol engine developing 14·92 kW consumes 0·1 litres of petrol in 43·25 s and air at the rate of 1·75 kg/min. If the relative density of the petrol is 0·731 and L.C.V. 45 500 kJ/kg, find: (*a*) fuel consumption, kg/kW h; (*b*) air–fuel ratio by mass; (*c*) brake thermal efficiency.
((*a*) 0·4031 kg/kW h; (*b*) 17·26 to 1; (*c*) 19·4 per cent)

15. A four-cylinder engine of 60 mm bore and 85 mm stroke was found to develop during a test 14·17 kW when running at a speed of 2500 rev/min. What brake mean effective pressure was being developed? (707·4 kN/m²) (C. and G.)

16. A six-cylinder petrol engine of 60 mm bore and 100 mm stroke, consumes 1·4 m³ of air/min when running at 2000 rev/min and developing 17·15 kW. Fuel is consumed at the rate of 0·146 l/min. (Relative density 0·731.)

Find: (*a*) volumetric efficiency; (*b*) fuel consumption, kg/kW h.
((*a*) 82·5 per cent; (*b*) 0·3733 kg/kW h)

17. At a certain speed and power output the brake thermal efficiency of an oil engine is 33 per cent, it is then consuming fuel at the rate of 15·65 l/h; relative density of fuel 0·855; L.C.V. 47 000 kJ/kg.

What is the brake power? (52·94 kW)

18. Describe any method of testing a multi-cylinder engine on the bench in order to determine its mechanical efficiency. (C. and G.)

19. A twin-cylinder, two-stroke motor-cycle engine with 76·2 mm bore and 101·6 mm stroke has an i.m.e.p. of 455 kN/m² when running at 3000 rev/min. If the mechanical efficiency is 90 per cent, what power is transmitted by the driving chain to the gear box? (18·972 kW)

20. An engine, tested against a dynamometer having a formula $P_b = \dfrac{F \text{ rev/min}}{30}$ gave the following results:

Rev/min	825	1000	1200	1400	2000	2500	3000	3800	4200	4750
Load F(N)	200	220	230	232	225	220	215	200	185	160

Plot the engine characteristic curve and from it deduce the approximate speed at which the engine develops its maximum power and the approximate speed at which it develops its maximum torque.

(4200 rev/min; 1400 rev/min)   (C. and G.)

21. When the speed of a certain engine was 2000 rev/min the air–fuel ration by mass was 12·4 to 1 and it was consuming fuel at the rate of 0·2 l/min.

Find the mass of air consumed per minute.

If the brake thermal efficiency was 15·3 per cent, what kW was being developed? (Relative density of petrol 0·731; L.C.V. 47 500 kJ/kg.)

(1·83 kg; 17·71 kW)

22. Modern car engines, when tested for P_b on the bench, are generally found to give three or four times the R.A.C.-rated power. Why is this so? Discuss some of the factors that have contributed to this result.

(C. and G.)

23. A four-cylinder oil engine working on the four-stroke cycle has a bore of 85 mm and stroke of 120·6 mm. When running at 1500 rev/min the brake load on the hydraulic dynamometer was 280 N, and 0·1 litre fuel was consumed in 65·5 s. (Relative density of fuel oil 0·848; K_c for brake, 2.)

Find: (*a*) capacity of engine in litres; (*b*) brake power developed; (*c*) torque; (*d*) fuel consumption, kg/kW h.

((*a*) 2·75 litres; (*b*) 14 kW; (*c*) 89·13 Nm; (*d*) 0·3328 kg/kW h)

24. A six-cylinder petrol engine was Morse tested when running at 1400 rev/min and the following brake loads F(N) were observed: all in 258 N; No. 1 out 198 N; No. 2 out 206·8 N; No. 3 out 211 N; No. 4 out 211 N; No. 5 out 209 N; and No. 6 out 205 N (each cylinder was cut out in turn). The brake constant $K_c = 2$.

Find: (*a*) brake power; (*b*) indicated power; (*c*) friction power; (*d*) mechanical efficiency.

((*a*) 12·04 kW; (*b*) 14·38 kW; (*c*) 2·34 kW; (*d*) 83·73 per cent)

25. A six-cylinder petrol engine has a bore 69·5 mm and stroke 100 mm and, when running at 4200 rev/min produced a torque of 87 Nm. The brake constant $K_c = 2$.

Find: (*a*) brake power; (*b*) brake load F(N); (*c*) power by the R.A.C. rating.

((*a*) 40·46 kW; (*b*) 289 N; (*c*) 17·96 hp)

26. A single-cylinder engine (four-stroke) of bore 125 mm and stroke 150 mm overcomes a resistance of 140 N at a radius of 534 mm when running at 550 rev/min. Calculate the power developed by the engine and the b.m.e.p. (4·305 kW; 510·4 kN/m²)   (C. and G.)

27. A certain fuel has a calorific value of 46 000 kJ/kg and is consumed in an engine of 'brake thermal efficiency' 22 per cent at the rate of 5·4 kg/h. Calculate the brake power developed by the engine. Give an approximate account of the disposal of the remaining 78 per cent of the heating value of the fuel.

(15·18 kW; P_f 6 per cent; C.W. 32 per cent; E and R 40 per cent)
(C. and G.)

28. A petrol engine burns 0·225 litres of fuel in 10 minutes and 1 kg of fuel gives out 47 500 kJ. (Relative density of fuel = 0·78.)

If 24·5 per cent of the heat in fuel is transformed into useful work, calculate the number of joules of work done by the engine per minute.
(204·2 kJ)   (U.E.I.)

29. Assuming 100 units of energy are supplied to a petrol engine in the fuel, give an account of the disposal of this energy on its passage through the engine. (C. and G.)

30. An engine was found by experiment to consume 1·56 kg of air per minute. Assuming a mixture of 15 to 1 with a fuel of calorific value 44 190 kJ/kg and brake thermal efficiency of 24 per cent, calculate the P_b of the engine. (18·39 kW)   (C. and G.)

31. An engine on test, running at 3000 rev/min, overcomes a resistance of 140 N at a radius of 360 mm and at the same time consumes fuel at the rate of 8 litres an hour. Given that the fuel consumption, at the rate of 1 litre per hour, is equivalent to a supply of energy at the rate of 8375 W, calculate the brake thermal efficiency.

(23·62 per cent)   (C. and G.)

32. A single-cylinder two-stroke diesel engine develops 6·71 kW at 2800 rev/min. Calculate the work done on the piston in joules in one stroke. If the piston is 100 mm diameter and the stroke is 150 mm, calculate the average pressure on the piston in kN/m².

(143·7 J; 122 kN/m²)   (U.E.I.)

33. During a test on an engine 64 m³ of air at 18°C are heated to 250°C. 1 m³ of air at 18°C has a mass of 1·233 kg and its specific heat capacity is 1·005. Calculate: (*a*) the number of kJ used in heating the air; (*b*) the power represented by this heat if the test lasted 15 min.

(18 410 kJ; 20·455 kW)   (U.E.I.)

34. A six-cylinder, four-stroke engine has a bore of 85 mm and stroke 85 mm, and it is tested against a dynamometer with a torque arm length of 0·67 m; P_b is given by $\dfrac{F}{K_{c1}}$ rev/min; torque in Nm by FK_{c2} and b.m.e.p. in kN/m² by FK_{c3} where

$$F = \text{brake load, in N}$$

and K_{c1}, K_{c2} and K_{c3} are constants depending on the given dimensions. Find the values of K_{c1}, K_{c2} and K_{c3}.

$$(K_{c1} = 14\cdot25;\ K_{c2} = 0\cdot67;\ K_{c3} = 5839)$$

12 Forces on a Vehicle

To study the mechanics of a moving vehicle and its component parts it is necessary to know the laws of motion concerned with mass, energy, momentum and centrifugal force.

Kinetics is a study of motion in terms of displacement, velocity, speed and acceleration. A motor car, travelling along a curved or winding road from point A to point B, covers a distance, say 7·5 km, which is the actual distance measured along the road. The displacement of this vehicle is a distance measured in a straight line from A to B, say 5 km, and is irrespective of the path followed by the vehicle.

Displacement is a vector quantity because it has direction, sense and magnitude.

Speed is the rate at which anything moves, or the actual distance travelled divided by time taken. Speed of a motor car is often given, but the direction of the motion is not given.

Velocity is the rate of change of displacement or displacement divided by time.

Velocity and speed are numerically the same if the movement is in a straight line, but a change in direction of a moving object changes its velocity but not its speed.

Example. The instantaneous speed of a vehicle at A (Fig. 12.1)

$$= \frac{\text{Short distance travelled}}{\text{Time taken to cover distance}}$$

$$= \frac{15\text{m}}{1 \text{ s}} \quad \text{or} \quad \underline{54 \text{ km/h}}$$

The instantaneous speed of a vehicle at B

$$= \frac{\text{Short distance travelled}}{\text{Time taken to cover distance}}$$

$$= \frac{10 \text{ m}}{1 \text{ s}} \quad \text{or} \quad \underline{36 \text{ km/h}}$$

If the time taken to cover distance A to B is 12 min,

$$\text{Average speed along road} = 7{\cdot}5 \times \frac{60}{12} \text{ km/h}$$

$$= 37{\cdot}5 \text{ km/h}$$

$$\text{Velocity A to B} = \frac{\text{Direct distance}}{\text{Time taken}}$$

$$= 5 \times \frac{60}{12} \text{ km/h}$$

$$= \underline{25 \text{ km/h in the direction } 20° \text{ N. of E.}}$$

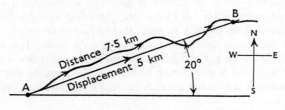

Fig. 12.1.

Relative Velocity

The velocity of anything moving is measured relative to another object, usually the earth, which is assumed to be fixed; actually it is moving at high velocity inside the solar system, which in turn is moving relative to fixed 'space'. An object can have two or more velocities. An example is a bus travelling due north at 24 km/h (v_1), while the conductor walks forward at 3 km/h (v_2) relative to the floor of the bus; his velocity relative to the ground is $v_1 + v_2$ or 27 km/h due north. On his return to the rear platform he walks at the same velocity, 3 km/h due south, so his velocity relative to the ground is $v_1 - v_2$ or 21 km/h due north.

Relative motion of a point P on a motor-vehicle tyre relative to the ground is shown in Fig. 12.2.

Let P = point on tyre

     v = velocity of wheel hub relative to the ground

     v_1 = velocity of point P

     R = velocity of point relative to the ground

The vectors indicate the direction and magnitude of point P relative to the ground. At its lowest position the velocity is zero except when the wheel is spinning or skidding.

Amgular Velocity

Many parts on a motor vehicle rotate, and it is common practice to refer to their speed of rotation as rev/min or rev/s. If the t.d.c. mark on a flywheel moves through five complete revolutions in 1 s, its angular velocity is 5 rev/s or 300 rev/min. This method of statement is not

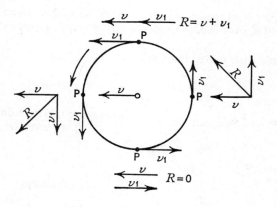

FIG. 12.2.

convenient for some calculations. The velocity is expressed in radians/s. The radian has been defined in Part 1 (one revolution or $360°$ equals 2π radians), so the angular velocity of the flywheel would be $5 \times 2\pi = 10\pi$ radians per second.

Let the total angle turned through by the flywheel in t s $= \theta$ radians.

Then average angular velocity

$$= \frac{\text{Total angle turned through (in radians)}}{\text{Time taken (s)}}$$

$$\therefore \omega = \frac{\theta}{t} \text{ radians/s}$$

Example. A road wheel rotates at 3000 rev/min. What is its angular velocity in radians/s?

$$3000 \text{ rev/min} = 50 \text{ rev/s}$$

$$\text{and } 1 \text{ revolution} = 2\pi \text{ radians}$$

$$\therefore 50 \text{ revolutions} = 2\pi \times 50 \text{ radians}$$

$$\therefore \text{ Angular velocity } \omega = 100\pi \text{ radians/s}$$

$$= \underline{314 \cdot 16 \text{ radians/s}}$$

Example. If an engine valve rocker arm moves through an angle of 30° in 0·01 s, what is its average angular velocity in radians/s?

$$\theta, \text{ the angle moved through} = 30°$$

$$= \frac{30}{360} \times 2\pi \text{ radians}$$

$$\text{Average angular velocity} = \frac{\text{Angle moved through (in radians)}}{\text{Time taken (s)}}$$

$$\therefore \omega = \frac{\theta}{t}$$

$$= \frac{30 \times 2\pi}{360 \times 0 \cdot 01} \text{ radians/s}$$

$$= \underline{52 \cdot 36 \text{ radians/s}}$$

In some calculations of rotation the linear speed, that is the speed of a point on the circumference, must be known. Consider again the t.d.c. mark on the flywheel at a radius r m from the centre, moving with a uniform speed of v m/s along the circumference and at an angular velocity of ω radians/s. The length of arc moved over in 1 s is v m, so the angle moved through in radians/s is:

$$\text{Velocity (m/s)} \div \text{radius (m)}$$

$$\therefore \text{ Angular velocity } \omega = \frac{v}{r} \quad \text{or} \quad v = \omega r$$

Example. A dynamo pulley, 100 mm diameter, rotates at 3000 rev/min. What is the average linear speed of the driving belt?

Equation:
$$\omega = \frac{v}{r}$$
$$\therefore v = \omega r$$
$$= \frac{2\pi \times 3000 \times 0\cdot 1}{60 \times 2} \text{ m/s}$$
$$= \underline{15\cdot 71 \text{ m/s}}$$

Angular Acceleration

This is the rate of change of angular velocity and is given the symbol α ('alpha' a Greek letter).

The equations used for angular velocity, angular acceleration and angle turned through are similar to those equations used for linear motion.

Let $\omega_1 = $ initial angular velocity

$\omega_2 = $ final angular velocity

$\theta = $ angle turned through

$\alpha = $ angular acceleration

$t = $ time in seconds

Then the equations:

$$v = u + at \quad \text{will become} \quad \omega_2 = \omega_1 + \alpha t$$
$$s = ut + \tfrac{1}{2}at^2 \quad \text{,,} \quad \text{,,} \quad \theta = \omega_1 t + \tfrac{1}{2}\alpha t^2$$
$$v^2 - u^2 = 2as \quad \text{,,} \quad \text{,,} \quad \omega_2{}^2 - \omega_1{}^2 = 2\alpha\theta$$

Centripetal Acceleration

If the road wheel of a car is moving with uniform speed a point P on the tyre follows a circular path on a circumference of radius r measured from the hub centre. Let the velocity of point P (see Fig. 12.3 (*a*)) at the position M be v m/s and the angular velocity be ω radians/s. The arrow from M indicates the direction of the velocity, it is always perpendicular to the radius; thus, as its path is not straight, its direction must always be changing to keep it on a curved path. At the position N the arrow indicates the new direction of the velocity of P; when the speed of rotation is uniform, it is the direction that changes, not the magnitude.

To find this change a vector diagram is constructed, Fig. 12.3 (*b*).

Let   *pm* = velocity of P at position M

   pn = velocity of P at position N

The change in velocity is represented by *mn* and it is in a direction radially inwards towards the hub O. We consider that a force is pulling the point P inwards and the change in velocity causes an acceleration towards the centre; this is known as the **centripetal acceleration.**

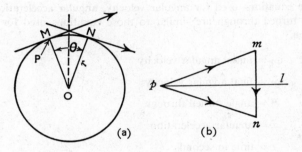

FIG. 12.3.

To calculate this centripetal acceleration:

$$\text{angle } \theta \text{ radians} = \text{MON}$$

$$= mpn$$

The angle θ is bisected by the line *pl* to produce two right-angled triangles whose angle is $\dfrac{\theta}{2}$.

Then $\sin \dfrac{\theta}{2} = \dfrac{\frac{1}{2}mn}{pm}$

$$\therefore \tfrac{1}{2}mn = \sin \frac{\theta}{2}\, pm$$

$$mn = 2 \sin \frac{\theta}{2}\, pm$$

But pm is the velocity v of point P at position M.

$$\therefore \text{ Change in velocity } mn = 2 \sin \frac{\theta}{2} \, v$$

$$= 2v \sin \frac{\theta}{2}$$

$$= v \sin \theta$$

$$= v\theta$$

The angle θ is always very small, and from the tables it can be seen that the sine of small angles is numerically about the same as the angle in radians.

$$\text{Acceleration} = \frac{\text{Change in velocity}}{\text{Time}}$$

$$= \frac{mn}{t}$$

If t is the time for point P to move from M to N, then the acceleration of

$$P = \frac{mn}{t} = \frac{v\theta}{t}$$

$$= v\omega$$

Since angular velocity $\omega = \dfrac{\theta}{t}$

also angular velocity $\omega = \dfrac{v}{r}$

$$\therefore \text{ Accleration of P} = v\omega = v \times \frac{v}{r}$$

$$= \frac{v^2}{r} \text{ or } \omega^2 r$$

* System of Units

Mechanical and **automobile engineers** use for all calculations the **International System of Units (SI)**

The unit of mass is called the **kilogramme (kg)**.

The unit of force is called the **newton (N)**, it is that force which, when applied to a body having a mass of one kilogramme gives an acceleration of one metre per second squared. In practice, we may have to multiply the mass of a body, in kg, by 9·8 in order to convert it to newtons.

$$\text{Force } (F) = \text{mass } (m) \times \text{acceleration } (a)$$

* See appendix p. 358.

Occasionally the mass is not constant; for example, the mass of a running car decreases as the fuel is burnt.

Determination of g (9·8 m/s²)

An experimental method of determining the value of g is by means of the apparatus known as **Fletcher's Trolley** (Fig. 12.4). This apparatus consists of a plane on which runs a trolley mounted on ball-bearing wheels. A bridge which spans the plane at one end carries a steel vibrator. The trolley is drawn along the plane by a string passing over a pulley which carries a mass that can fall vertically. A strip of paper ribbon is fixed to the top surface of the trolley, and the inked brush at the end of the vibrator draws a graph on the paper. From the graph the distances travelled by the trolley, in known intervals, can be measured. The friction of the trolley is eliminated by raising one end of the plane sufficiently for the trolley to run down at a slow uniform speed.

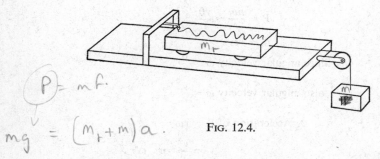

$$P = mf.$$

$$mg = (m_r + m)a.$$

FIG. 12.4.

The following table gives the results obtained from an experiment on a Fletcher's trolley. The times and distances measured from the graph on the paper ribbon were recorded in columns (1) and (2). By the subtraction of successive values in column (2) we obtain the values tabulated in column (3). For example $9·65 - 0·0 = 9·65$; $40·39 - 9·65 = 30·74$, and so on. The values in column (4) were obtained by dividing each value in column (3) by $0·2$, since column (3) gives the distances in mm covered in $0·2$ s. Column (5) was obtained by the subtraction of successive values in column (4). Column (6) was obtained by dividing the values in column (5) by $0·2$, because the differences in velocity occurred at intervals of $0·2$ s.

The force pulling the trolley was 0·89 N, and the vertical downward force of the trolley was 15 N.

Time from start in seconds (1)	Distance from start in mm (2)	Distance in mm during 0·2 seconds (3)	Velocity in mm per second (4)	Differences in velocity mm/s (5)	Acceleration mm/s² (6)
0·0	0·0				
		9·65	48·25		527·25
0·2	9·65			105·45	
		30·74	153·7		520·5
0·4	40·39			104·1	
		51·56	257·8		484·75
0·6	91·95			96·95	
		70·95	354·75		503·75
0·8	162·9			100·75	
		91·1	455·5		485
1·0	254			97	
		110·5	552·5		602·5
1·2	364·5			120·5	
		134·6	673		501
1·4	499·1			102	
		155	775		
1·6	654·1				

Average acceleration mm/s² 7)3621·75

517·39

Let F = force acting on trolley, in N
  W = vertical downward force of trolley, in N
  a = average acceleration, in m/s²
  g = acceleration due to gravity, in m/s²

Then

$$F \times g = (W + F) \times a$$

or

$$g = \frac{(W + F)}{F} \times a \, \text{m/s}^2$$

$$0·89 \times g = (15 + 0·89) \, 0·517 \, 39$$

$$g = \frac{15·89 \times 0·517 \, 39}{0·89}$$

$$= 9·868 \, \text{m/s}^2$$

Newton's Laws of Motion

Newton's first law states that if a body is at rest it tends to remain at rest unless compelled by an external force to move; also, if the body is already moving in a straight line at constant speed it will continue to do so, and only change its speed or deviate from the straight path if an external force is applied.

Two common forces exist near the earth's surface; they are gravitational pull and air resistance. If a motor car is to travel at a constant speed on a level road it requires power at the driving wheels to overcome air resistance and rolling resistance. If the power ceases, then the vehicle slows down and stops.

Newton's second law states that the rate of change of momentum is proportional to the force producing the change, and it takes place in the direction of the applied force.

The **momentum** of a moving body is the product of its mass (kg) and its velocity m/s. If the mass is assumed to remain constant, then the force is proportional to the rate of change of velocity, which is acceleration.

$\therefore$ Rate of change of momentum

$$= \text{Mass} \times \text{Rate of change of velocity}$$
$$= \text{Mass (kg)} \times \text{Acceleration (m/s}^2)$$
$$= ma$$

Newton's second law states that the force producing the change of momentum is proportional to the mass and the acceleration.

$$\therefore \text{Accelerating force } F = ma$$

Example. A motor vehicle of mass 3540 kg is travelling at a speed of 108 km/h. What force is necessary to slow it down to 36 km/h in 0·1 min?

$$\text{Mass of vehicle } m = 3540 \text{ kg}$$

$$\text{Time of 0·1 min} = 6 \text{ s}$$

$$\text{Speed of 108 km/h} = 30 \text{ m/s}$$

$$\text{Speed of 36 km/h} = 10 \text{ m/s}$$

$$\text{Now deceleration } a = \frac{\text{Change of velocity}}{\text{Time taken}}$$

$$= \frac{30 - 10}{6} \left(\frac{\text{m/s}}{\text{s}}\right)$$

$$= \underline{3 \cdot 333 \text{ m/s}^2}$$

Also, decelerating force $F = \text{Mass} \times \text{Deceleration}$

$$\therefore F \text{ (N)} = 3540 \times 3 \cdot 333 \left(\frac{\text{kg} \times \text{m/s}^2}{\text{m/s}^2}\right)$$

$$= \underline{11\,900 \text{ N}}$$

Note: When the mass of a vehicle is stated in kg it is sometimes necessary to know the vertical downward force that the vehicle exerts, this is found by kg $\times$ 9·8 = N.

Further examples using Newton's laws and momentum appear later in this chapter.

Forward Motion and Resistance of a Motor Vehicle

The power unit of a motor vehicle provides at the driving road wheels a **thrust** known as tractive effort or force. This thrust varies at different engine speeds and gear positions, but its purpose is to overcome forces opposing motion of the vehicle.

A vehicle travelling in a straight line has three main forces opposing its motion:

1. Rolling resistance
2. Gradient resistance
3. Air resistance

Rolling Resistance (R_r)

The **rolling** resistance of a vehicle may be regarded as the force necessary to maintain a constant speed of, say, 1 km/h on a level road. At this low speed air resistance to forward motion is negligible. The resistance is mainly due to friction between the tyres and road surface, although friction at the road wheel bearings does exist and increases if the mass of the vehicle increases. Friction between tyre and road depends on road surface, load on each tyre, inflation pressure and type of tyre tread.

The resistance R_r is measured in newtons and may be expressed as a percentage of the downward force exerted by the vehicle. Resistance on an average type of road surface is between 1 and 2 per cent of the downward force (F) exerted by the vehicle.

Rolling resistance $= R_r$ (newtons)

      when $F =$ downward force exerted by vehicle

      and $R_r =$ resistance as a percentage of the downward force

Gradient Resistance (R_g)

A gradient was defined in Part 1 as the distance measured along a path, divided by the vertical height of ascent or descent. A gradient of 1 in 8 means that a road rises 1 m for every 8 m measured along the road. It may be stated that the gradient is 8, since the distance is always stated as per metre of vertical rise.

The gradient G is represented in Fig. 12.5 as $\dfrac{b}{a}$ or sin α.

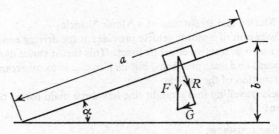

Fig. 12.5.

Therefore, assuming no friction or rolling resistance exists, the component of force down the gradient $= F\dfrac{b}{a}$ or $F \sin \alpha$.

Now $\dfrac{b}{a} = \dfrac{1}{8}$ and 8 is the gradient G

$\therefore$ Component of force down the gradient $= \dfrac{F}{G}$ or $F \sin \alpha$

A motor vehicle moving up a gradient has its forward motion opposed by a force known as the gradient resistance, which is equal to the component of force down the slope. The rolling resistance always exists, so it must be considered with the gradient resistance.

Forces opposing forward motion of a vehicle moving up a slope

$$= \text{Gradient resistance } (R_g) + \text{Rolling resistance } (R_r)$$

$$= F \sin \alpha + R_r \quad \text{or} \quad \frac{F}{G} + R_r$$

Forces producing forward motion of a vehicle moving down a slope

$$= \text{Gradient resistance} - \text{Rolling resistance}$$

$$= F \sin \alpha - R_r \quad \text{or} \quad \frac{F}{G} - R_r$$

Example. A motor vehicle standing on a gradient of 1 in 10 has a mass of 710 kg; the rolling resistance is 1 per cent of its mass. If the hand brake were released, how far would it travel in 30 s and what would be its final speed?

Total vertical downward force $F = 710 \times 9 \cdot 8 = 6958$ N

Force producing forward motion

$$= \text{Gradient resistance} - \text{Rolling resistance}$$

$$= \frac{F}{G} - R_r$$

$$= \frac{710 \times 9 \cdot 8}{10} - \frac{710 \times 9 \cdot 8}{100} \text{ N}$$

$$= 695 \cdot 8 - 69 \cdot 58 \text{ N}$$

$$= \underline{626 \cdot 22 \text{ N}}$$

The force producing motion (acceleration) down the gradient has been calculated in newtons (N), but in order to calculate **acceleration**, it is necessary to convert the vertical downward force of 6958 N into mass (kg). Since 9·8 is the conversion factor of N to kg, we divide N by 9·8 in order to obtain mass (kg).

Accelerating force $F = ma$

$$\therefore \text{ Acceleration } a = \frac{F}{m}$$

$$= \frac{626 \cdot 22 \text{ (N)}}{6958 \text{ (N)} \div 9 \cdot 8 \text{ (m/s}^2)}$$

$$= \underline{0 \cdot 8818 \text{ m/s}^2}$$

The distance travelled in 30 s:

$$s = \tfrac{1}{2}at^2$$
$$= 0.5 \times 0.8818 \times 30 \times 30 \text{ m}$$
$$= \underline{396.9 \text{ m}}$$

The final velocity of the vehicle:

$$s = \frac{v}{2}t$$
$$\therefore v = \frac{2s}{t}$$
$$= \frac{2 \times 396.9}{30} \text{ m/s}$$
$$= \underline{26.46 \text{ m/s or } 95.25 \text{ km/h}}$$

Example. A motor vehicle has a mass of 700 kg and is travelling at 36 km/h on a level road when neutral is engaged. How far will it travel before stopping if the rolling resistance is 155 N?

$$\text{Total vertical downward force } F = 700 \times 9.8 = 6860 \text{ N}$$
$$\text{Retarding force} = 155 \text{ N}$$
$$\text{The decelerating force } F = ma$$
$$\therefore a = \frac{F}{m}$$
$$= \frac{155 \text{ (N)}}{6860 \text{ (N)} \div 9.8 \text{ (m/s}^2)}$$
$$= \underline{0.221 \text{ m/s}^2}$$

The distance travelled by the vehicle:

$$v^2 - u^2 = 2as$$
$$\therefore s = \frac{v^2}{2a} \text{ since } u = 0$$
$$= \frac{10 \times 10}{2 \times 0.221} \left(\frac{\text{m/s} \times \text{m/s}}{\text{m/s}^2} \right)$$
$$\approx \underline{226.2 \text{ m}}$$

Example. A vehicle has a mass of 720 kg and is travelling at 36 km/h up a gradient of 1 in 10 when neutral is engaged. How far will it travel before stopping if the rolling resistance is 150 N?

Total vertical downward force $F = 720 \times 9 \cdot 8 = 7056$ N

Forces opposing motion = Gradient resistance + Rolling resistance

$$= \frac{F}{G} + R_r$$

$$= \frac{7056}{10} + 150 \text{ N}$$

$$= 705 \cdot 6 + 150 \text{ N}$$

$$= \underline{855 \cdot 6 \text{ N}}$$

The decelerating force $F = ma$

$$\therefore \text{Deceleration } a = \frac{F}{m}$$

$$= \frac{855 \cdot 6}{7056 \div 9 \cdot 8}$$

$$= \underline{1 \cdot 188 \text{ m/s}^2}$$

The distance travelled before stopping:

$$v^2 - u^2 = 2as$$

$$\therefore s = \frac{v^2}{2a}$$

$$= \frac{10 \times 10}{2 \times 1 \cdot 188}$$

Distance travelled $= \underline{42 \cdot 08 \text{ m}}$

Comparing the last two answers, we see that the gradient is a major factor in motor-vehicle operation.

Example. A motor vehicle of mass 10 tonne is driven up a slope of 1 in 10 at 18 km/h. The rolling resistance is constant at 2450 N. Find the propelling force and power required to maintain this speed.

Total vertical downward force $= 10\,000 \times 9 \cdot 8 = 98\,000$ N

Total propelling force = Gradient resistance + Rolling resistance

$$= \frac{F}{G} + R_r$$

$$= \frac{98\ 000}{10} + 2450 \text{ N}$$

$$= 12\ 250 \text{ N}$$

Power required = Force × Distance (18 km/h = 5 m/s)

$$= 12\ 250 \times 5 \text{ W}$$

$$= \underline{61\ 250 \text{ W or } 61{\cdot}25 \text{ kW}}$$

Air Resistance ($K_c v^2 A$)

The foregoing examples were calculated without considering **air resistance,** which varies with the shape and speed of the vehicle. Air resistance increases as the **square** of the vehicle's speed, and for this reason much importance is given to streamlining and the frontal area of modern motor vehicles.

Air resistance is calculated from a formula $K_c v^2 A$, the constant term K_c being given values depending on the shape of a vehicle. This formula must be considered as approximate, since the only accurate method of obtaining the air resistance of a vehicle is to test it in a wind tunnel, as is done with aircraft.

The following values for K_c are given:

0·044 38	Lorry and bus
0·031 44	Modern motor car
0·022 19	Sports car
0·0111	Racing car

These values show how streamlining of the vehicle affects the air resistance.

When calculating air resistance, the vehicle's road speed and both the speed and direction of any wind relative to the vehicle must be known. These must be added to the vehicle's speed if the wind is opposing its motion, or subtracted if it is helping the vehicle along. If, however, the direction of the wind is different from the direction in which the vehicle is moving, then the air resistance will vary as the angle sin θ, see Fig. 12.6, as θ approaches 0°, its sine approaches 0 and the air pressure decreases.

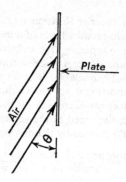

FIG. 12.6.

Example. Find the air resistance opposing motion of a vehicle whose frontal area is 1·67 m² and value of K_c is 0·031 44, at (a) 70 km/h, (b) 140 km/h, (c) 140 km/h against a 'head' wind whose velocity is 40 km/h.

(a) Air resistance $= K_c v^2 A$

$$= 0·031\ 44 \times 70^2 \times 1·67\ \text{N}$$

$$= \underline{257·2\ \text{N}}$$

(b) Air resistance $= K_c v^2 A$

$$= 0·031\ 44 \times 140^2 \times 1·67\ \text{N}$$

$$= \underline{1029\ \text{N}}$$

(c) The velocity of the vehicle relative to the air = Road speed of vehicle + Speed of wind (**plus** since wind opposes the motion of the vehicle).

$$\therefore\ \text{Velocity} = 140 + 40 = 180\ \text{km/h}$$

$$\therefore\ \text{Air resistance} = K_c v^2 A$$

$$= 0·031\ 44 \times 180^2 \times 1·67$$

$$= \underline{1701\ \text{N}}$$

The additional resistance of wind has increased the air resistance by about 70 per cent.

Tractive Effort (T_e) and Tractive Resistance (T_r)

The **thrust** of the driving road wheels of a motor vehicle is called the tractive effort or force. Opposing this tractive effort are the tractive resistances. To overcome these, a tractive force, at least equal to, or preferably greater, must be available. The tractive effort of the driving wheels is directly proportional to the engine torque. Both engine torque and tractive effort are increased by the reduction gears in the gear box and rear axle; the speed of the vehicle, however, is reduced.

The tractive effort (T_e) exerted by the driving wheels of the vehicle

$$= \frac{\text{Engine torque } (T) \times \text{Gear ratio } (gr) \times \text{Efficiency } (e)}{\text{Radius of driving wheels } (r)}$$

$$\therefore \ T_e = \frac{T \times gr \times e}{r}$$

Example. Calculate the torque in Nm that a propeller shaft must exert in order to propel a vehicle of mass 2500 kg up a gradient of 1 in 10, neglecting air resistance. The rear-axle ratio is 5 to 1, the tyre radius is 380 mm and the rolling resistance 360 N.　　　(C. and G.)

The tractive resistance is found and then used in the tractive effort formula.

Tractive resistance = Gradient resistance + Rolling resistance

$$= \frac{F}{G} + R_r$$

$$= \frac{2500 \times 9 \cdot 8}{10} + 360 \text{ N}$$

$$= \underline{2810 \text{ N}}$$

The tractive effort $T_e = \dfrac{\text{Torque} \times \text{Gear ratio}}{\text{Radius of road wheels}}$

$$T_e = \frac{T \times gr}{r}$$

$$\therefore \ \text{Torque in shaft } T = \frac{T_e \times r}{gr}$$

$$= \frac{2810 \times 0 \cdot 38}{5} \text{ Nm}$$

$$= \underline{213 \cdot 56 \text{ Nm}}$$

Example. A motor vehicle travelling at 90 km/h is accelerating up a gradient of 1 in 20. The mass of the vehicle is 1150 kg; frontal area 1·8 m²; rolling resistance 250 N; K_c for shape of body is 0·035. At this instant the engine is developing 56 800 W at 4000 rev/min and the transmission efficiency is 90 per cent. If the rear-axle ratio is 5·2 to 1 and rolling radius of the tyres is 350 mm, what is the acceleration?

Tractive resistance = Gradient resistance + Rolling resistance + Air resistance.

$$\therefore T_r = \frac{F}{G} + R_r + K_c v^2 A$$

$$= \left(\frac{1150 \times 9·8}{20}\right) + 250 + (0·035 \times 90^2 \times 1·8)$$

$$= \underline{1323·8 \text{ N}}$$

Tractive effort $= \dfrac{\text{Torque at road wheels}}{\text{Rolling radius of tyres}}$

$$= \frac{P \times \text{Axle ratio} \times \text{Efficiency} \times 60}{2\pi \times \text{rev/min} \times \text{Rolling radius}}$$

$$= \frac{56\,800 \times 5·2 \times 0·9 \times 60}{2 \times 3·1416 \times 400 \times 0·35}$$

$$= \underline{1812·4 \text{ N}}$$

Accelerating force = Tractive effort − Tractive resistance

$$= 1812·4 - 1323·8$$

$$= \underline{488·6 \text{ N}}$$

The acceleration equation $F = ma$

$$\therefore \text{Acceleration } a = \frac{F}{m}$$

$$= \frac{488·6}{1150}$$

$$= \underline{0·4248 \text{ m/s}^2}$$

Curves of Power required and Power available

A graph is shown in Fig. 12.7 of the curves of the following worked example. The power curve represents the available power, while the power required to overcome the resistances is represented by the power required curve.

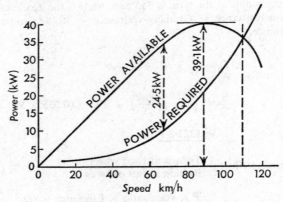

FIG. 12.7.

The power available at the road wheels is equal to the power at the engine flywheel, after making an allowance for the frictional 'losses' of the transmission. These 'losses' are about 10 per cent in top gear and about 18 per cent in the indirect gears.

The maximum speed of a vehicle is when the power at the road wheels is equal to the power required. This is shown on the graph as the intersection of the two curves; it occurs after the **'peak'** power point of the engine.

The speed at which maximum acceleration of the vehicle occurs is found by the greatest vertical distance between the two curves.

Example. The following figures apply to a certain car running in top gear on a level road:

Speed in km per hour .	40	60	80	100	120
P required to overcome resistance to motion .	1·87	7·46	17·5	29·8	44
P developed by engine .	21	31·8	38·8	38	29

Draw the curves of power required and power developed on a km/h base and determine: (*a*) maximum speed of the car on the level; (*b*) maximum power available for acceleration; (*c*) the speed at which (*b*) occurs; (*d*) the maximum power of the engine. (C. and G.)

The two curves are shown in Fig. 12.7 and the answers are:

(*a*) 109 km/h; (*b*) 24·5 kw; (*c*) 64 km/h; (*d*) 39·1 kW

Momentum

Momentum is the property of a moving body which tends to keep it moving with the same velocity; momentum depends on the mass of the body and the velocity at which it is moving.

$$\text{Momentum} = \text{Mass} \times \text{Velocity}$$
$$= mv$$

The units are: kg × m/s

The momentum of a body varies as its velocity, and two bodies having different masses but moving at the same velocity will have different momenta.

Like velocity, momentum is a **vector quantity** that can be represented in **direction** and **magnitude** by a line drawn to scale. Change of momentum of a body can be produced only by changing its velocity, since its mass is constant. The rate of change is therefore a change of velocity, which is acceleration.

The rate of change of momentum = ma.

Example. A motor vehicle of mass 700 kg is accelerated from 27 to 108 km/h. Find the change of momentum.

$$\text{Initial momentum} = m_1v_1$$
$$= 700 \times 7·5 \text{ kg m/s}$$
$$= 5250 \text{ kg m/s}$$

$$\text{Final momentum} = m_2v_2$$
$$= 700 \times 30 \text{ kg m/s}$$
$$= 21\,000 \text{ kg m/s}$$

$$\text{Change of momentum} = m_2v_2 - m_1v_1$$
$$= 21\,000 - 5250 \text{ kg m/s}$$
$$= 15\,750 \text{ kg m/s}$$

Impulse

When two moving bodies collide or a force is applied to a body for a very short time it is known as an **impulsive force**. If two motor cars collide and then move together the momentum after impact is equal to the momentum of each car before their collision. This may be represented by a vector diagram. Should they collide 'head on', one momentum is positive, the other negative.

Example. A car of mass 750 kg and travelling at 108 km/h runs into the back of a car of mass 1200 kg which is travelling at 54 km/h. Find: (*a*) separate momentum before impact; (*b*) combined momentum after impact; (*c*) velocity after impact.

(a) Momentum 1 $= m_1 v_1$

$= 750 \times 30$ kg m/s

$= \underline{22\ 500 \text{ kg m/s}}$

Momentum 2 $= m_2 v_2$

$= 1200 \times 15$ kg m/s

$= \underline{18\ 000 \text{ kg m/s}}$

(b) Total momenta $= m_1 v_1 + m_2 v_2$

$= 22\ 500 + 18\ 000$

$= \underline{40\ 500 \text{ kg m/s}}$

(c) Velocity after impact $= \dfrac{\text{Total momentum}}{\text{Total Mass}}$

$= \dfrac{40\ 500}{m^1 + m^2} \left(\dfrac{\text{kg m/s}}{\text{kg}} \right)$

$= \dfrac{40\ 500}{750 + 1200}$ kg m/s

$= \underline{20 \cdot 77 \text{ m/s} \quad \text{or} \quad 74 \cdot 772 \text{ km/h}}$

Example. A car of mass 750 kg and travelling at 108 km/h collides 'head on' with a car of mass 1200 kg and travelling at 54 km/h. Find the speed after collision and its direction.

Working the example in kg km/h:

$$\text{Momentum 1 (positive)} = m_1 v_1$$
$$= 750 \times 108 \text{ kg km/h}$$
$$= \underline{81\ 000 \text{ kg km/h}}$$

$$\text{Momentum 2 (negative)} = m_2 v_2$$
$$= 1200 \times 54 \text{ kg km/h}$$
$$= \underline{64\ 800 \text{ kg km/h}}$$

$$\text{Total momentum} = m_1 v_1 - m_2 v_2$$
$$= 81\ 000 - 64\ 800 \text{ kg km/h}$$
$$= \underline{16\ 200 \text{ kg km/h}}$$

Let v_3 = Final velocity in km/h.

$$\text{Total momentum} = \text{Total mass} \times \text{Final velocity}$$
$$= (m_1 + m_2) \times v_3$$
$$\therefore \text{Final velocity } v_3 = \frac{\text{Total momentum}}{m_1 + m_2}$$
$$= \frac{16\ 200}{750 + 1200} \left(\frac{\text{kg km/h}}{\text{kg}}\right)$$
$$= \underline{8 \cdot 3 \text{ km/h positive}}$$

that is, the direction of the smaller car.

Example. A motor car of mass 750 kg and travelling at 108 km/h due west collides with a car of mass 1200 kg travelling at 54 km/h due south. Find their direction and velocity after collision.

$$\text{Momentum 1 (west)} = m_1 v_1$$
$$= 750 \times 108 \text{ kg km/h}$$
$$= \underline{81\ 000 \text{ kg km/h}}$$

$$\text{Momentum 2 (south)} = m_2 v_2$$
$$= 1200 \times 54 \text{ kg km/h}$$
$$= \underline{64\ 800 \text{ kg km/h}}$$

The vector diagram (Fig. 12.8) shows how the resultant momentum may be calculated by using Pythagoras' theorem.

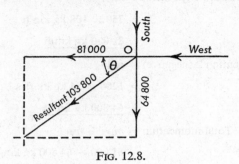

FIG. 12.8.

Resultant momentum^2 = Momentum 1^2 + Momentum 2^2

$\therefore$ Resultant momentum = $\sqrt{81\,000^2 + 64\,800^2}$ kg km/h

= 103 800 kg km/h

Direction after collision is solved by:

$$\sec \theta = \frac{\text{Resultant momentum}}{\text{Momentum 1}}$$

$$= \frac{103\,800}{81\,000} = 1 \cdot 28$$

= 38° 38′ S. of West

Velocity after collision:

Resultant momentum = $(m_1 + m_2)v_3$

$\therefore$ Final velocity $v_3 = \dfrac{\text{Resultant momentum}}{m_1 + m_2}$

$$= \frac{103\,800}{750 + 1200} \left(\frac{\text{kg km/h}}{\text{kg}}\right)$$

$$= \frac{103\,800}{1950}$$

= 53·23 km/h in direction 38° 38′ S. of West

Direct Impact

Impact is the result of a fast-moving body colliding with a stationary object, and the force of impact is a change of momentum. The moving body is brought to rest in a short interval of time at a high rate of retardation. The retarding force is the average force of impact, and this may be calculated from force exerted by mass of moving body × retardation.

Sometimes the stationary object does not move and the moving object is distorted. For example, a car crashing into a concrete wall comes to rest while the car crumples, in a time of, say, 0·1 s. If a car crashes into a fence it probably travels a short distance, breaking down the fence for a distance of, say, 5 metres before coming to rest, in the time of, say, 0·25 s.

Consider a force F produced by a moving body travelling at a velocity of v m/s and crashing into a solid object so that it is brought to rest in t seconds.

$$\text{Rate of retardation} = \frac{\text{Initial velocity} - \text{Final velocity}}{\text{Time taken for change of velocity}}$$

$$= \frac{v - 0}{t} \quad \text{or} \quad \frac{v}{t}$$

$$\text{Average force of impact} = \text{Force produced by mass} \times \text{Retardation}$$

$$F = m \times \frac{v}{t}$$

$$= ma$$

Example. A car of mass 750 kg and travelling at 54 km/h crashes into a solid wall, coming to rest in 0·1 s. What is the force of impact?

$$\text{Rate of retardation} = \frac{\text{Change of velocity}}{\text{Time taken}}$$

$$= \frac{15}{0·1} \left(\frac{\text{m/s}}{\text{s}}\right)$$

$$= \underline{150 \text{ m/s}^2}$$

$$\text{Force of impact} = \text{Mass} \times \text{Retardation}$$

$$= ma$$

$$= 750 \times 150 \ (\text{kg} \times \text{m/s}^2)$$

$$= \underline{112\,500 \text{ N}}$$

If the moving object embeds or crushes after impact and travels a distance of s metres, the rate of retardation a is calculated from the formula $v^2 = 2as$.

Example. A car of mass 750 kg and travelling at 54 km/h crashes into a fence, coming to rest after it has penetrated the fence for a distance of 2·5 m.

Find: (*a*) retardation; (*b*) force of impact.

(*a*) Rate of retardation:

$$v^2 = 2as$$

$$\therefore \text{ Rate of retardation } a = \frac{v^2}{2s}$$

$$= \frac{15 \times 15}{2 \times 2 \cdot 5} \left(\frac{\text{m/s} \times \text{m/s}}{\text{m}} \right)$$

$$= \underline{45 \text{ m/s}^2}$$

(*b*)
$$\text{Force of impact} = ma$$

$$= 750 \times 45 \text{ kg} \times \text{m/s}^2$$

$$= \underline{33\ 750 \text{ N}}$$

It should be noted by how much the force of impact is reduced when colliding with something which will move or give way.

Mechanical Energy

A body capable of doing work because of its position, velocity, composition, pressure or temperature possesses **energy**. The energy may be in any of these forms or a combination of them.

Potential Energy

This is the energy a body possesses because of its mass, which exerts a vertical downward force and its height above some suitable datum level. When a motor car is descending a hill it gives up **potential energy** due to the force of gravity; it is moving from a higher to a lower level. If the car later returns up the hill, work is done on the car by its engine and the potential energy is restored.

Let $\quad m$ = mass of body (kg)

$\quad\quad\quad h$ = height through which body moves (m)

Then $\quad$ Potential energy = $m \times 9{\cdot}8$ (N) $\times h$ (height m)

$$= 9{\cdot}8 \ mh \text{ (Nm or J)}$$

$\therefore$ P.E. (Nm or J) = $9{\cdot}8 \ mh$ (Nm or J)

Example. Find the P.E. given to a lift and car of mass 3000 kg when it goes up to a floor 18 m above ground level. If it takes 40 s to carry out the task, what power does it represent?

$$\text{Potential energy} = 9{\cdot}8 \ mh$$

$$= 3000 \times 9{\cdot}8 \times 18 \text{ Nm or J}$$

$$= \underline{529{\cdot}2 \text{ kNm or kJ}}$$

$$\text{Power (P)} = \frac{529 \ 200}{40} \left(\frac{\text{Nm or J}}{\text{s}}\right)$$

$$= \underline{13 \ 230 \text{ W or } 13{\cdot}23 \text{ kW}}$$

Example. An engine valve spring requires a force of 430 N to compress it 16 mm. How much P.E. does it contain when: (*a*) fully compressed and the valve wide open; (*b*) when compressed 6 mm and the valve is closed; (*c*) P.E. given out to close the valve?

(*a*) $\quad\quad$ Potential energy = Fs when F = force in N

$$s \text{ = distance in m}$$

$$= 430 \times 0{\cdot}016 \text{ Nm or J}$$

$$= \underline{6{\cdot}88 \text{ J}}$$

(*b*) $\quad\quad$ Potential energy = Fs

$$= 430 \times 0{\cdot}006 \text{ Nm or J}$$

$$= \underline{2{\cdot}58 \text{ J}}$$

(*c*) Potential energy given out by the spring to close the valve

$$= a - b$$

$$= 6{\cdot}88 - 2{\cdot}58 \text{ J}$$

$$= \underline{4{\cdot}3 \text{ J}}$$

This is an example of energy stored in a spring. This, like other examples, is equal to the work done to produce the potential energy.

Kinetic Energy

Kinetic energy is the **energy of motion** or the energy which a body possesses due to its mass and velocity.

To put a body in motion it must be subjected to a force; this overcomes its **inertia,** and the force acting on the body over a distance does work.

Let a force F be applied to a stationary mass of m kg so that the force F is used to overcome the inertia of the mass and give it motion. Then the mass is accelerated at the rate of a m/s^2.

Then accelerating force $F = $ Mass $(m) \times$ Acceleration (a)

Let the force accelerate the mass for t seconds.

Then distance s travelled in t seconds

$$= \text{Average velocity} \times \text{Time}$$

$$= \frac{at}{2} \times t = \tfrac{1}{2}at^2$$

The work done accelerating the mass

$$= \text{Force} \times \text{Distance}$$

$$= F \times \tfrac{1}{2}at^2$$

But $F = ma$.

$$\therefore \text{ By substituting, Work done} = ma \times \tfrac{1}{2}at^2$$

$$= \tfrac{1}{2}ma^2t^2$$

But $at = v$.

$$\therefore \text{ By substituting, Work done} = \tfrac{1}{2}mv^2$$

The work is done on the mass when accelerating it from rest to v m/s and, if the body then continues with a velocity of v m/s, it will contain the **kinetic energy** of $\tfrac{1}{2}mv^2$ J.

$$\text{Kinetic energy, K.E.} = \tfrac{1}{2}mv^2$$

Example. Find the K.E. of a motor vehicle of mass 750 kg and travelling at 90 km/h.

$$\text{K.E.} = \tfrac{1}{2}mv^2$$

$$= \frac{750 \times 25 \times 25}{2} \left(\frac{\text{N} \times \text{m/s} \times \text{m/s}}{\text{N m/s or J}} \right)$$

$$= \underline{234\ 375\ \text{J}}$$

Example. A goods vehicle of mass 5000 kg is braked from 108 km/h to 36 km/h.

Find: (*a*) Loss of kinetic energy. (*b*) If the kinetic energy is dissipated as heat, what heat is generated at the brakes?

(*a*) K.E. at 108 km/h $= \tfrac{1}{2}mv_1^2$

  K.E. at 36 km/h $= \tfrac{1}{2}mv_2^2$

  $\therefore$ Loss of K.E. $= \tfrac{1}{2}mv_1^2 - \tfrac{1}{2}mv_2^2$

  $= \tfrac{1}{2}m(v_1^2 - v_2^2)$

  $= \dfrac{1}{2} \times 5000\ (30^2 - 10^2)$

  $= \underline{2\ 000\ 000\ \text{J or Nm}\ \ \text{or}\ \ 2000\ \text{kJ or kNm}}$

(*b*) Heat generated $=$ Loss of K.E.

  $= \underline{2000\ \text{kJ}}$

Conservation of Energy

If a body moves from a higher to a lower level it gives up some of its potential energy, but gains an equal amount of kinetic energy, so that the total energy of a body at any position remains constant. This is known as the **conservation** or interchange of energy and is true if friction losses are neglected.

Example. An engine of mass 149 kg is suspended from a crane hook 2·5 m above ground level.

Find: (*a*) Its potential energy. (*b*) If the wire breaks and it falls freely to the ground, what is its velocity and kinetic energy on striking the ground? (*c*) What is its velocity, kinetic energy and potential energy after falling 2 m?

Downward vertical force = 149 × 9·8 = 1460 N.

(*a*)   Potential energy $= Fs$ (J)
$$= 1460 \times 2\cdot5 \text{ J}$$
$$= \underline{3650 \text{ J}}$$

(*b*) Velocity on striking the ground:

$$v^2 - u^2 = 2as$$
$$\therefore v^2 = 2as \quad \text{since } u = 0$$
$$v = \sqrt{2as}$$
$$= \sqrt{2 \times 9\cdot8 \times 2\cdot5}$$
$$= \underline{7 \text{ m/s}}$$

K.E. on striking the ground:

$$\text{K.E.} = \tfrac{1}{2}mv^2$$
$$= \frac{1}{2} \times 149 \times 49$$
$$= \underline{3650 \text{ J}} \checkmark$$

(*c*) Velocity after falling 2 m:

$$v = \sqrt{2gs}$$
$$= \sqrt{2 \times 9\cdot8 \times 2}$$
$$= \underline{6\cdot261 \text{ m/s}}$$

$v^2 = u^2 + 2as.$
$u = 0 \quad a = 9\cdot81$
$\therefore v = \sqrt{2as}$
$= \sqrt{4 \times 9\cdot81}$

K.E. after falling 2 m:

$$\text{K.E.} = \tfrac{1}{2}mv^2$$
$$= \frac{1}{2} \times 149 \times 6\cdot261^2 \text{ J}$$
$$= \underline{2920 \text{ J}}$$

P.E. after falling 0·5 m:

$$\text{P.E.} = Fs \text{ (} s = \text{distance to fall)}$$
$$= 1460 \times 0\cdot5 \text{ J}$$
$$= \underline{730 \text{ J}}$$

Check:

Original P.E. = P.E. + K.E.
$$3650 = 2920 + 730$$
$$\underline{3650} = \underline{3650}$$

Kinetic Energy of a Rotating Mass

Consider a mass m, Fig. 12.9, rotating in a circular path of radius r m about a centre O at a certain number of rev/s.

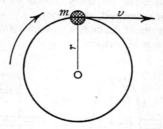

FIG. 12.9.

The linear velocity of mass m

$$= \text{Circumference} \times \text{rev/s}$$
$$= 2\pi r \times \text{rev/s}$$
$$= 2\pi \text{rev/s} \times r$$
$$= \text{radians/s} \times r \quad \text{or} \quad 2\pi \text{rev/s} \times r$$
$$\therefore v = \omega r$$

The kinetic energy of a moving mass $= \frac{1}{2}mv^2$
Substituting ωr for v

$$\text{K.E.} = \frac{1}{2}m(\omega r)^2$$
$$= \frac{1}{2}m\omega^2 r^2$$
$$= \frac{1}{2}mr^2\omega^2 \quad \text{or} \quad \frac{1}{2}mr^2(2\pi \times \text{rev/s})^2$$

From the formula we see that the K.E. stored in a revolving mass depends on the mass and the square of its radius r from the axis of rotation.

The quantity mr^2 is called the **Moment of Inertia** of the mass. One convenient way of storing energy is to use a flywheel. Flywheels required to store a large amount of energy must have a large moment of inertia; these are used for single-cylinder engines. The multi-cylinder engine which has several power impulses per revolution requires a smaller amount of stored energy to make it run smoothly, so its flywheel is smaller.

Radius of Gyration

This may be defined as a radius at which *all* the rotating masses are concentrated; it is given the symbol **k**. To obtain a large moment of inertia from a given mass, the mass should be concentrated at the extreme radius, or, if a flywheel, at the rim.

The **M. of I.** of an object depends on its mass and the location of its mass relative to the axis of rotation.

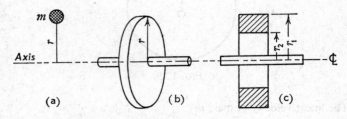

Fig. 12.10.

Fig. 12.10 (*a*) shows a mass connected to an axis of rotation by a cord.

$$\text{M. of I.} = mr^2$$

Fig. 12.10 (*b*) shows a solid disc of uniform thickness mounted on a shaft.

$$\text{M. of I.} = \frac{mr^2}{2} \quad \text{or} \quad mk^2$$

$$\text{since } k = \frac{r}{\sqrt{2}} = 0.7071r$$

The radius of gyration is the distance $0.7071r$ measured from the axis of rotation.

Fig. 12.10 (*c*) shows a hollow disc of uniform thickness.

$$\text{Radius of gyration } k = \sqrt{\frac{r_1^2 + r_2^2}{2}}$$

$$\text{M. of I.} = mk^2$$
$$= m\left(\frac{r_1^2 + r_2^2}{2}\right)$$

Example. The flywheel and clutch assembly on a motor vehicle engine has a mass of 18 kg and has a radius of 150 mm.

Find their M. of I. and K.E. when the engine speed is 4500 rev/min.

$$\text{M. of I.} = mk^2$$
$$= 18 \times (0 \cdot 7071 \times 0 \cdot 15)^2 \text{ kg m}^2$$
$$= \underline{0 \cdot 2025 \text{ kg m}^2}$$

$$\text{K.E.} = \tfrac{1}{2}mr^2\omega^2$$
$$= \tfrac{1}{2}mr^2(2 \times \pi \times \text{rev/s})^2$$
$$= \frac{1}{2} \times 18 \times (0 \cdot 15)^2 \times \left(2 \times 3 \cdot 1416 \times \frac{4500}{60}\right)^2 \text{ J}$$
$$= \underline{44\ 960 \text{ J}}$$

Example. The road wheel, brake drum and rotating parts of the wheel assembly have a mass of 18 kg and their radius of gyration is 220 mm. How much power is required to accelerate the road wheels from rest to 11 rev/s (about 72 km/h) in 20 s?

The kinetic energy stored in the rotating assembly when its speed is 11 rev/s is equal to the work done in overcoming the inertia to attain his speed.

$$\text{K.E.} = \tfrac{1}{2}mr^2\omega^2$$
$$= \tfrac{1}{2}mr^2(2 \times \pi \times \text{rev/s})^2$$
$$= \frac{1}{2} \times 18 \times (0 \cdot 22)^2 \times (2 \times 3 \cdot 1416 \times 11)^2 \text{ J}$$
$$= \underline{2081 \text{ J}}$$

$$\text{Total K.E. (4 wheels)} = 2081 \times 4 \text{ J}$$
$$= \underline{8324 \text{ J}}$$

$$\text{Power (P)} = \frac{8324}{20}$$
$$= \underline{416 \cdot 2 \text{ W}}$$

Circular Motion

If a mass m is moving along a straight path at a constant velocity it tends to continue at a constant velocity in a straight line; so to make it follow a curved path, a side force must be applied perpendicular to its motion, to force it round the curve. The side forces (see Fig. 12.11) are all perpendicular, so their radii intersect at O, the centre from which the curve is struck. An example of this is a locomotive going round a curve, the **radial** force being provided by the outer rail, which

presses on the wheel flanges. If a piece of metal is swung round on the
end of a cord the metal is kept on its curved path by the radial pull on
the cord. This radial or inward force towards the centre is called the
Centripetal Force.

Centrifugal force is the equal and opposite force, that is, the outward
pull the body exerts on the cord and not a force on the body.

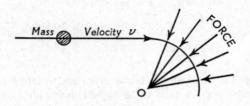

FIG. 12.11.

Centripetal acceleration was dealt with earlier in this chapter (p. 215)
and the inward acceleration of a mass moving in a circular path of r m
radius with a constant speed of v m/s was given as $\dfrac{v^2}{r}$ m/s or $\omega^2 r$. To
obtain this acceleration, a force must act towards the centre; this force,
the centripetal force,

$$= \text{Mass} \times \text{Acceleration}$$

$$= m \times \frac{v^2}{r}$$

$$= m\omega^2 r$$

When a motor vehicle travels round a curve it must be forced round
by an inward radial force, the **centripetal** force, but the passengers in
the vehicle feel that they are being flung radially outwards; this is the
centrifugal force.

$$\therefore \text{Centrifugal force} = \frac{mv^2}{r}$$

Example. A balance 'weight' of mass 0·05 kg becomes dislodged
from the rim of a motor-vehicle road wheel 500 mm in diameter. Find
the pull on the road wheel bearing due to the out-of-balance effect
when the wheel speed is 10 rev/s.

$$\text{C.F.} = \frac{mv^2}{r}$$

$$= \frac{0 \cdot 05}{0 \cdot 25} \times (2\pi \times 0 \cdot 25 \times 10)^2$$

$$= \underline{49 \cdot 2 \text{ N}} \text{ (about 50 newtons)}$$

The mass of $0 \cdot 05$ kg requires a force of $0 \cdot 05$ N to produce an acceleration of 1 m/s².

Example. When balancing an engine flywheel which is 400 mm diameter, a mass of 50 grammes is attached to the rim to produce static balance. What mass of metal must be removed by drilling at a point diametrically opposite the attached 'weight', at a radius of 175 mm?

What would the pull on the rear engine bearing be at 4500 rev/min if the balancing was not carried out?

This problem can be solved by equating the two C.F. involved.

Let m be the 50 gramme mass at radius r m and m_1 be the mass of metal removed at radius r_1 m.

Then

$$m\omega^2 r = m_1\omega^2 r_1$$

$$mr = m_1 r_1$$

$$\therefore m_1 = \frac{m r}{r_1}$$

$$= \frac{0 \cdot 05 \times 0 \cdot 2}{0 \cdot 175}$$

Mass removed $= 0 \cdot 057$ kg

$$\text{C.F.} = \frac{mv^2}{r}$$

$$= \frac{0 \cdot 05}{0 \cdot 2} \left(2 \times 3 \cdot 1416 \times 0 \cdot 2 \times \frac{4500}{60}\right)^2 \text{ N}$$

$$\underline{2225 \text{ N pull on main bearing}}$$

Centre of Gravity above Ground Level

The height of the centre of gravity (c.g.) above ground level is an important factor in the overturning speed of a motor vehicle when cornering. Generally, should the height of the c.g. fall outside the wheel track, the vehicle overturns, see Fig. 12.12; note that the line of the c.g. always remains at right-angles to the vehicle.

When a vehicle is travelling up a gradient or accelerating its c.g. moves towards the rear of the vehicle; thus the load on the front axle becomes less while the load on the rear axle becomes greater.

The following examples illustrate methods of determining the height of the c.g. above ground level.

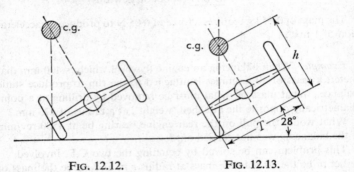

FIG. 12.12.   FIG. 12.13.

Example. During the test of a double-decker bus for stability the angle of tilt was recorded as 28 degrees. If the wheel track was 2·28 m, determine the height of the centre of gravity above ground level.

Fig. 12.13 shows a line diagram of the lay-out.

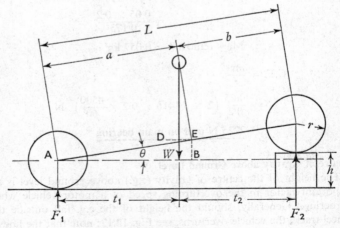

FIG. 12.14.

Let h = height of c.g. above ground level, in m

     T = wheel track, in m

then
$$h = \frac{0 \cdot 5\, T \text{ m}}{\tan 28°}$$
$$= \frac{1 \cdot 14 \text{ m}}{0 \cdot 5317}$$
$$= \underline{2 \cdot 144 \text{ m}}$$

Another experimental method of determining the height of the centre of gravity is:

The axle loads are noted while one pair of wheels is supported at a higher level than the other pair, Fig. 12.14. Either the front axle or the rear axle can be raised. Using the diagram, Fig. 12.14,

let H = height of c.g. above ground level, in m

    r = wheel radius, in m

Then θ is given by $\sin \theta = \dfrac{h}{L}$

Taking moments about A,

$$F_2(t_1 + t_2) \quad Wt_1$$
or
$$Wt_1 = F_2 L \cos \theta$$
but
$$t_1 = \text{AB} - \text{ED}$$
$$= a \cos \theta - (H - r) \sin \theta$$
$$F_2 L \cos \theta = Wa \cos \theta - W(H - r) \sin \theta$$
$$\therefore H - r = \left(\frac{Wa - F_2 L}{W} \right) \cot \theta$$
$$\therefore H = \left\{ \left(\frac{Wa - F_2 L}{W} \right) \cot \theta \right\} + r$$

For convenience during calculation the line running through the wheel centres is used, but the wheel radius r is added at the end to determine the value of H.

Example. A vehicle has a wheelbase of 2·4 m, a total mass of 2 tonne and the road wheels are 0·6 m in diameter.

When the rear axle is raised, the distance of the c.g. from the rear axle is 0·75 m. The mass of the rear axle is 1·15 tonne and the mass on the front axle is 0·85 tonne. Determine the height of the c.g. above ground level.

Fig. 12.14 shows the required layout.

Since $\sin \theta = \dfrac{0·3}{2·4} = \dfrac{1}{8} = 7° \ 11'$

Then $\cot \theta = 7·93$, $\cos \theta = 0·992$ and $\sin \theta = 0·125$, $a = 1·65$ m and the road wheels have a radius r of 0·3 m.

As height of c.g. only has to be calculated, there is no need to change mass (tonne) into downward force (N).

$$H - r = \left(\frac{2 \times 1·65) - (1·15 \times 2·4)}{2} \right) \times 7·93$$

$$H - 0·3 = \left(\frac{3·3 - 2·76}{2} \right) \times 7·93$$

$$H = (0·135 \times 7·93) + 0·3$$

$$= 1·07 + 0·3 = 1·37 \text{ m}$$

Height of c.g. above ground level = <u>1·37 m</u>

Overturning of a Motor Vehicle

Modern motor vehicle are designed so that **overturning** will not occur under normal conditions. Fast cornering makes a vehicle skid sideways before it overturns. Should the vehicle strike a kerb when cornering, the sudden shock sometimes causes the vehicle to overturn.

Fig. 12. 15 shows a line diagram of a vehicle viewed from the rear and the forces which exist when it is turning left.

$$\text{Overturning moment} = \text{C.F.} \times \text{Height of c.g.}$$

$$= \frac{mv^2}{9·8 \, r} \times h$$

The righting or correcting moment

$$= \frac{m}{2}d$$

If the overturning moment is equal to the **righting** moment the vehicle pivots on the road wheels at R_A with the road wheel at R_B just about to leave the road.

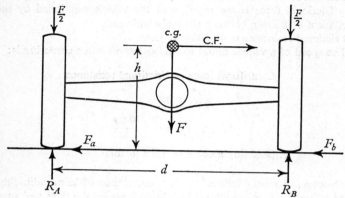

Fig. 12.15.

Overturning moment = Righting moment

$$\frac{mv^2h}{9\cdot8\ r} = \frac{m}{2}d$$

$$\therefore\ v^2 = \frac{md}{2} \times \frac{9\cdot8\ r}{mh}$$

$$\therefore\ \text{Overturning speed } v = \sqrt{\frac{9\cdot8\ rd}{2h}}\ \text{(m/s)}$$

Example. A vehicle has a track of 2 m and its c.g. is 500 mm above ground level. It travels round a bend of 36 m radius on a level road. What is the maximum speed at which it can travel round the bend without overturning?

Overturning moment = Righting moment

$$\frac{mv^2}{9\cdot8\ r} = \frac{m}{2}d$$

$$\therefore\ \text{Max. speed } v = \sqrt{\frac{9\cdot8\ rd}{2h}}$$

$$= \sqrt{\frac{9\cdot8 \times 36 \times 2}{2 \times 0\cdot5}}\ \text{m/s}$$

$$= \underline{26\cdot57\ \text{m/s}}\quad\text{or}\quad\underline{95\cdot63\ \text{km/h}}$$

Skidding when Cornering on a Level Road

When cornering, a vehicle will **skid** or **slide** outwards when the centrifugal force exceeds the frictional force $F_a + F_b$ (see Fig. 12.15). The frictional force is the reaction of the vehicle multiplied by the coefficient of friction between the tyres and road.

Frictional resistance to skidding $= \mu m$.

The speed of a vehicle about to skid outwards when cornering is:

$$\text{Centrifugal force} = \text{Frictional resistance}$$

$$\frac{mv^2}{9 \cdot 8 \, r} = \mu m$$

$$\therefore \; v^2 = \mu m \times \frac{9 \cdot 8 \, r}{m}$$

$$\therefore \; \text{Skidding speed } v = \sqrt{9 \cdot 8 \; \mu r} \; \text{m/s}$$

Example. A motor vehicle travels round a bend of 36 m radius; the road is level and the coefficient of friction between the tyres and road is 0·8. Find the maximum speed at which the vehicle can be driven round the bend without skidding.

$$\text{Centrifugal force} = \text{Frictional resistance}$$

$$\frac{mv^2}{9 \cdot 8 \, r} = \mu m$$

$$\text{Max. speed } v = \sqrt{\mu \, 9 \cdot 8 \, r}$$

$$= \sqrt{0 \cdot 8 \times 9 \cdot 8 \times 36} \; \text{m/s}$$

$$= \underline{16 \cdot 8 \; \text{m/s} \quad \text{or} \quad 60 \cdot 47 \; \text{km/h}}$$

The student should compare this answer for skidding with the previous example for overturning.

Vehicle Motion on a Curved Banked Track

We have already seen that the motor vehicle is prevented from skidding outwards when cornering by the frictional resistance between the tyres and road, see Fig. 12.15. The frictional resistance required on any corner can be reduced by **banking**, and this is actually done on modern roads. For a given speed and angle of banking, no radial inward force need be supplied by the road to keep the vehicle on its circular path.

Consider the vehicle P shown in Fig. 12.16 travelling at a constant speed of v m/s on a curve banked at an angle α and a radius of r m.

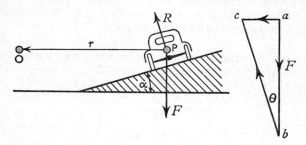

FIG. 12.16.

The forces on the vehicle are:

1. Its vertical force F downward on track (N).
2. Reaction of the track R (N) acting perpendicular to the track.
3. The centripetal force $\dfrac{mv^2}{r}$ acting from P to O in a horizontal direction (equal and opposite to the centrifugal force).

A force diagram is constructed:

Vector ab is drawn vertically downwards to represent the downward force.

A horizontal line is drawn from a.

A line is drawn from b, perpendicular to the track to intersect the horizontal line at point c. The vector ac represents the centripetal force. From this can be calculated the speed the vehicle travels on the banked curve without **lateral support**. When this condition exists the angle of the track α is equal to the angle θ of the force diagram,

$$\therefore \tan \alpha = \tan \theta$$
$$= \frac{ac}{ab}$$
$$= \frac{mv^2}{9 \cdot 8\,r} \div m$$

Angle of track $\tan \alpha = \dfrac{v^2}{9 \cdot 8\,r}$

This equation should be used on problems when friction is not considered, i.e. no lateral support.

If the track is insufficiently banked a radial inward or centripetal force exerted by the track and the angle θ of the force diagram is greater than the angle of the track banking α.

Example. At what speed can a vehicle travel on a curved track of 25 m radius, which is banked at an angle of 22°, and require no lateral support?

$$\tan \alpha = \frac{v^2}{9 \cdot 8 \, r}$$

$$\therefore \; v^2 = 9 \cdot 8 \, r \tan \alpha$$

$$\therefore \text{ Max. speed } v = \sqrt{9 \cdot 8 \, r \tan \alpha}$$

$$= \sqrt{9 \cdot 8 \times 25 \times 0 \cdot 404} \text{ m/s}$$

$$= \underline{9 \cdot 93 \text{ m/s} \quad \text{or} \quad 35 \cdot 82 \text{ km/h}}$$

Skidding on a Curved Banked Track

Fig. 12.17 shows the vehicle on the track, banked at an angle α. The gravitational pull on the vehicle, together with the reactions $R_A + R_B$ at the points where the road wheels contact the track, produces on the vehicle an inward radial force equal to the C.F. $\frac{mv^2}{9 \cdot 8 \, r}$.

The components m and $\frac{mv^2}{9 \cdot 8 \, r}$ of the reactions R_A, R_B, F_a and F_b will now be considered.

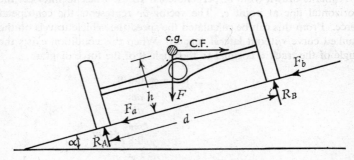

FIG. 12.17.

The components of $F_a + F_b$ along the track

$$= \frac{mv^2}{9.8\,r} \cos \alpha - m \sin \alpha \qquad \text{Eq. 1}$$

The components of $R_A + R_B$ perpendicular to the track

$$= m \cos \alpha + \frac{mv^2}{9.8\,r} \sin \alpha \qquad \text{Eq. 2}$$

Taking friction into consideration, $R_A + R_B$ becomes

$$\mu(R_A + R_B)$$

Then, from Eq. 2,

$$\mu \left(m \cos \alpha + \frac{mv^2}{9.8\,r} \sin \alpha \right) \qquad \text{Eq. 3}$$

The point at which side-slipping occurs is when

$$F_a + F_b = \mu(R_A + R_B)$$

By substituting their component forces,

$$\frac{mv^2}{9.8\,r} \cos \alpha - m \sin \alpha = \mu \left(m \cos \alpha + \frac{mv^2}{9.8\,r} \sin \alpha \right)$$

$$v^2 = 9.8\,r \left(\frac{\mu + \tan \alpha}{1 - \mu \tan \alpha} \right)$$

$$\therefore \text{Max. speed } v = r \sqrt{9.8\,r \left(\frac{\mu + \tan \alpha}{1 - \mu \tan \alpha} \right)} \text{ m/s}$$

Example. A car travels on a curved track of 30 m radius; the co-efficient of friction between the tyres and road is 0·6.

Find the speed at which skidding occurs when: (*a*) the track is not banked; (*b*) the track is banked at an angle of 22°.

(*a*)
$$v = \sqrt{9.8\mu r}$$
$$= \sqrt{9.8 \times 0.6 \times 30}$$
$$= \underline{13.28 \text{ m/s}}$$

or $\quad \underline{47.8 \text{ km/h}}$

(*b*) When the track is banked at 22°.

$$v = \sqrt{9.8\,r \left(\frac{\mu + \tan \alpha}{1 - \mu \tan \alpha} \right)}$$

$$= \sqrt{9.8 \times 30 \left(\frac{0.6 + 0.404}{1 - (0.6 \times 0.404)} \right)} \text{ m/s}$$

$$= \underline{19.7 \text{ m/s}}$$

or $\quad \underline{70.92 \text{ km/h}}$

Overturning on a Curved Track

To calculate the overturning speed on a curved banked track, moments are taken about the centre of gravity of the vehicle.

Taking moments about the c.g. (see Fig. 12.17),

Anti-clockwise moments = Clockwise moments

$$R_B \times \frac{d}{2} = \left(R_A \times \frac{d}{2} \right) + (F_a \times h) + (F_b \times h)$$

$$(R_B - R_A)\frac{d}{2} = (F_a + F_b)h$$

By substituting values for $F_a + F_b$ from Eq. 1 in previous example for skidding,

$$(R_B - R_A)\frac{d}{2} = \left(\frac{mv^2}{9 \cdot 8\ r} \cos \alpha - m \sin \alpha \right) h$$

$$= mh \frac{v^2}{9 \cdot 8\ r} \cos \alpha - mh \sin \alpha$$

$$\therefore\ R_B - R_A = mh \left(\frac{2}{d} \right) \left\{ \left(\frac{v^2}{9 \cdot 8\ r} \right) \cos \alpha - \sin \alpha \right\} \qquad \text{Eq. 4}$$

By subtracting Eq. 2 from Eq. 4 and putting $R_A = 0$ for the overturning speed, we get:

$$\text{Equation: } v^2 = 9 \cdot 8\ r \left(\frac{h \tan \alpha + \dfrac{d}{2}}{h - \dfrac{d}{2} \tan \alpha} \right)$$

Then,   overturning speed $v = \sqrt{9 \cdot 8\ r \left(\dfrac{h \tan \alpha + \dfrac{d}{2}}{h - \dfrac{d}{2} \tan \alpha} \right)}$ m/s

Example. A car travels on a curved track of 30 m radius which is banked at an angle of 22°. The car track is 1·5 m and its c.g. is 0·75 m above ground level.

At what speed will it overturn?

$$\text{Overturning speed } v = \sqrt{9{\cdot}8\, r \left(\frac{h \tan \alpha + \dfrac{d}{2}}{h - \dfrac{d}{2} \tan \alpha} \right)}$$

$$= \sqrt{9{\cdot}8 \times 30 \left(\frac{0{\cdot}75 \times 0{\cdot}404 + 0{\cdot}75}{0{\cdot}75 - (0{\cdot}75 \times 0{\cdot}404)} \right)} \text{ m/s}$$

$$= \underline{26{\cdot}31 \text{ m/s} \quad \text{or} \quad 94{\cdot}7 \text{ km/h}}$$

Load (Mass) Distribution on Road Wheels

Change of mass occurs from rear to front wheels during braking. When a vehicle is braked its mass tends to carry on and, in effect, produces a forward force of F (N) through the centre of gravity (see Fig. 12.18).

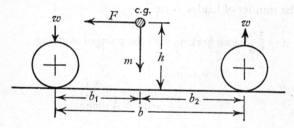

FiG. 12.18.

$$\text{Force } F = \text{Mass} \times \text{Retardation}$$
$$= ma$$

This force produces a turning moment Fh Nm equivalent to the turning moment producing the change of mass to the road wheels.

Equating the moments:

$$Fh = wb_1 + wb_2$$
$$= wb$$

$$\therefore \text{ Change of load } w = F\frac{h}{b}$$

The ratio $\dfrac{h}{b}$, when multiplied by the retarding force F, determines the transfer of mass at any road speed.

If the vehicle is braked to the point of skidding, the retarding force $F = \mu m$.

So $$w = F\frac{h}{b} \quad \text{or} \quad \mu m \frac{h}{b}$$

The retarding force F may also be calculated from the equation $F = ma$, when a is calculated from the stopping distance equation.

Example. A lorry fully laden has a mass of 18 tonne, its wheelbase is 5 m and c.g. is 1 m above ground level. The mass distribution is 30 per cent front axle, 70 per cent rear axle.

Find the mass on each axle when the vehicle is braked to the point of skidding and: (*a*) retardation is 3·9 m/s²; (*b*) coefficient of adhesion is 0·6.

(*a*) The transfer of load $w = \mu m \dfrac{h}{b}$

Now $\mu = \dfrac{3 \cdot 9}{9 \cdot 8}$, since braking is to the point of skidding.

$$\therefore w = \mu m \frac{h}{b}$$

$$= \frac{3 \cdot 9}{9 \cdot 8} \times 18 \times \frac{1}{5} \text{ tonne}$$

$$= \underline{1 \cdot 43 \text{ tonne}}$$

Mass on front axle = 30 per cent of mass + Transfer of mass

$$= (0 \cdot 3 \times 18) + 1 \cdot 43 \text{ tonne}$$

$$= \underline{6 \cdot 83 \text{ tonne}}$$

Mass on rear axles = 70 per cent of mass − Transfer of mass

$$= (0 \cdot 7 \times 18) - 1 \cdot 43 \text{ tonne}$$

$$= \underline{11 \cdot 17 \text{ tonne}}$$

(*b*) The transfer of mass $w = \mu m \dfrac{h}{b}$

$$= 0 \cdot 6 \times 18 \times \frac{1}{5} \text{ tonne}$$

$$= \underline{2 \cdot 16 \text{ tonne}}$$

Mass on front axle $= (0.3 \times 18) + 2.16$ tonne

$= \underline{7.56 \text{ tonne}}$

Mass on rear axles $= (0.7 \times 18) - 2.16$ tonne

$= \underline{10.44 \text{ tonne}}$

The braking conditions were better in example (*b*) as the transfer of load was greater.

Change of Load (Mass) when Cornering

The **change** of load from inner to outer road wheels depends on mass of vehicle, speed, height of centre of gravity, width of track, radius of curvature of road and angle of banking.

Fig. 12.19 shows a line diagram of the forces involved.

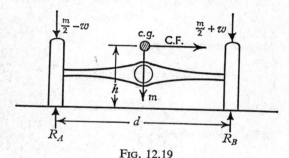

FIG. 12.19

Let $m =$ Total mass of vehicle

$w =$ Change of load, $+ w$ for downward loads, $- w$ for upward loads

The mass on each wheel is proportional to the static axle loads, but the mass on the inner wheels is half the mass of the vehicle or $\dfrac{m}{2}$.

By taking the moments about R_A when the vehicle is turning, the change of mass produces a clockwise moment wd equal to the force producing it, $\dfrac{mv^2}{9.8\,r} \times h$.

So

$$wd = \frac{mv^2}{9.8\,r} \times h$$

$\therefore$ Change of load $w = \dfrac{mv^2}{9.8\,r} \times \dfrac{h}{d}$

The change of mass is proportional to the height of the c.g. and track when the mass and speed remain constant.

Example. A lorry fully laden has a mass of 18 tonne and travels at a speed of 27 km/h round a curve of 38 m radius; its track is 2 m and height of c.g. 1 m above ground level. Find the downward mass on the inner and outer road wheels.

$$\text{First } 27 \text{ km/h} = 7 \cdot 5 \text{ m/s}$$

$$\text{Transfer of mass } w = \frac{mv^2}{9 \cdot 8 \, r} \times \frac{h}{d}$$

$$= \frac{18 \times (7 \cdot 5)^2}{9 \cdot 8 \times 38} \times \frac{1}{2} \text{ tonne}$$

$$= 1 \cdot 35 \text{ tonne}$$

$$\text{Mass on inner wheels} = \frac{m}{2} - w$$

$$= \frac{18}{2} - 1 \cdot 35 \text{ tonne}$$

$$= \underline{7 \cdot 65 \text{ tonne}}$$

$$\text{Mass on outer wheels} = \frac{m}{2} + w$$

$$= \frac{18}{2} + 1 \cdot 35 \text{ tonne}$$

$$= \underline{10 \cdot 35 \text{ tonne}}$$

Exercise 12

1. A road runs in a curve of 180 m radius and is to be banked so that vehicles may travel at a speed of 72 km/h on the curve without any tendency to skid outwards. Determine the angle of banking.

(12° 46′)   (C. and G.)

2. A certain vehicle has a mass of 1·5 tonne. Its track is 1·2 m and the height of its centre of gravity above ground is 0·6 m. When running straight, the mass is equally distributed between near and offside wheels. What proportion of the mass is carried by the outside wheels when the vehicle is taking a corner, 60 m radius, at 54 km/h? (Assume the road to be uncambered.)   (69 per cent)   (C. and G.)

3. A car is 'cornering' at a speed of 27 km/h in a radius of 10 m measured to its centre of gravity, which is 0·6 m above ground. The wheel track is 1·2 m and the car has a mass of 2 tonne. Calculate the total transfer of mass from the inner to the outer wheels during the process. (Assume the road to be uncambered.) (573·9 kg) (C. and G.)

4. A car has a wheelbase of 2·4 m and the height of the centre of gravity is 0·4 m. Find the extra mass imposed on the front wheels when the rear wheels only are braked to their maximum capacity without skidding. The static mass on the two rear wheels together may be taken as 1·1 tonne and the coefficient of friction between tyres and road as 0·6. (100 kg) (C. and G.)

5. A vehicle has a mass of 1·5 tonne, its wheelbase is 3 m and the centre of gravity 0·6 m above ground level. When at rest the mass on the front axle is 800 kg. Calculate the mass on the front wheels when the brakes are applied so as to produce a deceleration of 3 m/s^2.

(891·83 kg) (C. and G.)

6. A vehicle has a mass of 1·5 tonne and is moving at 54 km/h. It is brought to rest by the brakes in 20 m. Calculate the force applied by the brakes. (843·75 N)

7. A motor vehicle has a mass of 1·2 tonne, a wheelbase of 2·4 m and the c.g. is 0·6 m above ground level. Find the downward mass on the front and rear axle when the braking is 80 per cent and the static distribution is: (*a*) 50/50; (*b*) 40/60.

((*a*) 0·84 tonne; 0·36 tonne; (*b*) 0·72 tonne; 0·48 tonne)

8. A motor vehicle travels round a curve of 30 m radius. If the coefficient of friction between the tyres and road is 0·8, find its maximum speed if: (*a*) the curve is unbanked; (*b*) the curve is banked at an angle of 22°. ((*a*) 55·2 km/h; (*b*) 82·3 km/h)

9. A motor vehicle, when travelling on an unbanked curve of 24 m radius at a speed of 45 km/h, is just at the point of skidding. At what speed could it travel if the curve was banked at an angle of 18°?

(62 km/h)

10. A vehicle has a mass of 1·2 tonne, a track of 1·5 m and its c.g. is 0·6 m above ground level. It travels round a bend of 150 m radius on a level road.

Find: (*a*) maximum speed without overturning; (*b*) centrifugal force at this speed; (*c*) the smallest radius of curve when travelling at 90 km/h.

((*a*) 154 km/h; (*b*) 14700 N; (*c*) 51·02 m)

11. A car has a mass of 920 kg and a force of 2300 N is applied to it at rest.

Find the acceleration produced on a level road and time required to reach 90 km/h.

Also find the retarding force necessary to bring it to rest at a steady rate in 10 s. (2·5 m/s²; 10 s; 1916·6 N)

12. The track of a vehicle is 1·8 m and its c.g. is 0·6 m above ground level. What is the smallest radius of a curve that it can be driven round at 90 km/h without overturning? (42·5 m)

13. The speed of a vehicle which has a mass of 920 kg is reduced from 72 km/h to 27 km/h by the action of a mean retarding force of 2300 N. Find the distance covered during this reduction of speed.

(68·75 m) (C. and G.)

14. At what speed would a vehicle overturn on a level road when turning a corner of 20 m radius; its track is 1·2 m and c.g. is 0·6 m above the ground?

By how many km/h would its overturning speed be increased by if the curve was banked at an angle of 18°? (50·4 km/h; 20·16 km/h)

15. Given the following data, calculate the tractive effort required to drive a vehicle up a gradient of 1 in 7. State how much power is required.

Total mass 900 kg; frontal area 2 m²; road resistance 350 N; speed 60 km/h; constant K_c 0·03. (1626 N; 27·09 kW) (C. and G.)

16. A car of mass 750 kg has a constant rolling resistance of 200 N and a constant propelling force of 900 N.

If it starts from rest, find its velocity after 10 s.

It then ascends a gradient of 1 in 40. Find its velocity after a further 20 s.

It then runs on the level for a further 5 s. Find its velocity.

It is then at the top of a down gradient of 1 in 20; neutral is engaged. Find its velocity after a further 10 s.

(9·3 m/s; 23·06 m/s; 27·71 m/s; 30·16 m/s)

17. A disc flywheel has a mass of 20 kg and has a radius of 0·3 m. Find its moment of inertia and the kinetic energy it stores at 2400 rev/min. (0·9 kg m²; 56 830 N)

18. A vehicle has a mass of 1350 kg and is travelling at 54 km/h on a level road. If, under these conditions, the total resistance to motion is 500 N and the total power available at the road wheels is 29·84 kW, calculate the maximum acceleration possible. (1·1 m/s²) (C. and G.)

19. A motor vehicle has a mass of 1·2 tonne and travels at 54 km/h round a curve of 36 m radius. The track of the vehicle is 1·5 m and its c.g. is 0·75 m above ground level.

What is the downward mass on the inner and outer wheels?

(0·9827 tonne; 0·2173 tonne)

20. A vehicle having a mass of 1400 kg and travelling at 45 km/h is brought to rest by the brakes in a distance of 18 m. Calculate the average braking force and time taken to stop. (6076 N; 2·88 s)

21. A vehicle has a mass of 1200 kg and is acted upon by a tractive effort of 2700 N.

(*a*) How long will it take to accelerate from 27 to 54 km/h if the average resistance to motion during this period is 220 N?

(*b*) By how much will its kinetic energy have increased during the acceleration? ((*a*) 3·63 s; (*b*) 102·25 kJ) C. and G.)

22. A motor vehicle has a mass of 1500 kg and is accelerated from 27 to 54 km/h.

Find: (*a*) the change of momentum; (*b*) K.E. at 54 km/h.

((*a*) 11 250 kg m/s; (*b*) 168·75 kJ)

23. A car has a mass of 1350 kg and, starting from rest, is allowed to roll freely down an incline of 1 in 15. What distance will it travel before reaching 54 km/h, assuming that the mean resistance to motion during that period is 360 N?

If the speed is maintained at 54 km/h by applying the rear brakes, determine the braking torque at the rear axle if the wheels have a diameter of 670 mm, the resistance now being steady at 450 N.

(291 m; 24·12 Nm) (C. and G.)

24. A motor lorry with a load has a mass of 2 tonne, and it is driven up an incline of 1 in 20 at a uniform speed of 36 km/h. If the resistances on a level road are 100 N per tonne and the efficiency of the transmission is 75 per cent, calculate the power of the engine. (15·733 kW) (I.M.I.)

25. A wheel is rotating at 2000 rev/min and, when a brake is applied, the wheel is brought to rest with uniform retardation in 400 revolutions. Find the time taken to bring the wheel to rest and the angular retardation in rad/s². (23·95 s; 8·75 rad/s²) (I.M.I.)

26. The engine of a bus develops 59·68 kW at a speed of 63 km/h. If the efficiency of the transmission gear is 85 per cent, what is the effective propelling force if the road is horizontal? (2898 N) (E.M.E.U.)

27. A car has a wheel track of 1·36 m and the centre of gravity is 0·7 m above ground level. Determine the angle through which the car can be tilted before it overturns. (44° 10′)

28. During a Fletcher's Trolley Experiment it was found that the trolley moved through a distance of 75 mm during 0·1 s and through 82·5 mm during the next 0·1 s.

If the vertical downward force of the trolley was 29·25 N and the force of the suspended mass 2·475 N, determine the experimental value of the acceleration due to gravity.   (9·616 m/s²)   (C. and G.)

29. The piston of an engine moved 25 mm in $\frac{1}{100}$ s and 30 mm in the next $\frac{1}{100}$ s, the piston mass was 2·5 kg. Find the average acceleration and the force required to produce this acceleration.   (50 m/s²; 125 N)

30. A car of mass 750 kg and travelling at 72 km/h runs into the back of a heavy lorry of mass 20 tonne which is travelling in the same direction at 27 km/h.

Find: (a) combined momenta after impact; (b) velocity after impact.
((a) 165 000 kg m/s; 28·62 km/h)

13 Periodic Motion and Balancing

Vibration

When a force is applied to a mass elastically secured to another mass, then the first mass will move in the direction of the applied force. Directly this movement finishes, the mass will return some distance and then move once again in the direction of the applied force. This to-and-fro movement, which may continue for some time, is called a **vibration** or **oscillation**.

Spring Vibration

When a spring is deflected from its normal resting position the spring absorbs the energy given to it by the force which caused the deflection. The absorbed energy is given out by the spring as a **rebound**. This rebound may carry the spring beyond its normal rest position and the to-and-fro action continues until the spring finally returns to rest. The time taken for one complete vibration is called the **period** of oscillation, or the **periodicity**.

Natural Frequency

This is the speed at which a mass oscillates or the number of vibrations per minute; it is sometimes expressed as the number of oscillations per minute or the number of **cycles** per minute.

Amplitude

This is the maximum distance covered by the mass when it moves from the central or rest position. **Amplitude** can be described as half the travel or stroke of the movement and is usually given as displacement in mm.

Chassis Springs

One of the most important specifications of a chassis spring is the **static** (stationary) deflection under maximum load. This factor determines the following:

(a) The frequency of the spring and therefore passenger comfort: the most comfortable rate is about 90 complete oscillations per minute.
(b) The relative softness of the spring and its ability to cushion or absorb shocks. As the static deflection increases, the riding qualities of the vehicle improve.

Example. What is meant by the period of oscillation of a spring? The rear springs of a vehicle when fully loaded have a static deflection of 120 mm; what will be their natural period of oscillation? (C. and G.)

The period of oscillation of a spring is the time taken for one complete vibration.

The natural period of oscillation of springs with a given static deflection is found by using the following formula.

$$t = \sqrt{\frac{d}{254}}$$

where d = deflection in mm, t = time for one complete vibration in seconds.

$$\text{Natural period of oscillation} = \sqrt{\frac{120}{254}} = \underline{0.6874 \text{ s}}$$

The formula $\sqrt{\dfrac{d}{254}}$ was derived from the basic pendulum formula $t = 2\pi \sqrt{\dfrac{l}{g}}$,

where t = time for one complete vibration, in s

l = length of pendulum, in m

$g = 9.8 \text{ m/s}^2$

Simple Harmonic Motion

The term 'simple motion' describes to-and-fro motion or a simple vibration. The term 'harmonic' indicates that the motion or vibration is repeated at regular intervals. The motion of an engine valve is a good example of **simple harmonic motion (s.h.m.)**.

Simple harmonic motion may be described as follows:

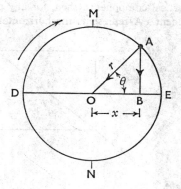

Fig. 13.1.

Fig. 13.1 shows a circle with point O as centre. Suppose a point A on the circumference moves in a circular path of radius r m with a constant speed of v m/s and another point B is always at the foot or lower end of the vertical line AB on the diameter DE of the circle. Then, while point A travels completely round the circumference of the circle, point B will move along the diameter of the circle from E to D and then back again to E; thus B makes a complete motion.

The time taken by point B is called the **Period** of a complete motion or complete vibration, and its value as a time is given as **t** seconds.

Thus,
$$t = \frac{\text{Circumference}}{\text{Velocity } (v)} = \frac{2\pi r}{v}$$

Since $\dfrac{v}{r} = \omega$, the angular velocity of A,

then
$$t = \frac{2\pi}{\omega}$$

The radius r of the circle, which is half the stroke or travel of the motion, is called the **Amplitude** of the motion or vibration.

Acceleration During s.h.m.

When point A is moving in a circular path its acceleration will be $\frac{v^2}{r}$ from A to O. If we resolve the vector for acceleration into its horizontal and vertical components, then, for any position of A, the horizontal component FA represents the horizontal acceleration (see Fig. 13.2).

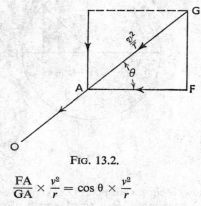

Fig. 13.2.

Now

$$\frac{\text{FA}}{\text{GA}} \times \frac{v^2}{r} = \cos\theta \times \frac{v^2}{r}$$

since

$$\text{GA} = \frac{v^2}{r} \quad \text{and} \quad \frac{\text{FA}}{\text{GA}} = \cos\theta$$

If $\cos\theta \, \frac{v^2}{r}$ is the horizontal acceleration of A it must also be that of B, in Fig. 13.1.

Then

$$\cos\theta \, \frac{v^2}{r} = \frac{\text{OB}}{r} \times \frac{v}{r}$$

$$= \text{OB} \times \frac{v^2}{r^2}$$

Since $\omega^2 = \frac{v^2}{r}$, then horizontal acceleration of B is distance $\text{OB} \times \omega^2$ in the direction B to O (units m/s^2), in Fig. 13.1.

Thus the horizontal acceleration is proportional to distance BO, and for any position of B it is always towards O. It is maximum when A is in positions E and D, and minimum in positions M and N.

We can now define simple harmonic motion. If a body moves to and fro so that its acceleration is directed towards a fixed point at any instant and the acceleration is proportional to its distance from the fixed point, then the body is moving with simple harmonic motion.

If a body of mass m kg moves in with point B, then a force must have acted on it to give the body the required acceleration. This force is derived from:

$$\text{Mass} \times \text{Acceleration} = m\omega^2 \times \text{OB}$$

Therefore, when $\qquad F = \text{force, in N}$

then $\qquad F = m\omega^2 \times \text{OB (N)}$

Because the acceleration of a body is proportional to any given distance OB, then the force F on the body will also be proportional to the distance OB and the force F will always be directed towards O.

Velocity During s.h.m.

The velocity of a point moving with s.h.m. is given by the following expression:

$$v = \omega r \sin \theta, \text{ Fig. 13.3.}$$

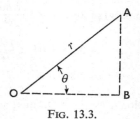

FIG. 13.3.

In terms of the displacement x of the point B in Fig. 13.1, from Fig. 13.3

$$\sin \theta = \frac{\text{AB}}{\text{OA}}$$

Thus $\qquad v = \omega r \dfrac{\text{AB}}{\text{OA}}$

$$= \frac{\omega r \sqrt{r^2 - x^2}}{r}$$

Since $AB^2 = r^2 - x^2$

$$AB = \sqrt{r^2 - x^2}$$

then $\qquad v = \omega\sqrt{r^2 - x^2}$

The maximum velocity V_m occurs when $x = 0$, thus $V_m = \omega r$. The equations used in this section are as follows:

$$t = \frac{2\pi r}{v} = \frac{2\pi}{\omega} \text{ s}$$

$$a = OB \times \frac{v^2}{r^2} = OB \times \omega^2 \text{ m/s}^2$$

$$F = m\omega^2 \times OB \text{ (N)}$$

$$v = \omega\sqrt{r^2 - x^2} \text{ m/s}$$

$$V_m = \omega r \text{ m/s}$$

Example. A crank 40 mm long is driven by a piston and makes 1400 rev/min. Find the acceleration of the piston when it is 9 mm from the end of its stroke, taking the motion as s.h.m.

$$\text{Velocity of crank } (v) = 2\pi \times r \times \frac{\text{rev/min}}{60} \text{ m/s}$$

$V = r\omega$

$$= 2\pi \times 0 \cdot 04 \times \frac{1400}{60} \text{ m/s}$$

$$= 5 \cdot 866 \text{ m/s}$$

$$\text{Acceleration } (a) = \frac{v^2}{r^2} \times OB \text{ m/s}^2$$

$$OB = 0 \cdot 04 - 0 \cdot 009 = 0 \cdot 031 \text{ m}$$

$$a = \frac{5 \cdot 866^2}{0 \cdot 04^2} \times 0 \cdot 031$$

$$= \frac{34 \cdot 41 \times 0 \cdot 031}{0 \cdot 0016}$$

$$= \underline{666 \cdot 7 \text{ m/s}^2}$$

Example. In a 12·6 litre c.i. engine a piston drives a crank 80 mm long and a connecting rod 460 mm long. Assuming the acceleration of the piston to be simple harmonic, calculate its velocity and acceleration when the crank has moved 60° from the t.d.c. position. If the crank speed is 1800 rev/min, what is the maximum velocity of the piston?

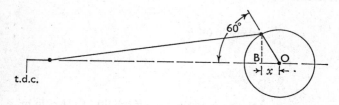

FIG. 13.4.

The motion of a piston is not s.h.m. unless the connecting rod is at least six times the length of the crank.

$$\omega = 2\pi \times \frac{\text{rev/min}}{60} = \frac{2\pi \times 1800}{60} = 188 \cdot 5 \text{ rad/s}$$

From Fig. 13.4,

$$x = \text{OB} = 0 \cdot 08 \times \cos 60° = 0 \cdot 04 \text{ m}$$

$$v = \omega \sqrt{r^2 - x^2}$$

$$= 188 \cdot 5 \sqrt{0 \cdot 08^2 - 0 \cdot 04^2}$$

$$= 188 \cdot 5 \sqrt{0 \cdot 0048}$$

$$= \underline{13 \cdot 06 \text{ m/s}}$$

$$a = \omega^2 x$$

$$= 188 \cdot 5^2 \times 0 \cdot 04$$

$$= \underline{1421 \text{ m/s}^2}$$

$$V_m = \omega r$$

$$= 188 \cdot 5 \times 0 \cdot 08$$

$$= \underline{15 \cdot 08 \text{ m/s}}$$

Example. The full lift of an engine valve, whose motion may be taken as s.h.m., is 6·4 mm. The time taken to open and close the valve is 0·01 s and the mass of the valve is 0·135 kg. Calculate the accelerating force at each end of the valve stroke.

$$t = \frac{2\pi}{\omega}, \quad \text{then} \quad 0\cdot01 = \frac{2\pi}{\omega}$$

$$\omega \doteq \frac{2\pi}{0\cdot01} = 200\pi$$

$a = \omega^2 s$, where s is stroke or half full lift of valve, in m

$s = 0\cdot0032$, i.e. $0\cdot0064 \div 2$

$$\therefore a = (200\pi)^2 \times 0\cdot0032 \text{ m/s}^2$$

$$F = m \times \omega^2 s \text{ N}$$

$$\therefore F = 0\cdot135 \times (200\,\pi)^2 \times 0\cdot0032 \text{ N}$$

$$= \underline{170\cdot5 \text{ N}}$$

Balancing

The importance of road wheel balance in vehicle operation is well known. Wheel unbalance can cause violent oscillation and tramp, and unless corrected may cause rapid wear on the 'front-end' parts and tyre treads. Correct balance in fan assemblies, flywheel–clutch assemblies and propeller shafts is carefully obtained during the manufacture of quality and racing cars.

There are two forms of balance, namely **Static** and **Dynamic** balance. Static or stationary balance means the equal distribution of the mass of an assembly about its axis of rotation, so that when the assembly is rotated it will not come to rest in the same position every time it stops. Fig. 13.5 shows a wheel with a heavy spot at A. When this wheel is rotated it always comes to rest with the spot A at the bottom. To balance the wheel a suitable 'weight' is fixed to the wheel rim at B, as shown in Fig. 13.5. The wheel is now in static balance only, and is not fully balanced.

Dynamic or running balance means that an assembly must rotate over its speed range on an axis which runs through the centre of the assembly and at the same time the assembly must be perpendicular to the axis of rotation.

Although an assembly has correct static balance, it may not have correct dynamic balance. For example, in Fig. 13.5, when the wheel is rotated the two opposed centrifugal forces F_1 and F_2 are not in line with each other. As the wheel rotates, because the forces are offset they

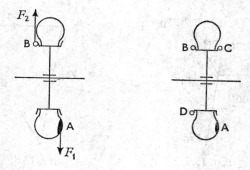

FIG. 13.5.   FIG. 13.6.

try to tilt the wheel first one way and then the other, thus producing a vibration which increases as the speed of the wheel increases. This condition is known as a 'rocking couple', and although the wheel is in static balance, it is not in dynamic balance.

To obtain dynamic balance two 'weights' B and C are placed one on each side of the wheel rim as shown in Fig. 13.6, and a further 'weight' at D to compensate for 'weight' C; this eliminates the rocking couple, and dynamic balance is obtained.

In practice, 'weights' B and D can often be removed without affecting correct balance.

Example. A wheel and tyre assembly, in complete dynamic balance, has three small lead 'weights' attached to the wheel rim. Assuming that one of the 'weights' is missing, determine, either graphically or by calculation, the magnitude and relative angular position of a replacement 'weight' to restore dynamic balance. The two balancers remaining in position have a mass of 56 g and 85 g respectively, and the angle between them is 120 degrees.   (C. and G.)

The graphic method of answering this type of question is far simpler than by direct calculation. Figs. 13.7 and 13.8 show the space and force diagrams. The force diagram shows that the magnitude of the missing 'weight' is 75 g and the position of the 'weight' 100 degrees relative to the 56 g 'weight' and 140 degrees relative to the 85 g 'weight'.

$$75 \text{ g}; \quad 100°; \quad 140°$$

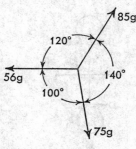

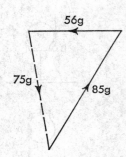

Fig. 13.7.   Fig. 13.8.

Engine Balancing

The reciprocating parts of an engine are the piston complete with gudgeon pin and about one-third of the connecting rod. The big-end assembly, part of the connecting rod and crankpin are considered as rotating parts plus the rest of the crankshaft and the flywheel.

The purpose of engine balancing is to minimize the effects of engine vibration caused by the following:

(1) Unbalanced centrifugal forces and couples set up by the rotating parts.

(2) Unbalanced forces and couples set up by the inertia effects of the reciprocating parts.

To obtain a smooth-running engine the designer must neutralize all these forces and couples so as to reduce stresses in the engine and its supports to a minimum.

Single-cylinder Engine

In this type of engine one rotating mass is balanced by two other masses rotating in separate planes. The mass to be balanced is usually taken as: (*a*) the crankpin; (*b*) the rotating part of the connecting rod; and (*c*) one-**half** the mass of the reciprocating parts. If this mass is not balanced a reaction of considerable magnitude is imposed on the main bearings.

Example. An engine has a 100 mm stroke and is running at 3500 rev/min. If the rotating parts have a mass of 1·36 kg, calculate the reaction on the main bearings.

Let $F =$ reaction force, in N

$m =$ mass of rotating parts, in kg

$r =$ crank radius, in metres

$90 =$ a constant

Then

$$F = \frac{mr \; (\text{rev/min})^2}{90}$$

$$\therefore F = \frac{1·36 \times 0·05 \times (3500)^2}{90}$$

$$= \underline{9257 \text{ N}}$$

This force is caused by the rotating masses only.

Fig. 13.9 shows a single cylinder crankshaft with a crank arm radius

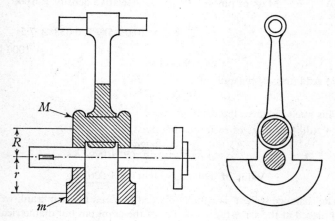

Fig. 13.9.

R; the combined rotating and half the reciprocating mass is denoted by M. Thus the 'mass moment' of the unbalanced mass M can be denoted by MR; the mass moment of the 'balance weight' m is denoted by mr. To effect balance, MR must equal mr ($MR = mr$) and the 'balance weight' m should be placed diametrically opposite to and in the same plane as the unbalanced mass M. But this is not practicable, and it is usual to divide the 'balance weight' m equally and place one-half on each crank web as shown in Fig. 13.9, so as to make room for the connecting rod when the crankshaft rotates.

The balancing equation will now be:

$$\frac{MR}{2r} = \frac{m}{2}$$

Example. A single-cylinder crankshaft has symmetrical crank webs. The crank pin is 63·5 mm dia. and 38 mm long, and the relative density is 7·5. The mass of the reciprocating parts is 0·726 kg, and the mass of the lower end of the connecting rod is 0·34 kg.

Assume that the whole of the rotating masses and half the reciprocating masses are to be balanced, determine the value of the counterbalance 'weights' and make a sketch showing where they should be placed. (C. and G.)

First calculate the mass of the crankpin.

(*a*) Mass of pin $= \frac{\pi}{4}D^2 \times L \times$ Relative density $\times\ 1000$

$$= \frac{22}{7} \times \frac{1}{4} \times (0{\cdot}0635)^2 \times 0{\cdot}038 \times 7{\cdot}5$$
$$\times\ 1000\ \text{kg}$$
$$= 0{\cdot}9033\ \text{kg}$$

(*b*) Add mass of big end $= 0{\cdot}9033 + 0{\cdot}34$
$$= 1{\cdot}2433\ \text{kg}$$

This mass balances the rotating mass.

(*c*) Add half mass of reciprocating mass:

$$1{\cdot}2433 + \frac{0{\cdot}726}{2} = 1{\cdot}6063\ \text{kg}$$

$\therefore$ Value of 'balance weight' $= \underline{1{\cdot}6063\ \text{kg}}$

The 'balance weight' is equally divided between the two crank webs and placed at the same radius as that of the crankpin but diametrically opposite. Fig. 13.9 shows the required sketch.

In a single-cylinder engine, because only half the mass necessary to balance the reciprocating mass is used, the remainder is left unbalanced in the vertical line of the stroke. This, unfortunately, produces a horizontal as well as a vertical force effect, thus, only partial balance is obtained. It is not possible to balance completely a single-cylinder engine by adding 'balance weights' to the crank.

90° Twin Engine

The reciprocating and rotating parts are balanced by the addition of 'balance weights' opposite the crankpin. Because of the 90° angle between the cylinders the engine is balanced for the primary (inertia) forces, but not for those known as secondary forces, which are caused by the comparatively short connecting rods.

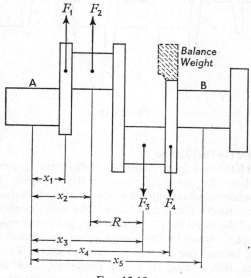

Fig. 13.10.

Horizontally Opposed Twin Engine

In these engines the pistons move in opposite directions and at the same speed, so that the centrifugal and inertia forces oppose and thus balance each other. In practice, the centre lines of the cylinders are offset, distance R, Fig. 13.10. This introduces a rocking couple which, however, can be practically eliminated by adding 'balance weights', one to each crank web.

Fig. 13.10 shows the derivation of a formula for determining the magnitude of the load on the main bearings B and A.

Taking moments about bearing A, then:

$$Bx_5 = (F_1x_1 + F_2x_2) - (F_3x_3 + F_4x_4)$$

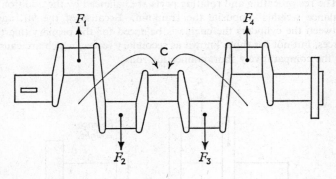

FIG. 13.11.

Four-cylinder (In-line) Engine

Fig. 13.11 shows a four-cylinder crankshaft; the arrows F_1, F_2, F_3 and F_4 indicate the centrifugal forces on the crankpins. When these forces are added algebraically the result is zero, which shows that the engine is balanced for all inertia forces. The term algebraically means that some of the forces have a negative sign, in this example F_1 and F_4.

The couples, shown by the arrows C, set up in each half of the crankshaft, balance one another but tend to spring the intermediate crank webs, thus causing stresses in crankshaft, main bearings and crankcase. 'Balance weights', however, are sometimes fitted to reduce the effect of these stresses, which are particularly severe on the centre main bearing of a normal three bearing four-cylinder engine.

The four-cylinder engine is not balanced for the secondary forces.

Six- and Eight-cylinder Engines

These engines are in complete balance.

Torsional Vibration

Engines designed with six and eight cylinders in line are often subjected to crankshaft oscillation which produces a torsional vibration. This oscillation produced by power impulses may be reduced to a small angle of twist by fitting a 'damper' to the front end of the crankshaft. The damper may have a rubber-bonded inertia member, viscous or frictional controlled member. Adjustment must not be made to any damper unless the manufacturer's specification is known.

Exercise 13

1. (a) Calculate the frequency of a spring which has a maximum deflection of 100 mm.

(b) Calculate the maximum deflection of a spring which has a frequency of 90 oscillations per minute.

((a) 95·63 oscs/min; (b) 112·8 mm)

2. The spring of a vehicle suspension deflects 0·15 m under load. Find the speed at which the vehicle should not be driven over a series of bumps, 1·8 m apart from crest to crest, due to resonance effects which would be encountered. (8·433 km/h) (I.M.I.)

3. The stroke of a high speed diesel engine is 150 mm, and it runs at 1800 rev/min. Find the maximum acceleration of the crankpin in m/s. (665·5 m/s²)

4. During opening and closing a valve moves a total distance of 0·01 m in 0·006 s. Calculate: (a) the maximum velocity of the valve, and (b) its maximum acceleration. The motion of the valve may be taken as simple harmonic. ((a) 2·661 m/s; (b) 2796 m/s²)

5. A car is brought in with wheel wobble. During the check it is noticed that the nearside front wheel has a 56 g 'weight' and a 28 g 'weight' 120 degrees apart, but a third 'weight' is missing. Find the magnitude of the 'weight' and its position relative to the other 'weights' in order to restore balance. The rim diameter is 406 mm.
(49 g; 90° from 28 g 'weight', 150° from 56 g 'weight') (C. and G.)

6. The rotor or turbine of a torque converter recorded an out of balance of 85 g mm on the balancing machine.

Calculate the length of a strip of steel 12·5 mm wide × 1·58 mm thick to be attached to the rotor at a radius 114 mm from its centre (relative density of steel 7·3). (51·71 mm)

7. The flywheel of an engine required a mass of 14 g to be attached to the rim, 190 mm from the centre of the wheel.

Calculate how many holes 9·2 mm in diameter and 10 mm deep must be drilled on the heavy side of the wheel at a radius of 170 mm from the centre of the wheel to produce perfect balance (relative density of cast iron 7·8).   (3 holes)

8. An unbalanced single-cylinder engine has the following data: mass of piston and gudgeon pin 0·36 kg; total mass of connecting rod 0·45 kg (0·32 kg rotating, 0·13 kg reciprocating); mass of crankpin (calculated) 0·09 kg.

Calculate the mass required to obtain balance and show by means of a diagram where the 'weights' would normally be placed. The unbalanced mass and the 'balance weights' are assumed to act at equal radii.

(0·655 kg)   (C. and G.)

9. Sketch the normal crankshaft arrangement for a four-cylinder in-line engine. Indicate in your diagram the centrifugal forces on the crankpins and explain how these balance without the use of 'balance weights'. Why, in spite of this, are 'balance weights' sometimes fitted?

(C. and G.)

14

Bending and Twisting

Many parts of a motor vehicle acted on by forces at right angles to their length can conveniently be called **beams**. Examples are a hand-brake lever, an axle, a chassis frame member, a leaf spring, etc.

Two simple forms of a loaded beam are shown in Figs. 14.1 (*a*) and (*b*). Fig. 14.1 (*a*) shows a form of beam called a **cantilever**, e.g. a bracket for a running-board. The bracket is fixed to the chassis at one end; it has no other support and is shown carrying a load W at the free end.

Fig. 14.1 (*b*) is a horizontal beam supported at each end; it carries a load W midway between the supports.

The following definitions have been previously stated in Part 1:

$$\text{Stress} = \frac{\text{Force}}{\text{Area}}$$

$$\text{Strain} = \frac{\text{Change of length}}{\text{Original length}}$$

Three fundamental types of stresses were also given:

(1) Tensile stress σ
(2) Compressive stress σ
(3) Shearing stress τ

To understand the stress and strain in a loaded and bent beam, we shall assume that the beam shown in Fig. 14.1 (*c*) is made of rubber or some flexible material. This beam has a number of equidistant parallel lines scribed on one side, and when the beam is bent, by applying a load at the centre, the lines are no longer parallel with each other. The distance between these lines decreases on the upper side and increases on the lower side; on the XY line, however, they remain the same length. Since the upper fibres of the beam are shortened, they are therefore in compression. The lower fibres of the beam are stretched, and they are therefore in tension. The middle fibre of the beam is free from both stress and strain; it is called the **neutral axis** of the beam. The intensity of stress is zero at the neutral axis, but steadily increases as the outer edges of the beam are approached. The loaded beam shown in Fig. 14.1 (*a*) has the upper fibres in tension and the lower fibres in compression.

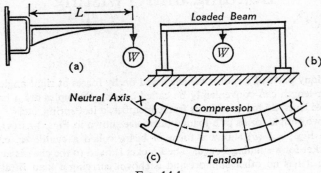

FIG. 14.1.

Bending Stresses

The distribution and calculation of all the stresses in a beam are beyond the scope of the book, but enough information is given to enable students to solve the practical problems likely to be met.

The stress produced in a beam by the loads or forces acting on it are

FIG. 14.2.

not simply proportional to these loads or forces, but to the **moment** or torque of the forces. This moment or torque is called the **bending moment**, abbreviated to B.M. or M.

To show the principle of bending moments let us take, for example, the cantilever shown in Fig. 14.2. The free end has a load W, the total length of the beam outside the support is denoted by l and the maximum bending moment occurs at the support, i.e. B.M. $= Wl$. The B.M. at any point X along the beam is Wx, where x is the distance from the point X to the free end.

Example. See Fig. 14.2.

Let $W = 100$ N and $l = 1500$ mm, then

$$\text{Maximum B.M.} = 100 \times 1.5$$
$$= 150 \text{ Nm}$$

Let $x = 600$ mm, then

$$\text{B.M. at X} = 100 \times 0.6$$
$$= \underline{60 \text{ Nm}}$$

A beam loaded in the centre and supported at its ends (Fig. 14.3) has the maximum B.M. at the centre. The reaction at the supports are

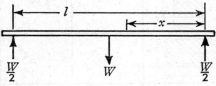

FIG. 14.3.

$\dfrac{W}{2}$, and the distance from either end to the middle of the beam is $\dfrac{l}{2}$. Neglecting the mass of the beam, there is only the reaction or force $\dfrac{W}{2}$ acting upward on each side; the moment of the force about the middle of the beam is $\dfrac{W}{2} \times \dfrac{l}{2} = \dfrac{Wl}{4}$ and the B.M. at any point is $\dfrac{W}{2}x$.

Example. See Fig. 14.3.

Let $W = 100$ N and $l = 1500$ mm, then

$$\text{Maximum B.M.} = \frac{Wl}{4}$$
$$= \frac{100 \times 1.5}{4} \text{ Nm}$$
$$= \underline{37.5 \text{ Nm}}$$

Let $x = 600$ mm, then

$$\text{B.M. at X} = \frac{W}{2}x$$
$$= \frac{100 \times 0.6}{2} \text{ Nm}$$
$$= \underline{30 \text{ Nm}}$$

Moment of Inertia and Modulus of Section

The term **moment of inertia** refers to a property of the shape of a beam section. It is a measure of the ability of a beam section to resist bending. Moment of inertia is expressed in metres to the fourth power (m)[4].

SECTION	MOMENT OF INERTIA I_{xx}	MODULUS OF SECTION Z
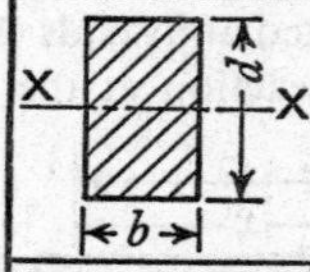	$\frac{1}{12}bd^3$	$\frac{1}{6}bd^2$
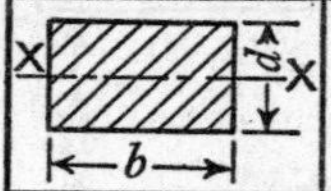	$\frac{1}{12}bd^3$	$\frac{1}{6}bd^2$
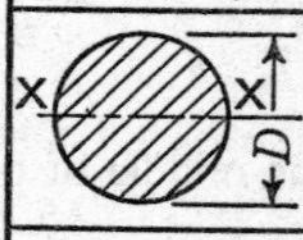	$\frac{\pi}{64}D^4$	$\frac{\pi}{32}D^3$
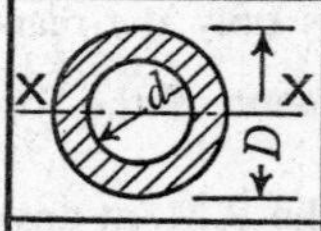	$\frac{\pi}{64}\left(D^4-d^4\right)$	$\frac{\pi}{32}\left(\frac{D^4-d^4}{D}\right)$
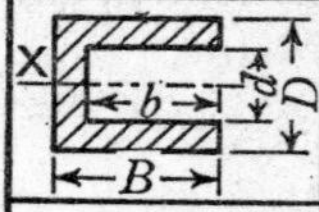	$\frac{1}{12}\left(BD^3-bd^3\right)$	$\frac{1}{6D}\left(BD^3-bd^3\right)$
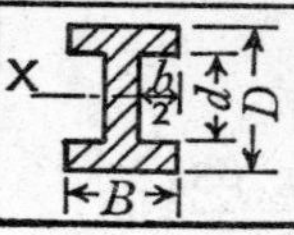	$\frac{1}{12}\left(BD^3-bd^3\right)$	$\frac{1}{6D}\left(BD^3-bd^3\right)$

Fig. 14.4.

Modulus of section is an expression which occurs in some bending calculations; it is the moment of inertia divided by the distance from the neutral axis to the outermost fibre of the beam.

The following equations have been developed for bending calculations:

$$M = \sigma\frac{I}{y} = fZ; \quad \sigma = \frac{M}{Z}; \quad Z = \frac{M}{\sigma}$$

where M = bending moment, in Nm

I = moment of inertia, in $(m)^4$ units

y = distance from neutral axis to the outermost fibre, in metres

Z = modulus of section, in $(m)^3$ units = $\dfrac{I}{y}$

σ = stress in material, in kN/m²

In Fig. 14.4 a number of standard sections are shown, each with its moment of inertia and modulus of section.

Example. A straight bar of rectangular section is secured in a wall at one end and projects 500 mm. The section of the bar is 75 mm by 37·5 mm with the larger dimension parallel to the direction of the load 1800 N, which is applied at the free end of the bar. Calculate the maximum stress in the material at the fixed end.

Fig. 14.5 shows a line diagram of the bar.

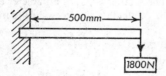

Fig. 14.5.

Now
$$\text{B.M.} = 1800 \times 0.5 = 900 \text{ Nm}$$

Modulus of section $Z = \tfrac{1}{6}bd^2$

$$= \tfrac{1}{6} \times 0.375 \times 0.75^2 \text{ m}^3$$

$$= 0.000\ 035\ 17 \text{ m}^3$$

Since stress in material $\sigma = \dfrac{\text{B.M.}}{Z}$

$$\therefore \sigma = 900 \div 0.000\ 035\ 17 \text{ N/m}^2$$

$$= 25\ 600\ 000 \text{ N/m}^2$$

$$= \underline{25\ 600 \text{ kN/m}^2}$$

Example. A channel-section frame member is subjected to a bending moment of 1000 Nm. The section is 125 mm deep and 50 mm wide; the thickness of the material is 3 mm. Calculate the tensile stress in the material in kN/m².

$$\text{Stress in material } \sigma = \frac{\text{B.M.}}{Z}$$

$$= \frac{1000}{Z} \text{ N/m}^2$$

$$\text{Modulus of section } Z = \frac{BD^3 - bd^3}{6D} \text{ (see Fig. 14.4)}$$

$$= \frac{(0 \cdot 05 \times 0 \cdot 125^3) - (0 \cdot 047 \times 0 \cdot 119^3)}{6 \times 0 \cdot 125} \text{ m}^3$$

$$= 0 \cdot 000 \ 024 \ 63 \text{ m}^3$$

$$\therefore \sigma = 1000 \div 0 \cdot 000 \ 024 \ 63 \text{ N/m}^2$$

$$= 40 \ 590 \ 000 \text{ N/m}^2$$

$$= \underline{40 \ 590 \text{ kN/m}^2}$$

Example. A tubular frame member is subjected to a bending moment of 560 Nm. The section is 75 mm diameter and the thickness of the material is 3 mm. Calculate the stress in the material in kN/m².

$$\text{Stress in material } \sigma = \frac{\text{B.M.}}{Z}$$

$$= \frac{560}{Z} \text{ N/m}^2$$

$$\text{Modulus of section } Z = \frac{\pi}{32} \left(\frac{D^4 - d^4}{D} \right) \text{ (see Fig. 14.4)}$$

$$= \frac{\pi}{32} \left(\frac{0 \cdot 075 - 0 \cdot 069^4}{0 \cdot 075} \right) \text{ m}^3$$

$$= 0 \cdot 000 \ 011 \ 77 \text{ m}^3$$

$$\therefore \sigma = 560 \div 0 \cdot 000 \ 011 \ 77 \text{ N/m}^2$$

$$= 47 \ 570 \ 000 \text{ N/m}^2$$

$$= \underline{47 \ 570 \text{ kN/m}^2}$$

Bending Moments and Shearing Forces

The side chassis member of a motor vehicle is designed to withstand bending and shearing forces. Its depth of section varies along its length proportionately to the bending moment, so that the material from which the chassis is made is uniformly stressed. Downward loads occur at points where the power unit and body or platform are mounted; the reactions to these loads or the supports are at the axles or spring attachments. This chassis member may be regarded as a beam, and the bending moments and shearing forces can be calculated and represented by diagrams.

In the calculations, two rules must be observed:

1. The bending moment at *any point* along a loaded beam is the algebraic sum of all the moments of the vertical forces acting on *one side* of the *point* about that *point*.
2. The **shearing force** at *any* point along a loaded beam is the algebraic sum of all the vertical forces acting on *one* side of the point.

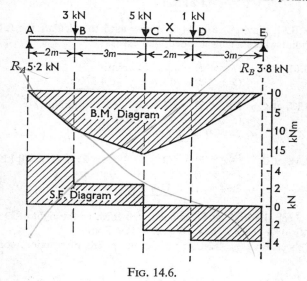

Fig. 14.6.

Two different diagrams are used, the bending moment (B.M.) and the shearing force (S.F.) diagrams. On both diagrams all forces which make the beam sag are shown downwards below the datum or zero line. Upward loads and reactions are shown upwards in both diagrams (see Fig. 14.6).

A loaded beam is shown in Fig. 14.6. The reactions at R_A and R_B are calculated first:

$$10 R_A = [(1 \times 3) + (5 \times 5) + (3 \times 8)]$$
$$\therefore R_A = 5.2 \text{ kN} \quad \text{and} \quad R_B = 3.8 \text{ kN}$$

Consider the B.M. at point X which is midway between the points C and D. The clockwise moment to the left of X and about X is $R_A \times 6$ kNm. The anticlockwise moments to the left of X and about X are $(5 \times 1) + (3 \times 4)$ kNm. The B.M. which exists at the point X is the difference between the anticlockwise and clockwise bending moments; since the beam sags under this load, the B.M. is plotted downwards.

$$\begin{aligned}
\therefore \text{ B.M. at X} &= (R_A \times 6) - [(5 \times 1) + (3 \times 4)] \text{ kNm} \\
&= (5 \cdot 2 \times 6) - (5 \times 1) - (3 \times 4) \text{ kNm} \\
&= 31 \cdot 2 - 5 - 12 \text{ kNm} \\
&= \underline{14 \cdot 2 \text{ kNm}}
\end{aligned}$$

The B.M. diagram, Fig. 14.6, is now used to calculate the B.M. at each point where a concentrated load exists.

$$\begin{aligned}
\text{B.M. at B} &= (R_A \times 2) - (3 \times 0) \text{ kNm} \\
&= (5 \cdot 2 \times 2) - 0 \text{ kNm} = \underline{10 \cdot 4 \text{ kNm}}
\end{aligned}$$

$$\begin{aligned}
\text{B.M. at C} &= (R_A \times 5) - [(3 \times 3) + (5 \times 0)] \text{ kNm} \\
&= (5 \cdot 2 \times 5) - 9 - 0 \text{ kNm} \\
&= 26 - 9 = \underline{17 \text{ kNm}}
\end{aligned}$$

$$\begin{aligned}
\text{B.M. at D} &= (R_A \times 7) - [(3 \times 5) + (5 \times 2) + (1 \times 0)] \text{ kNm} \\
&= (5 \cdot 2 \times 7) - 15 - 10 - 0 \text{ kNm} \\
&= 36 \cdot 4 - 25 = \underline{11 \cdot 4 \text{ kNm}}
\end{aligned}$$

To check the B.M. at D, calculate the B.M. to the right of D (anticlockwise); it is $R_B \times 3$ or $3 \cdot 8 \times 3 = 11 \cdot 4$ kNm.

To check that the B.M. is zero at the points of reaction, consider point R_A.

$$\text{B.M.} = R_A \times \text{Distance} = R_A \times 0 \quad \text{or} \quad 5 \cdot 2 \times 0$$

which is zero.

The shear-force diagram, Fig. 14.6, shows the shearing forces plotted at the reaction and other points where the concentrated loads exist.

$$\begin{aligned}
&\text{S.F. at A} = 5 \cdot 2 \text{ kN upwards} \\
&\text{S.F. at B} = 3 \text{ kN downwards} \\
&\text{S.F. at C} = 5 \text{ kN downwards} \\
&\text{S.F. at D} = 1 \text{ kN downwards} \\
&\text{S.F. at E} = 3 \cdot 8 \text{ kN upwards}
\end{aligned}$$

The following example resembles a chassis side member (see Fig. 14.7).

Example. Reactions were calculated and the results are shown in Fig. 14.7 as $R_A = 5\cdot25$ kN; $R_B = 8\cdot75$ kN.

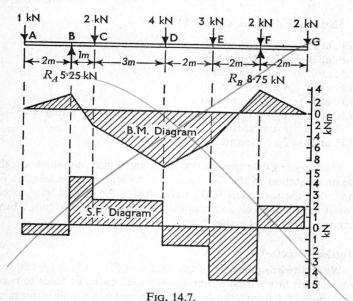

FIG. 14.7.

B.M. at A $= -(1 \times 0) = \underline{0 \text{ kNm}}$

B.M. at B $= -(1 \times 2) = \underline{-2 \text{ kNm}}$

B.M. at C $= (R_A \times 1) - (1 \times 3) \text{ kNm}$
$= 5\cdot25 - 3 = \underline{2\cdot25 \text{ kNm}}$

B.M. at D $= (R_A \times 4) - [(1 \times 6) + (2 \times 3)] \text{ kNm}$
$= 21 - 6 - 6 = \underline{9 \text{ kNm}}$

B.M. at E $= (R_A \times 6) - [(1 \times 8) + (2 \times 5) + (4 \times 2) \text{ kNm}$
$= 31\cdot5 - 8 - 10 - 8 = \underline{5\cdot5 \text{ kNm}}$

B.M. at F $=$
$(R_A \times 8) - [(1 \times 10) + (2 \times 7) + (4 \times 4) + (3 \times 2)] \text{ kNm}$
$= 42 - 10 - 14 - 16 - 6 = \underline{-4 \text{ kNm}}$

B.M. at G $= (R_A \times 10) + (R_B \times 2)$
$= [(1 \times 12) + (2 \times 9) + (4 \times 6) + (3 \times 4) + (2 \times 2)]$ kNm
$= 52 \cdot 5 + 17 \cdot 5 - 12 - 18 - 24 - 12 - 4$
$= 70 - 70 = \underline{0 \text{ kNm}}$

Shear force diagram, see Fig. 14.7.

S.F. at A $= 1$ kN downwards
S.F. at B $= 5 \cdot 25$ kN upwards
S.F. at C $= 2$ kN downwards
S.F. at D $= 4$ kN downwards
S.F. at E $= 3$ kN downwards
S.F. at F $= 8 \cdot 75$ kN upwards, 2 kN downwards, giving $6 \cdot 75$ kN
               upwards
S.F. at G $= 2$ kN downwards

The foregoing diagrams are typical for any vehicle, and show why the depth of section of the side member is varied along its length. We note that the maximum B.M., which makes the chassis 'sag', is between the road wheels and also that the chassis tends to 'hog', bend convex, at the wheel arches.

Torsion (*Twisting*)

When a **twisting moment** or torque T (see Fig. 14.8) is applied to a round shaft firmly fixed at one end the shaft twists or tends to twist. The forces, $F F$ form a **couple**, and the **moment** of a couple is measured by multiplying *one* of the forces by the perpendicular distance between them, called the **arm** of the couple. In the foregoing example the arm of the couple is represented by d and one of the forces by F.

If we take a circular cross-section of the shaft at XY, in Fig. 14.8, we shall find that all the material is under shear stress. The material to the left of XY tends to turn the fixed end in a clockwise direction, but the material to the right of XY exerts equal and opposite forces on the free end of the shaft to give an anticlockwise moment. The twisting shear stress which exerts this resisting moment or torque varies in intensity from maximum at the circumference of the shaft (*ab*, Fig. 14.8) to zero at the axis of the shaft. The distance *ab* is proportional to θr, so that as r approaches zero (axis) the distance becomes less and also the stress. Stress is proportional to tangential force multiplied by radius r.

Experiments have shown that the strength of a solid shaft is directly proportional to the cube of its diameter, e.g. a shaft of 100 mm diameter can transmit with safety 8 times more torque than a shaft of 50 mm diameter.

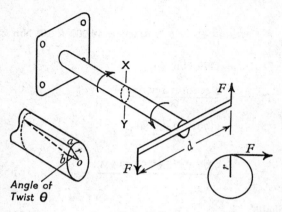

FIG. 14.8.

Let σ equal the maximum intensity of stress at the outer surface of the shaft in kN/m² and let d equal the diameter of the shaft in metres. Then the total resisting torque of the shaft is:

$$T = \frac{\pi}{16} d^3 \sigma$$

where T is in kNm and d is in metres.

$$\therefore \quad \sigma = \frac{16T}{\pi d^3} \text{ kN/m}^2$$

Example. A clutch shaft of 30 mm diameter transmits a torque of 120 Nm. Find the torsional stress to which the material of the shaft is subjected. (C. and G.)

Since
$$T = \frac{\pi}{16} d^3 \sigma$$

$$\therefore \quad \sigma = \frac{16T}{\pi d^3} = \frac{16 \times 0 \cdot 12}{\pi \times 0 \cdot 03^3}$$

$$= \underline{22\ 630 \text{ kN/m}^2}$$

Example. What torque may be transmitted in a shaft 50 mm diameter with a maximum shear stress of 48 000 kN/m²? If the shaft makes 80 rev/min, what power may be transmitted?

Now $\qquad T = \dfrac{\pi}{16}d^3\tau = \dfrac{\pi}{16} \times 0.05^3 \times 48\ 000 \times 10^3$ Nm

$$= 1179 \text{ Nm}$$

$$\text{Power} = \frac{T \times 2\pi \times \text{rev/min}}{60}$$

$$= \frac{1179 \times 2\pi \times 80}{60} \text{ W}$$

$$= \underline{9879 \text{ W} \quad \text{or} \quad 9.879 \text{ kW}}$$

Hollow Shafts

When a solid shaft is under a torsional load the material near the axis of the shaft is only under a small shearing stress and the moment arm is also small. Therefore we can obtain a stronger shaft of the same mass by removing some of the material from the centre and putting it at the circumference of the shaft where it is all at maximum stress.

Shafts of large diameter, e.g. propeller shafts, are made hollow for the sake of lightness and, mass for mass, a hollow shaft is stronger than a solid shaft.

Torque transmitted by a hollow shaft is given by the equation

$$T = \frac{\pi}{16}\tau\left(\frac{D^4 - d^4}{D}\right)$$

where $D =$ outside diameter of shaft, in metres

$d =$ inside diameter of shaft, in metres

For an applied torque, the stress in the shaft is calculated:

$$\tau = \frac{16T}{\pi\left(\dfrac{D^4 - d^4}{D}\right)} \text{ kN/m}^2$$

Example. A tubular propeller shaft has an outside diameter of 40 mm and an inside diameter of 30 mm. The shaft is subjected to a torque of 465 Nm. Calculate the shear stress in the material in kN/m².

$$\tau = \frac{16T}{\pi\left(\dfrac{D^4 - d^4}{D}\right)}$$

$$= \frac{16 \times 465}{\pi\left(\dfrac{0\cdot04^4 - 0\cdot03^4}{0\cdot04}\right) \times 1000} \text{ kN/m}^2$$

$$= \underline{54\ 120 \text{ kN/m}^2}$$

Torsional Stiffness and Angle of Twist

The **torsional stiffness** of a shaft means its resistance to twisting when subjected to a torque or twisting moment. For a given torque the **angle of twist** (i.e. the amount of twist produced when torque is applied to a shaft) is directly proportional to the length and inversely proportional to the fourth power of the diameter of the shaft.

Example. A shaft 1·5 m long is twisted through an angle of 9° when a torque of 2025 Nm is applied to it. Determine the angle through which a similar shaft 1·8 m long will be twisted by a torque of 2700 Nm.

A 1·5 m shaft twisted by 2025 Nm torque through 9°

„ 1 m   „   „   „   1 Nm   „   „ $\dfrac{9}{1\cdot5} \times \dfrac{1}{2025}$ °

„ 1·8 m   „   „   „   2700 Nm   „   „ $\dfrac{9}{1\cdot5} \times \dfrac{2700 \times 1\cdot8}{2025}$

$$= \underline{14\cdot4°}$$

Exercise 14

1. (*a*) A shaft 1·5 m long is twisted through an angle of 8 degrees when a torque of 2025 Nm is applied to it. Determine the angle through which a similar shaft 2 m long will be twisted by a torque of 2700 Nm.

(*b*) Calculate the average value of the shear stress in a solid gudgeon pin, 25 mm in diameter, when the shearing load on it is 37 800 N.

((*a*) 14·2°; (*b*) 38 500 kN/m²)   (E.M.E.U.)

2. A straight brake lever has a force of 360 N applied to its end at right angles to its length. At a point 350 mm from the point of application of the force the section of the lever is rectangular, 25 mm by 12·5 mm, with the larger dimension parallel to the direction of the load. Calculate the maximum stress in the material in this section.

(96 768 kN/m²)   (C. and G.)

3. Determine the maximum stress in a solid steel shaft 25 mm diameter, produced by a torque of 580 Nm.

(189 100 kN/m²)   (C. and G.)

4. A solid propeller shaft 28·5 mm diameter transmits 29·84 kW at 1000 rev/min. Calculate the maximum stress in the material under these conditions.   (62 700 kN/m²)   (C. and G.)

5. What factors set a limit to the torque or twisting effort that a driving-axle half-shaft can be called upon to transmit?

Determine the maximum stress in a solid steel shaft 25 mm diameter produced by a torque of 580 Nm.   (189 100 kN/m²)   (C. and G.)

- **6.** (a) A tubular frame member is subject to a bending moment of 580 Nm. The section is 75 mm diameter and the thickness of the material 3 mm. Calculate the stress in the material in kN/m².

(b) A similar tube is subject to a twisting moment of 580 Nm. Calculate the shear stress in the material in kN/m².

((a) 49 280 kN/m²; (b) 24 640 kN/m²)   (C. and G.)

7. A tubular shaft is subjected to a twisting moment of 600 Nm. The section is 75 mm outside diameter and the thickness of the material is 3 mm. Calculate the shear stress in the material in kN/m².

(25 490 kN/m²)

8. A torsion bar with an effective diameter of 22 mm is fitted with a lever arm of 300 mm. When the arm is horizontal the maximum static load at its end is 3600 N. Calculate the stress in the material of the bar.

(516 500 kN/m²)

9. A front axle is connected to the chassis frame by semi-elliptic springs. The front track is 1250 mm and the distance between the spring seats is 650 mm.

If the load on the axle is 5800 N, determine; (a) the maximum bending moment in the vertical plane containing the axle; (b) if the modulus of section is $0·1 \times 10^{-3}$ m³, determine the maximum value of the stress induced.   ((a) 0·87 kNm; (b) 8700 kN/m²)

10. A certain motor vehicle is to be fitted with a solid propeller shaft instead of the usual tubular shaft, which is 76 mm outside diameter and 69 mm inside diameter. The engine develops a torque of 350 Nm and the lowest gear ratio is 4 to 1. Calculate: (*a*) the stress in the tubular shaft; and (*b*) the diameter of the solid shaft required to transmit the same torque at the same stress.

((*a*) 50 630 kN/m²; (*b*) 52·02 mm)

15

Materials

This chapter deals with metals used in the construction of the motor vehicle.

Metals are divided into two groups:

> (1) **Ferrous** metals
> (2) **Non-ferrous** metals

Ferrous metals are all those metals containing iron and include cast iron, wrought iron, malleable iron, plain carbon steels, alloy steels (an **alloy** is a mixture of metals).

Non-ferrous metals are all metals not containing iron; they include copper and its alloys, aluminium and its alloys, bearing metals.

The ferrous metals are more widely used because they are usually stronger, cheaper than the non-ferrous metals and can be heat-treated.

Non-ferrous metals are used because they resist rusting and corrosion, are lighter in weight, are good conductors of heat, have a low coefficient of friction and low electrical resistance.

Mechanical Properties of Metals

(1) **Strength.** This is the resistance of metal to stress when under a steady load. The strength of a metal is determined by breaking a standard test-piece in a special tensile testing machine; the maximum load sustained by the test-piece before breaking is known as the Tensile strength.

The tensile strength of steel is about 400×10^3 kN/m^2 for mild steel to about 1500×10^3 kN/m^2 for certain types of heat-treated alloy steel, but these figures are reduced if the load fluctuates or is applied suddenly. In practice, failure under direct load is rare, and breakages that occur are usually caused by fatigue.

(2) **Ductility.** This is the property of a cold metal when formed or stretched into shape without its breaking or cracking. Ductility is important in sheet-metal work, such as headlamp bodies, which are

drawn out from a flat sheet of metal. A certain amount of ductility is, however, necessary in most other metal parts, otherwise they are liable to break under sudden applications of loads.

(3) **Malleability.** A metal is malleable when it is easily formed by compression.

Lead, for example, is a metal possessing high malleability, since it is easily hammered and **extruded** (forced to pass through a die at room temperature) into various shapes. Although malleability and ductility are applied properties, it is possible to find a combination of high malleability and low ductility in a metal, lead for example.

(4) **Hardness.** Hardness is the resistance of metal to wear and **indentation** (scratching or scoring). This property is important in parts subjected to rubbing and crushing loads, e.g. ball and roller bearings, cams, gears, etc.

(5) **Toughness.** Toughness is the resistance of a metal to fracture.

The quality of toughness can best be described as the opposite of brittleness. Toughness should not be confused with hardness, since it is possible to have a combination of hardness and negligible toughness, e.g. a file is both hard and brittle.

(6) **Fatigue Resistance.** When subjected to a continuous load the **tensile strength** of a metal, is the maximum load sustained before breaking. It is usually expressed as a stress of so many newtons per square metre. If the load is repeatedly applied or continuously reversed, then the ultimate strength of the metal is reduced.

A part of a vehicle which resists reversals or variations of load, and therefore stress, for long periods, without breaking has a high fatigue resistance. When a part fails after a number of load reversals the part fails through fatigue.

Factor of Safety

The **safe working stress** of a metal is the stress it withstands without any fear of breaking; it is usually a simple fraction of the tensile strength of the metal. Motor-vehicle parts should be made of such a size that the maximum stress in the material does not exceed a certain amount, called the safe working stress.

The ratio of the tensile strength to the safe working stress of the metal is known as the **factor of safety.** Thus

$$\text{Factor of safety} = \frac{\text{Tensile strength (stress)}}{\text{Safe working stress}}$$

Example. Calculate the diameter of a steel tie-rod which is required to transmit a pull of 50 kN if the tensile strength of the steel is $463 \cdot 2 \times 10^3$ kN/m² and the factor of safety is to be 6. (U.L.C.I.)

$$\text{Safe working stress} = \frac{\text{Tensile strength}}{\text{Factor of safety}}$$

$$= \frac{463\ 200}{6} = 77\ 200 \text{ kN/m}^2$$

$$\text{Area of rod} = \frac{\text{Load in kN}}{\text{Stress in kN/m}^2}$$

$$= \frac{50}{77\ 200}\left(\frac{\text{kN}}{\text{kN/m}^2}\right) = 0 \cdot 006\ 477 \text{ m}^2$$

$$\text{Diameter of rod} = \sqrt{\frac{0 \cdot 006\ 477 \times 4}{\pi}}$$

$$= \underline{28 \cdot 72 \text{ mm}}$$

Cast Iron and Steel

Both cast iron and steel are alloys of iron and carbon together with small quantities of other elements (manganese, silicon, sulphur, phosphorus) which improve the quality of the metal or are present as impurities. The main difference between cast iron and steel is the **carbon content**; up to 1·7 per cent carbon the alloy is known as steel, over 1·7 per cent carbon it is considered to be cast iron. There is, however, no exact dividing line between steel and cast iron; the 1·7 per cent carbon content is the conventional value. In addition to the carbon content there are two other differences between cast iron and steel:

(1) In cast iron some of the carbon is always free in the form of flakes of graphite. It is the graphite flakes which give cast iron its self-lubricating properties and are the main reason for its brittleness. In steel the carbon is always combined, i.e. steel never contains graphite.

(2) Owing to the method of manufacture, cast iron contains more impurities than steel, which has the effect of reducing the strength and ductility of cast iron as compared with steel.

Cast iron possesses the following properties: it is brittle, with little ductility; weak in tension but much stronger in compression; the compressive strength of cast iron is about four times its tensile strength.

Cast iron forms an excellent bearing surface when 'run-in', e.g. a cylinder bore. It is cheaper than steel and can be cast into intricate shapes, e.g. a cylinder block.

The carbon in cast iron may exist either as combined carbon or as free or graphitic carbon. Cast iron containing combined carbon is known as white iron, because it shows a silvery white fracture. Cast iron containing graphitic carbon is known as grey iron, because it shows a dark grey fracture.

White iron is hard and brittle and is difficult to work, but it is often used for parts subject to much wear.

Grey iron is weaker and softer than white iron, but it is more generally used owing to its excellent machining properties.

Malleable Iron

By a special heat treatment, iron castings can be given a certain amount of ductility; this specially treated iron is known as **malleable** iron.

To convert ordinary castings to malleable iron castings, the ordinary castings are heated for a period at a temperature sufficient to break up the flakes of graphite into small spheres or balls. The graphite flakes are the main cause of the brittleness in cast iron, thus an improvement in ductility results. Test bars of malleable cast iron can withstand bending up to 90 degrees without breaking.

Malleable iron castings are a cheap substitute for steel castings. They are used for parts of intricate form which prove uneconomical to machine from the solid, and where an ordinary casting has not enough ductility to allow for sudden or shock loading. Another reason for using malleable iron castings, often the only reason, is their excellent machinability. Rear-axle casings are often made of malleable iron.

Alloy Cast Irons

To improve the tensile strength and certain other properties of cast iron, additional elements are alloyed with the iron and carbon. The principal element used is nickel, up to 3 per cent; other elements used with or without nickel are chromium, molybdenum, copper and manganese. The main purpose of adding these elements is to reduce the size of the graphite flakes in the cast iron and thus increase the tensile strength.

Engine crankshafts and camshafts are sometimes cast in alloy iron. The cast part is cheaper to produce than the equivalent forged steel part, and it also has the advantage of improved fatigue resistance. A typical alloy cast iron has the following composition: carbon 1·25–1·4 per cent; silicon 1·9–2·1 per cent; manganese 0·5–0·6 per cent; chromium 0·35–0·4 per cent; and copper 2·5–2·75 per cent.

Plain Carbon Steels

The term 'plain carbon' is used to distinguish between steels without special alloying elements and those steels containing these elements.

The properties of a plain carbon steel are determined, almost entirely, by the percentage of carbon it contains. As the carbon content increases so does the strength and hardness, but at the expense of ductility and malleability.

Carbon steels are usually divided into three groups:

(1) **Mild steel.** Carbon content up to about 0·3 per cent. Mild steels are soft and ductile; they cannot be hardened by heating and quenching, but they can be case hardened. Mild steel is used extensively for body panels, where the high amount of ductility permits easy forming without danger of cracking. In general, mild steel is used for all parts not requiring great strength or resistance to wear and not subjected to high temperature or corrosion.

(2) **Medium carbon steel.** Carbon content about 0·3–0·75 per cent. In this range the steels can be hardened appreciably by quenching; the amount of hardness obtained increases as the carbon content increases. The increased strength of medium carbon steels enables them to be used for a number of moving parts, such as connecting rods, gears, transmission shafts, etc. For most applications in the modern motor vehicle, however, medium carbon steel has been replaced by alloy steels.

(3) **High carbon steels.** Over 0·75 per cent carbon. Plain high carbon steels are seldom used in the modern motor vehicle; they have been superseded by the various alloy steels. High carbon steel, however, can be hardened to give an excellent cutting edge, and is used for reamers, scrapers, etc.

Nickel improves strength, ductility and case-hardening properties.

Chromium gives increased hardness and strength.

Nickel and chromium. Nickel–chrome steels are widely used; the penetration of hardening is greatly improved. Some of these steels can be hardened simply by cooling in air. The steel is also corrosion and heat resisting when high percentages of nickel and chromium are added (12–20 per cent nickel and up to 20 per cent chromium).

Vanadium, which is used with other elements, improves the strength and elastic limit of the steel and gives extra resistance to fatigue loading. **Chrome–vanadium** steel is used for axle half-shafts, connecting rods, valve springs and torsion bars.

Molybdenum. This material improves the penetration of the hardening and the strength at high temperatures.

Silicon is a relatively cheap alloying element; it is used as a deoxidizing agent. Silicon also has the effect of slightly improving the hardness penetration.

Silicon–manganese steel, about 2 per cent silicon and 0·8 per cent manganese, is often used for both road and valve springs. The use of silicon–manganese steel enables the spring to be fully hardened across the entire section; if an inferior steel is used the centre of the spring is left soft, and it is liable to take a permanent set.

Tungsten is added to give improved properties at high temperatures, greater strength and hardness. For example, valve steels usually contain tungsten in order to resist **scaling** at high temperatures.

Alloy steels are usually employed in the heat-treated condition, i.e. hardened and tempered, because this condition gives the best combination of strength, ductility and fatigue resistance.

Alloy steels can be classified into three groups:

(1) Low carbon alloy steels which contain about 0·10–0·25 per cent carbon. These are chiefly used for case-hardened parts.
(2) Medium carbon alloy steels which contain about 0·25–0·50 per cent carbon. These are either oil or air hardened, according to their composition, and they are mainly used in the hardened and tempered condition.
(3) High carbon alloy steels which contain about 0·50–0·75 per cent carbon. Steels in this group are used for springs, torsion bars and wear-resisting parts; they are always hardened and tempered.

In addition to the ordinary alloy steel, there are special corrosion-resisting (**stainless** steels) and heat-resisting steels. These special steels are often used for exhaust valves which operate at high temperatures and are subjected to the corrosive action of the burning gases.

Copper and its Alloys

Copper is a comparatively soft and ductile material; in the annealed state its tensile strength is about half that of mild steel. This metal can, however, be cold work hardened, by rolling or drawing, and, when fully cold worked, its tensile strength and hardness are about equal to mild steel.

Copper is a good conductor of electricity and is used extensively for electrical equipment. It is also a good conductor of heat and is used for radiators and oil coolers. Owing to its good formability and resistance to corrosion, copper is used for oil and petrol pipes.

The most important copper alloys are the **brasses**. Brass is obtained by alloying copper with zinc, the percentage of zinc ranging from 5 to 40. The addition of zinc increases the tensile strength; the ductility increases when up to 30 per cent zinc is added, but further additions of zinc result in reduced ductility. The principal straight brasses, containing copper and zinc only, are:

Cartridge brass contains about 70 per cent copper. This alloy has the highest ductility of the range of brasses; it combines high ductility with strength and is used for parts made from sheet or strip. This alloy makes easier such difficult operations as forming headlamp bodies, radiator shells, cores, etc.

Basic brass and 65/35 brass have 61–65 per cent copper and the rest zinc. This alloy is not so ductile as cartridge brass; it is used as a cheaper substitute for parts formed cold from sheet and strip.

All brasses can be strengthened and hardened by cold working. When fully work hardened the tensile strength and hardness of brass are greater than copper, e.g. the strength of cartridge brass can be increased from 300×10^3 to $700 \times 10^3 \text{ kN/m}^2$ by cold rolling or drawing.

Compared with sheet steel, the higher content brasses, used for sheet-metal working, can be formed in press-tool operations at two to three times the speed of the softest steel. This fact enables the total cost of the job to be reduced, even though sheet brass is a more expensive material than sheet steel.

An additional advantage of brass is that it forms the most satisfactory base for nickel or chromium plating. Steel requires undercoats of copper and nickel before chromium plating, and there is always a risk of the chromium flaking off.

To obtain improved mechanical properties, aluminium, iron, manganese, tin, nickel and silicon in proportions up to a total of 7 per cent are alloyed with 60 per cent copper and the remainder zinc to give high-tensile brasses.

Another important group of copper alloys is the **bronzes**. Phosphor-bronze is an alloy of copper and tin with the addition of up to 1 per cent phosphorus. In the cast form, phosphor-bronze is used for worm wheels, bearing bushes and other parts where a low coefficient of friction is required, together with the ability to withstand heavy loading.

Aluminium bronze contains 1–14 per cent of aluminium with the remainder copper. The aluminium bronzes can be divided into two groups:

(1) The wrought alloys containing up to 7 per cent aluminium.
(2) The cast alloys containing 8–14 per cent aluminium. The cast alloys can be heat-treated in a similar manner to the higher carbon steels by quenching, which gives increased hardness and tensile strength. When heat-treated, the hardness, tensile strength and ductility of these alloys are comparable with heat-treated medium carbon steel; they have good corrosion resistance, heat resistance and resistance to wear. Typical motor-vehicle applications are selector forks (gear box), valve guides and inserts.

Aluminium and its Alloys

Pure aluminium is mechanically weak and cannot be used for any load-carrying or moving part of the motor vehicle. Another disadvantage, which restricts its use, is the poor machining properties of pure aluminium, since the tendency to tear results in a poor surface finish. To improve the strength and machinability other elements are added; the resulting aluminium alloys retain the desirable properties of the pure metal.

These properties are:

(a) Lightness, about one-third the mass of cast iron or steel.
(b) Good conductivity of heat and electricity; it is second in order to copper among the base metals.
(c) Good corrosion resistance, owing to the formation of a protective film of oxide. This natural process can be assisted by an electrical process known as **anodizing**, which gives a thicker and more adherent film resulting in improved resistance to corrosion.

The number of aluminium alloys in use is many, and it is beyond the scope of this book to go into details of composition, etc. The principal groups are:

(1) **Aluminium copper**, up to 12 per cent copper.
(2) **Aluminium silicon**, up to 15 per cent silicon.

(3) **Aluminium zinc, copper**, 10–14 per cent zinc and 2–3 per cent copper.

(4) **Aluminium magnesium**, up to 10 per cent magnesium.

(5) The complex alloys: an example is the well-known alloy **duralumin**, whose composition is copper about 3·5–4·5 per cent, manganese 0·4–0·7 per cent, magnesium 0·4–0·7 per cent, silicon about 0·4 per cent, iron up to 0·5 per cent.

Applications of aluminium alloys in the motor vehicle can be divided into three groups:

(1) Sheet for wings, body panels, etc.

(2) Ordinary constructional uses such as gear-box cases.

(3) Parts subjected to high temperatures, e.g. pistons and cylinder heads.

The use of aluminium-alloy pistons and cylinder heads are typical examples of the third group. Here the high heat conductivity of the material gives rapid heat transfer, with a consequent reduction in temperature.

The lightness of aluminium alloys is an advantage for pistons and connecting rods as the reduced mass lightens the bearing loads and gives higher engine speeds.

Bearing Metals

The bearing metals generally used in the motor vehicle, arranged in order of increasing hardness, are:

(1) **Lead-**base **white** metals, which contain mainly lead with small proportions of tin, antimony and copper.

(2) **Tin-**base **white** metals, which contain tin up to 90 per cent, and the remainder copper, antimony and sometimes lead.

(3) **Copper–lead** alloys, which contain 10–30 per cent lead and the remainder copper.

(4) **Lead–bronze** alloys, which contain 4–22 per cent lead, 5–11 per cent tin and the remainder copper.

(5) **Phosphor-bronze**, which we have mentioned earlier in this chapter.

Testing of Metals

The mechanical testing of metals to be used in the manufacture of motor-vehicle components is essential for the efficient operation of these components.

There are three main tests in general use:

(1) **Tensile test.**
(2) **Hardness test.**
(3) **Impact test.**

Other tests sometimes used include fatigue, bend, torsion, creep and crack detection.

Tensile Test (Destruction Test)

A test piece of mild steel machined and gauge marked as shown in Fig. 15.1 is placed in a tensile testing machine, Fig. 15.2. The test

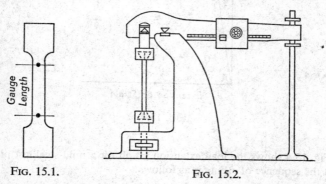

FIG. 15.1.   FIG. 15.2.

piece is then subjected to a steadily increasing tensile load. If the increase in length caused by the load is measured it will be found that up to a certain load the extension of the test piece is directly proportional to the load, Fig. 15.3. Thus, if the load is doubled the extension will also be doubled.

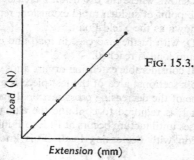

FIG. 15.3.

Continuing the test, a load value is soon reached at which a very rapid extension of the test piece suddenly takes place. When further load is applied the extension of the test piece continues to increase until it cannot support any further load. At this point considerable extension of the test piece occurs, it will 'waist' and finally fracture.

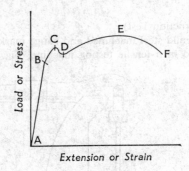

Fig. 15.4.

Fig. 15.4 shows the load/extension graph for a mild-steel test piece, and the sequence of events is as follows:

(1) The straight line from A to B represents that part of the test where extension remains proportional to the load. This is known as the Elastic Line, and the point B denotes the Elastic Limit of the steel.

(2) B to C shows where the extension increases more rapidly.

(3) C is the point of sudden rapid extension, represented by C to D. C is known as the Yield Point.

(4) After D, with further increase in load and extension, point E of maximum load is reached.

(5) From E considerable extension occurs and 'waisting' takes place; the cross-sectional area of the test piece is greatly reduced.

(6) Because of the decreasing cross-sectional area, a lesser load than that at E is required to continue the elongation; thus the load decreases until facture occurs at F. E to F indicates the continued extension with decreasing load. F is known as the **Breaking Point**.

Test Requirements

The following values are usually obtained so as to satisfy test requirements.

(1) Tensile strength $= \dfrac{\text{Maximum load}}{\text{Original cross-sectional area}}$

(2) Elastic limit stress $= \dfrac{\text{Load at yield point}}{\text{Original cross-sectional area}}$

(3) Yield-point stress $= \dfrac{\text{Load at yield point}}{\text{Original cross-sectional area}}$

(4) Percentage elongation $= \dfrac{\text{Increase in length} \times 100}{\text{Original length}}$

(5) Percentage reduction in area $= \dfrac{\text{Reduction in area} \times 100}{\text{Original area}}$

$\quad$ or $\dfrac{\text{Original area} - \text{Fracture area} \times 100}{\text{Original area}}$

The following examples show the method of calculation.

Example. The following figures were obtained during a tensile test of mild steel:

Original diameter	12·5 mm
Gauge length	200 mm
Final length	257 mm
Diameter at fracture	7·85 mm
Load at yield point	34 575 N
Maximum load	49 023 N

Determine (*a*) tensile strength; (*b*) stress at yield point; (*c*) percentage reduction in area; (*d*) percentage elongation.

Original cross-sectional area $= \dfrac{\pi}{4} \times 0\cdot0125^2$

$$= 0\cdot000\ 122\ 8 \text{ m}^2$$

Area at fracture $= \dfrac{\pi}{4} \times 0\cdot007\ 85^2$

$$= 0\cdot000\ 048\ 41 \text{ m}^2$$

(*a*) $\quad$ Tensile strength $= \dfrac{49\cdot023}{0\cdot000\ 122\ 8} = \underline{380\ 600 \text{ kN/m}^2}$

(b)   Stress at yield point $= \dfrac{34 \cdot 575}{0 \cdot 000\ 122\ 8} = \underline{268\ 300\ kN/m^2}$

(c)   Percentage reduction in area

$$= \dfrac{(0 \cdot 000\ 122\ 8 - 0 \cdot 000\ 048\ 41) \times 100}{0 \cdot 000\ 122\ 8}$$

$$= \underline{60 \cdot 57\ per\ cent}$$

(d)   Percentage elongation $= \dfrac{(257 - 200) \times 100}{200}$

$$= \underline{28 \cdot 5\ per\ cent}$$

Example. The following figures were obtained during a tensile test on a certain nickel steel (heat-treated).

Original diameter	14 mm
Gauge length	50 mm
Load at elastic limit	109·6 kN
Maximum load	139·5 kN
Total elongation	9·5 mm
Diameter at fracture	9·5 mm

Determine (a) tensile strength; (b) elastic limit stress; (c) percentage elongation; (d) percentage reduction in area.

(a)   Tensile strength $= \dfrac{139 \cdot 5}{0 \cdot 000\ 153\ 9} = \underline{906\ 500\ kN/m^2}$

(b)   Elastic limit stress $= \dfrac{109 \cdot 6}{15 \cdot 39 \times 10^{-5}} = \underline{712\ 400\ kN/m^2}$

(c)   Percentage elongation $= \dfrac{9 \cdot 5 \times 100}{50}$

$$= \underline{19\ per\ cent}$$

(d) Percentage reduction in area $= \dfrac{(15 \cdot 39 \times 10^{-5}) - (70 \cdot 87 \times 10^{-6})}{15 \cdot 39 \times 10^{-5}}$

$$= \underline{53 \cdot 96\ per\ cent}$$

Students should compare the results of the two tests, mild steel and nickel steel, and draw their own conclusions.

Hardness Testing

Hardness tests relate to the resistance offered by a metal to indentation by a hardened steel ball or diamond **indentor** under a known load. Hardness tests are necessary in order to determine the following:

(a) The resistance that a metal offers to indentation.
(b) The quality of any tempering carried out on the metal.
(c) The effect of different methods of heat treatment on the metal.
(d) To test finished articles.
(e) The effect of different processes of manufacture on the metal.

Brinell Hardness Tests

Fig. 15.5 shows one type of Brinell hardness machine.

The Brinell hardness test is carried out by pressing a hardened steel ball of standard diameter into the metal under a specified load. The

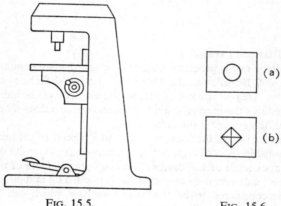

(a)

(b)

FIG. 15.5.   FIG. 15.6.

Brinell hardness number (B.H.N.) is obtained by dividing the applied load in kilogrammes by the spherical area of the indentation in square millimetres. The diameter of the indentation, Fig. 15.6 (a), is obtained by means of a special microscope and micrometer scale.

The formula used to obtain the Brinell hardness number is as follows, or reference tables may be used.

$$\text{B.H.N.} = \frac{F}{\frac{\pi}{2}D\left\{D - \sqrt{(D^2 - d^2)}\right\}}$$

where F = applied load, in kg
$\quad\quad D$ = diameter of ball, in mm
$\quad\quad d$ = diameter of indentation, in mm

Example. When testing the hardness of an induction-hardened steel specimen on a Brinell machine it was found that a 10-mm diameter ball when subjected to a load of 3000 kg made an impression measuring 2·93 mm across its diameter. Determine the Brinell hardness number. Assume the formula:

$$\text{B.H.N.} = \frac{F}{\frac{\pi}{2}D\left\{D - \sqrt{(D^2 - d^2)}\right\}}$$

$$\therefore \text{B.H.N.} = \frac{6000}{3\cdot142 \times 10\left\{10 - \sqrt{(10^2 - 2\cdot93^2)}\right\}}$$

$$= \frac{6000}{13\cdot79}$$

$$= \underline{435}$$

Vickers Diamond Pyramid Test

The Brinell test is generally used only for hardness test numbers up to about 600 Brinell, because above this number deformation of the ball results. This deformation increases the diameter of the indentation and so reduces the hardness number below its true value. The harder the metal, the greater is the deformation.

For harder metals the Vickers Diamond Pyramid test is used. The Vickers machine uses as an indentor a square-base pyramidal diamond with an apex angle of 136 degrees between opposite faces of the pyramid. The loads generally employed lie between 5 kg and 30 kg, while 100 kg is considered to be the maximum load which can be used without damage to the diamond indentor.

Fig. 15.6 (*b*) shows the shape of the Vickers indentation on a normal flat surface. A special microscope is used to measure the diagonals of the indentation, and a mean measurement is recorded. The Vickers Pyramid hardness number (V.P.N.) is calculated by dividing the applied load in kilogrammes by the pyramidal area in square millimetres, or by use of reference tables.

$$\text{V.P.N.} = \frac{2F\sin\left(\frac{\theta}{2}\right)}{d^2} = 1\cdot85\frac{F}{d^2}$$

where $F =$ applied load, in kg

$d =$ mean diagonal, in mm

$\theta =$ apex angle of pyramid (136°)

Example. The following data were recorded during a hardness test on a nickel–chrome steel using a Vickers machine.

Load	30 kg
Length of mean diagonal	0·445 mm

Determine the Vickers Pyramid hardness number.

$$V.P.N. = \frac{1·85F}{d}$$

$$= \frac{1·85 \times 30}{(0·455)^2}$$

$$= \underline{268}$$

Izod Impact Tests

This test detects differences in a metal caused by mechanical and heat treatment not indicated by other tests. For example, brittleness and the tendency of a metal to crack in service is often not discovered by the tensile and other tests, whereas the impact test does indicate these defects.

Fig. 15.7 shows an Izod impact testing machine.

The **notched** test piece, either 10 mm square section (Fig. 15.8) or 10

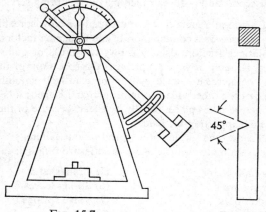

FIG. 15.7.   FIG. 15.8.

mm in diameter, is held in the machine vice with the bottom of the notch in line with the top of the vice jaws. The pendulum is raised to a specified height and, when released, it strikes the test piece on the same side as the notch and thus uses part of its energy to break the test piece. Because of its residual energy the pendulum continues its swing to actuate a pointer which indicates the actual energy in joules required to break the test piece.

Fatigue Failures in Metals

The term **fatigue failure** is given to the fracture of a metal subjected to repeated stresses, and which fails at a stress below that of its ultimate tensile stress. In general, the greatest number of fatigue failures are caused by reversed or alternating torsional and bending stresses.

The factors affecting fatigue failures are:

(1) Incorrect heat treatment, which may change the grain structure of the metal.
(2) Quenching cracks caused by too rapid or severe a quench.
(3) Decarburization and oxidation because of careless heat treatment.
(4) Sharp corners and sudden changes of section because of poor design.
(5) Machining or filing marks and other surface scratches or indentations which may occur because of careless manufacturing methods and handling.
(6) Wear scores and grooves which may arise during service.

Fatigue failure in a metal is often caused by a slow spreading crack caused by any one or a combination of the foregoing factors. Inspection of a fatigue fracture usually shows two areas of quite different appearance. One area, which represents the spreading of the fatigue crack, may be crescent shaped with a comparatively smooth surface. The surface of the other area is often rough and jagged; it is here that the final fracture takes place, usually by shear, because of the reduced area of metal supporting the load.

Fig. 15.9 shows the surface of a typical fatigue failure.

The parts of a motor vehicle likely to suffer from fatigue failure are:

(1) Axle half-shafts
(2) Steering arms
(3) Torsion bars
(4) Stub axles
(5) Crankshafts
(6) Spring leaves
(7) Valve springs
(8) Piston rings

To determine if fatigue has been a factor in the failure of a part, an area of the metal perpendicular to the fracture is prepared and then tested to see if local hardening has taken place.

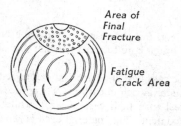

Area of
Final
Fracture

Fatigue
Crack Area

FIG. 15.9.

Heat Treatment

Most of the ferrous metals can be hardened by heating to a red heat and cooling rapidly, usually by quenching in water or oil. The limitations to this process are:

(1) The carbon content must be about 0·4 per cent or more to get appreciable hardness.
(2) The shape and size of the part must enable it to be quenched without danger of cracking.

It is this last factor which prevents large parts from being hardened in this way. Small simple castings can be hardened by quenching, but most castings cannot, because of the liability to crack when quenched.

The hardening process increases both strength and hardness, but at the expense of ductility, and it is well known that a fully hardened part is extremely brittle. In practice, parts are usually tempered after quenching to improve the toughness, and the tempering is adjusted to give the desired combination of strength, hardness and ductility.

The process of **tempering**:

The part is first fully hardened by heating to a cherry red and then quenching. The part is next heated to the required tempering temperature and again quenched. In practice, the colour of the heated part is often used as an indication of the tempering temperature, e.g. a centre-punch point could be brown when quenched. Where the temper has to be more exact, special instruments are used to indicate the required tempering temperatures.

Tempering temperatures go up to about 300°C; the higher the tempering temperature, the lower the final hardness but the greater the toughness.

Case Hardening

Certain parts, e.g. the gudgeon pin, require a hard surface to resist wear and also a tough core to resist shocks; this object is obtained by **case hardening**.

The parts to be case hardened are first **carburized** by heating them in contact with a material rich in carbon. This process converts the outer layers of the steel to a high carbon steel, while the core retains its original carbon content. The material used is generally mild steel or a low carbon alloy steel, to give the required ductility in the core. After carburizing, the parts are hardened in the usual way by heating and quenching.

Low carbon alloy steel with a nickel content from 3 to 5 per cent is favoured for case hardening, as it gives a tougher core and a gradual transition from case (layer) to core, which reduces the risk of the hardened case peeling off when the part is in service.

Normalizing and Annealing

These processes are similar, as the effect on the metal is much the same, that is to soften it.

Normalizing is carried out by heating the metal to a cherry red, same temperature as for hardening, and then cooling in still air. Normalizing relieves internal stresses set up by cold working, machining, welding, etc., and it tends to soften the steel.

Annealing of steel is carried out by heating the metal to a cherry red and then cooling it slowly in sand, lime or with the furnace. Most non-ferrous metals are annealed by heating and cooling, the rate of cooling, however, does not affect the result, e.g. copper can be annealed by heating to red and then quenching in water.

The effect of annealing is to soften the metal; it also relieves internal stresses.

Nitriding

Nitriding is a surface hardening process, like case hardening, but it can only be applied to certain steels and cast irons. Nitriding differs from ordinary case hardening:

(1) A special alloy steel or cast iron known as **Nitralloy** is necessary.
(2) The hard **case** or layer is thinner than the layer obtained by case hardening, but it is harder.
(3) The part to be nitrided is heated to a temperature of about 500°C in an atmosphere of ammonia gas for a period of up to 10 hours. The surface of the metal absorbs nitrogen, which is the main hardening agent. After heating, the nitrided parts are free from scale and the slight greying of the surface is easily removed by polishing.

Nitriding is applied to cast-iron cylinder liners, stems of alloy steel valves, crankshafts, pump shafts, etc. Besides a high resistance to wear, nitriding gives increased resistance to corrosion and increased fatigue strength.

Solders and Soldering

Soft solder consists of tin and lead in various proportions. Solder has one surprising property: its melting point is about 220°C, which is below the melting point of its constituents, lead (320°C), tin (232°C).

Soft solder is made to about the following proportions:

Tinman's solder, 50 per cent tin and 50 per cent lead.
Tinman's fine solder, 66 per cent tin and 34 per cent lead.

The melting point of a solder is reduced as the percentage of tin is increased, up to a limit of about 67 per cent.

Soldering is the method of joining two pieces of clean metal together by means of heat and molten solder. It is essential that the solder penetrates the surfaces of the metal. When cool, the thin film of solder between the surfaces of the metal forms a firm joint.

Fluxes. A flux is used to exclude air, thus preventing and removing, if present, oxidation. Oxidation is the formation of a 'skin' or film on the heated surfaces of the metal. This film prevents the solder coming into proper contact with the metal, thus obstructing the penetration of the surfaces by the solder and giving a faulty joint.

The two fluxes generally used for motor-vehicle work are:

(*a*) **Zinc-chloride** (killed spirits), which is made by adding zinc to hydrochloric acid. This flux is usually bought ready-made; there are several brands of soldering 'fluid'. Fluid flux is usually corrosive, and it must be washed off the completed work in order to avoid rusting.

(*b*) **Resinous paste**, which is made by mixing resin, vaseline and turpentine. This flux can be used for all metals, and it is particularly useful for electrical connections. A fluid flux should never be used for electrical work, since it may corrode and thus cause the joint to fail.

Brazing

The term **brazing** is applied to the following processes: **silver** and **hard** 'soldering', **true** brazing, **bronze welding**.

The main differences between the processes are the materials used and the temperature range over which they are carried out.

An alloy of silver, copper, zinc and cadmium, with a melting range of 615–850°C, is used for silver and hard soldering.

An alloy of copper and zinc, known as spelter, with a melting range of 850–950°C is used for true brazing.

A brass alloy of about 60 per cent copper and 40 per cent zinc, with the addition of silicon, nickel, manganese and tin in small amounts, with a melting point of about 900°C, is used for bronze welding.

For silver soldering and true brazing the rod or spelter is melted by the heat of the job, whereas in bronze welding the rod is melted mainly by the blowpipe, while the job remains at a dull, red heat.

Welding

Welding is the operation of melting the edges of metal parts to be joined so that the edges will fuse together. Welding employs the direct application of a concentrated **oxy-acetylene** flame (3000°C) or **electric arc** (3500°C).

The equipment used is well known and requires no description.

Most metals and alloys can be welded: a suitable filler rod is necessary and a suitable flux is generally used for most metals. A notable exception is mild steel.

Welding has a wide application; it is used for body manufacture, the repair of cylinder blocks and castings and for the fusing of special alloys on to worn surfaces, e.g. shackle pins, cams, axle casings, etc.

Also the repair of zinc-base alloys, e.g. door handles, carburettor and petrol-pump bodies.

Welding Symbols (B.S. 499, Part 2: 1965)

Fig. 15.10 shows the symbols applicable to the types of welded joint used in motor-vehicle manufacture and the repair trade.

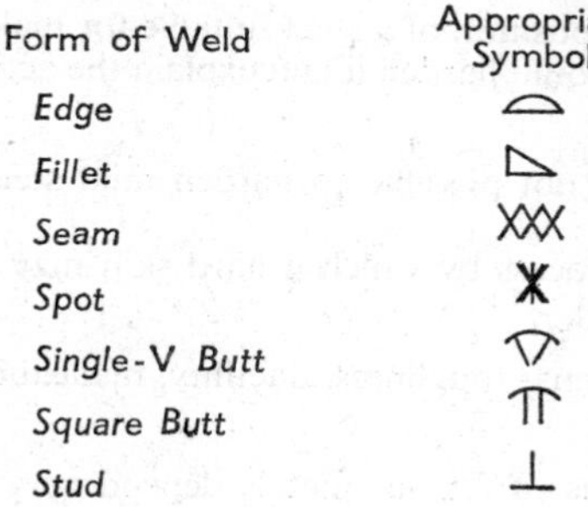

Form of Weld	Appropriate Symbol
Edge	⌒
Fillet	◁
Seam	XXX
Spot	X
Single-V Butt	▽
Square Butt	⊤⊤
Stud	⊥

Fig. 15.10.

Exercise 15

1. Describe either (*a*) the process of case hardening, or (*b*) the hardening and tempering of a piece of plain carbon steel. (E.M.E.U.)

2. What are the essential differences between soldering, brazing and welding? Give examples of the use of each process in motor-vehicle practice. (C. and G.)

3. What is meant by (*a*) case hardening, (*b*) tempering, (*c*) forging and (*d*) annealing? Describe briefly how each process is carried out and give examples of their application. (C. and G.)

4. What is meant by the normalizing of steel?

5. What are the principal reasons for using expensive alloy steels in motor vehicles? Give an example of the use of one of these alloys. (C. and G.)

6. What is meant by nitriding?

7. What are the differences between plain carbon and alloy steels?

8. Engine pistons are made of (*a*) aluminium or (*b*) cast iron. Explain how the choice of the respective metals is influenced by the type of engine to which the pistons are fitted. (E.M.E.U.)

9. A list of automobile parts is given below. Describe a material for each, giving reasons why this material is chosen for the particular duty involved: (*a*) connecting rod; (*b*) cylinder liner; (*c*) exhaust valve; (*d*) front axle; (*e*) chassis frame; (*f*) main bearings for crankshaft.

(C. and G.)

10. Give the composition of a steel suitable for making a cold chisel, describe how you would harden it and explain the action of the process you adopt.

11. (*a*) Why is it not possible to harden mild steel by heating and quenching?

(*b*) Describe a process by which a hard skin may be placed on the surface of mild steel.

12. Define the terms: toughness, ductility, malleability, as applied to metals. (C. and G.)

13. The properties of ferrous metals depend very largely upon the proportion of carbon present in the metal. What are the chief properties associated with 0·1 per cent, 0·8 per cent and 3·5 per cent carbon? Where would you expect each type to be used? (C. and G.)

14. Heat treatment plays a very important part in the production of motor vehicles. What is the object of such treatment and how is it carried out? Why is it important that the repair man should have a knowledge of the general principles of heat treatment? (C. and G.)

15. What are the essential differences between mild steel, high carbon steel and cast iron? What special properties are possessed by each? Give examples of the use of each in motor-vehicle practice.

(C. and G.)

16. Explain what is meant by the 'factor of safety'. The compressive load on a hollow cast-iron column is 398·5 kN and the column is 150 mm external diameter. If the compressive strength for cast iron is 618×10^3 kN/m², calculate the metal thickness required, using a factor of safety of 5. (7·2 mm) (I.M.I.)

17. The following results were obtained during a tensile destruction test on a nickel–chrome valve steel specimen:

Original dia. of specimen	12·5 mm
Original length between gauge marks	50 mm
Load at elastic limit	119·6 kN
Ultimate load	149·5 kN
Total elongation	10 mm
Diameter at fracture	8·9 mm

Determine (*a*) elastic limit stress, (*b*) tensile strength, (*c*) percentage elongation, (*d*) percentage reduction of area.

((*a*) 974 700 kN/m²; (*b*) 1 218 000 kN/m²; (*c*) 20 per cent, (*d*) 49·34 per cent)

18. In a Brinell hardness test on a steel specimen the following data were recorded: load 3000 kg; diameter of ball 10 mm; diameter of indentation 4·2 mm.

Calculate the Brinell hardness number for the specimen. (211)

19. (*a*) How does the carbon percentage affect the mechanical properties and subsequent heat-treatment of low, medium and high carbon steels?

(*b*) Give one use of each type of steel. (U.L.C.I.)

20. (*a*) What is the main difference between a brass and a bronze? Give typical percentages of the constituents of each.

(*b*) State a use of each, giving reasons for your choice. (U.L.C.I.)

21. (*a*) Name three different plastics used in engineering.

(*b*) State one engineering use of each, giving a reason in each case. (U.L.C.I.)

22. (*a*) What is meant by 'fatigue of metals'?

(*b*) State four different components of a motor vehicle which are likely to suffer fatigue failure.

(*c*) Describe how a particular component which has failed in service could be examined and tested to determine if fatigue contributed to the failure. (C. and G.)

16　Electricity

Further Practical Units

The **coulomb** (C) is the practical unit of the **quantity** of electricity, symbol Q, and is that quantity passing when a current of 1 ampere flows for 1 second. This unit is used for capacitor calculations, see p. 323. For many purposes a larger unit, the **ampere-hour**, is more convenient; it is used for battery calculations, see Part 1.

$$1 \text{ ampere-hour} = 3600 \text{ C}$$

The **microhm** is a millionth of an ohm; it is used when calculating the resistance of a conductor, e.g. a starter cable. The resistance of any conductor is directly proportional to its length, i.e. the resistance increases as the length of the conductor increases, and vice versa. It is inversely proportional to the cross-sectional area of the conductor, i.e. the larger the area, the less the resistance, and vice versa. The resistance is also directly proportional to the **resistivity** of the material used for the conductor. For example, copper has a lower resistivity than iron, therefore it is a better conductor. Resistivity can be defined as the resistance between the two opposite sides of a cube, maintained at $0°C$, having sides each 10 mm long.

Temperature and Resistance

Most conductors of electricity change their resistance with a change of temperature and the change in resistivity of a material (per $1°C$ change in temperature) is known as the **temperature coefficient** of the material. The operating temperature of motor-vehicle electrical equipment varies considerably; at times the temperature of the windings may reach $80°C$. Therefore, the prevailing temperature must be considered when calculating the resistance of cables, windings, etc.

The resistance of all pure metals, such as silver and copper, increases with increase of temperature, but the resistance of carbon and insulators decreases with increase of temperature. Certain alloys, e.g. Eureka and Manganin, are almost unaffected by changes in temperature. These alloys are used for electrical measuring instruments so that the accuracy of the instrument is not affected by temperature changes. The following list gives the resistivities and temperature coefficients of a number of materials:

Material	Resistivity (ρ) at 0 °C ($\mu\Omega$ mm)	Temperature coefficient (α) 0–100°C
Silver	15·4	0·004
Copper	15·9	0·004 28
Aluminium	30	0·004 23
Brass	75	0·0015
Iron	88·5	0·006 25
Nickel	122	0·006 22

The resistance of a conductor at 0°C can be calculated from the formula:

$$R = \rho \times \frac{l}{A}$$

where R = resistance, in ohms

ρ = resistivity, in $\mu\Omega$ mm

l = length, in mm

A = cross-sectional area, in mm²

The change in resistance due to a change in temperature of a material may be calculated from the formula:

$$R_2 = R_1 + R_1\alpha t$$
$$= R_1(1 + t\alpha)$$

where R_1 = initial resistance, in ohms

R_2 = final resistance, in ohms

α = temperature coefficient

t = temperature change (°C)

Example. The stop-lamp cable of a lorry is 7620 mm long and its nominal cross-sectional area is 0·97 mm².

Calculate: (a) the resistance of the cable at 0°C; (b) the resistance of the cable at 25°C.

(a) Let R_1 = resistance of cable at 0°C

$$R_1 = \rho \times \frac{l}{A}$$

$$= \frac{15 \cdot 9 \times 7620}{1\,000\,000 \times 0 \cdot 97} \text{ ohms}$$

$$= \underline{0 \cdot 125 \text{ ohms}}$$

(b) Let R_2 = resistance of cable at 25°C

$$R_2 = R_1(1 + \alpha t)$$

$$= 0 \cdot 125(1 + 0 \cdot 004\,28 \times 25)$$

$$= \underline{0 \cdot 138 \text{ ohms}}$$

In the foregoing example (b), if a 12-V 18-W bulb is used in the stop light, calculate the voltage drop due to cable resistance.

From Part 1,   Watts $= I \times E$ and $E = I \times R$

$$\therefore I = \frac{\text{Watts}}{E} = \frac{18}{12} = 1 \cdot 5 \text{ A}$$

Also $E = 1 \cdot 5 \times 0 \cdot 138$

$$= \underline{0 \cdot 2 \text{ voltage drop}}$$

Example. A copper field coil of a vehicle dynamo has a resistance of 10 ohms when cold at 16°C and of 12·5 ohms when hot after a long run. If the temperature coefficient of copper is 0·004 28 per degree C, calculate the hot temperature of the coil from the equation:

$$R_2 = R_1[1 + \alpha(t_2 - t_1)]$$

Now t_2 = final temperature after run, °C

t_1 = initial temperature when cold, °C

Using the symbols in the same way as for the last example, then

$$R_2 = R_1[1 + \alpha(t_2 - t_1)]$$
$$= R_1 + \alpha R_1(t_2 - t_1)$$
$$R_2 - R_1 = \alpha R_1(t_2 - t_1)$$
$$t_2 - t_1 = \frac{R_2 - R_1}{\alpha R_1}$$
$$t_2 = \left(\frac{R_2 - R_1}{\alpha R_1}\right) + t_1$$
$$= \left(\frac{12 \cdot 5 - 10}{0 \cdot 004\ 28 \times 10}\right) + 16$$
$$= \left(\frac{2 \cdot 5}{0 \cdot 0428}\right) + 16$$
$$= 58 + 16$$
$$= \underline{74°C}$$

The Ignition System

The purpose of the ignition system of a motor vehicle is to produce a spark between the points of the sparking plug. The voltage required to produce this spark is between 4000 and 15 000 V.

The ignition coil uses the principle of mutual induction described in Part 1.

Fig. 16.1 shows a diagram of an ignition coil and earth return circuit. The primary winding of the coil has a few hundred turns of comparatively thick wire and it is in circuit with the battery through the **contact breaker** which acts as an automatic mechanical switch. The secondary winding may have more than 20 000 turns of comparatively fine wire, and one end of the winding is connected to the primary winding. The other end of the secondary winding is connected to the plugs by way of the distributor.

Both the primary and secondary windings are wound on a laminated soft iron core with the primary winding wound on the outside of the secondary winding. This method of coil winding has been adopted to dissipate the heat produced in the primary winding.

With the ignition switch 'on' and the contact-breaker points closed, a current of about 4 A passes from the battery through the primary winding, thus creating a magnetic field round the windings and iron core. When the contact-breaker points open, current ceases to pass through the primary winding and the magnetic field collapses. This collapse causes the lines of force to cut through both the primary and the secondary windings; thus a voltage is induced in both these windings. The voltage induced in the primary winding is in proportion to the number of turns and its value is about 200 V; the voltage in the secondary winding is also in proportion to the number of turns, therefore its value is several thousands of volts. This high voltage is sufficient to produce a spark at the plug points.

To produce a really efficient spark, however, capable of igniting the air–fuel mixture under all conditions of engine speed and loading, a **capacitor** is fitted across the contact-breaker points as shown in Fig. 16.1.

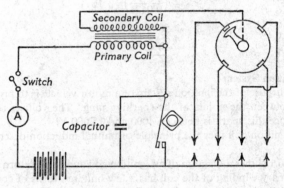

FIG. 16.1.

The purpose of the capacitor is:

(a) To reduce the sparking across the contact-breaker points, thus minimizing the burning and pitting of these points.

(b) The foregoing causes the primary current to fall more rapidly to zero, thus producing a higher secondary voltage.

Capacitance

The property of a capacitor to store an electric charge is known as its **capacitance**.

The **farad** (F) is the unit of capacitance, symbol C, and is defined as the capacitance of a capacitor requiring 1 V for a charge of 1 C.

$$C = \frac{\text{Charge (in coulombs)}}{\text{Applied voltage}} = \frac{Q}{E}$$

where C = capacitance, in farads.

In practice, the capacitance is usually expressed in **microfarads**, which is one-millionth of a farad.

Example. A coil ignition capacitor has a capacitance of 0·2 microfarads. When the points open the primary voltage is 200 V. Calculate the charge in coulombs.

Now
$$C = \frac{Q}{E}$$

$$\therefore Q = CE$$

$$= \frac{0·2}{1\,000\,000}\,(F) \times 200\,(V)\,C$$

$$= \underline{0·000\,04\,C}$$

The Dynamo (Generator)

The principles of electromagnetism govern the operation of the dynamo. We have seen in Part 1 that an electric current can be produced in a coil of wire by moving the coil in a magnetic field. The practical dynamo has a number of coils of wire (windings) wound on a laminated iron core which is fitted to a shaft. Each coil has its ends connected to a **commutator** fitted to one end of the shaft. The complete assembly is called an **armature**. The commutator consists of separate copper segments insulated from each other and from the shaft by mica.

When a dynamo armature revolves between the poles of an electromagnet current is produced; this current, however, is **alternating** (a.c.) and therefore is not suitable for charging the vehicle battery, which requires **direct current** (d.c.). The purpose of the commutator is to change or convert alternating to direct current; the principle of commutation is beyond the scope of this book.

Two or more fixed, spring-loaded **carbon brushes** press on the commutator and collect the current from the segments. These brushes pass the current into the main external circuit, which includes the battery, and return it to the armature.

In the practical dynamo an electromagnet, called a **field** magnet, is used to produce the necessary magnetic field. The field magnets, usually called the 'field', consist of two or more **pole shoes** of soft iron on which are mounted the magnetizing coils of insulated wire (windings).

The armature revolves between the faces of the pole shoes, which are usually fitted opposite each other, see Fig. 16.2; a small air gap prevents actual contact between the armature and the shoes. Since the pole shoes are of soft iron, they retain what is known as the **residual magnetism** of the pole shoes.

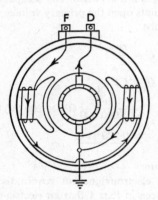

Fig. 16.2.

The field magnet of the dynamo is magnetized or **excited** as follows, see Fig. 16.2. When the armature revolves past the pole shoes it cuts the weak magnetic field caused by the existing residual magnetism of the pole shoes. The weak current produced in the armature windings then passes to the field coils, where it increases the strength of the magnetic field. The increased strength of the magnetic field produces a stronger current in the armature, which in turn increases the strength of the magnetic field, the ultimate effect being that the correct current and voltage output of the dynamo is obtained.

When referring to dynamo output we usually express its value as so many volts, e.g. 15 V. The voltage of a dynamo depends on:

(1) The strength of the magnetic field, i.e. the number of lines of force cut by the armature windings.

(2) The number of armature coils cutting the magnetic field. Voltage is produced between the ends of each armature coil and all the voltages are added up.

(3) The speed of rotation of the armature, i.e. the speed with which the armature windings cut the lines of force in the magnetic field.

Example. The voltage of a d.c. dynamo is 16 V when the armature is driven at 1000 rev/min. What would the voltage be with the armature speed at 3000 rev/min?

Since the armature speed is trebled, the voltage is trebled also.

$$\text{Voltage at 3000 rev/min} = 16 \times 3 \text{ V}$$
$$= \underline{48 \text{ V}}$$

The Shunt-type Dynamo

The **shunt**-type dynamo is generally used for the motor vehicle (Fig. 16.2).

First, it should be realized that in this dynamo two complete parallel circuits exist:

(*a*) **The Field Circuit.** The diagram shows that the field coils are connected or 'shunted' across the two brushes. Current from the armature passes through one brush, round the field coils and then back through the other brush to the armature.

(*b*) **The External Circuit.** Current from the armature is collected at one brush; it passes directly through the external circuit and then back through the other brush to the armature.

The current passing to the field coils is always proportional to the current supplied to the external circuit; therefore if the current through the field coils is 'heavy', then the current through the external circuit is also heavy. The output of a dynamo is therefore dependent on the current produced in both the field coils *and* the armature. A fault in either may result in reduced or even no output; in workshop language, no charge!

Example. The e.m.f. of a d.c. dynamo is 16 V when the armature is driven at 1000 rev/min and the field winding is carrying a current of 1 A. What would you expect the e.m.f. to be with the following speed and field current:

3000 rev/min and 2 A?

At 1000 rev/min and a field current of 1 A the e.m.f. is 16 V. At 3000 rev/min and a field current of 2 A the e.m.f. will be six times as much because the speed of the armature has trebled and the field current is doubled.

$$\therefore \text{e.m.f.} = 16 \times 6 = \underline{96 \text{ V}}$$

Dynamo Control

The foregoing example shows that at high speeds there is a possibility of the dynamo e.m.f. rising to such a high value that the life of the bulbs and contact points will be shortened; also damage may be caused to the insulation of the various parts. It is therefore necessary to **control** or **regulate** the dynamo output.

Two popular methods of control are:

(1) **Compensated voltage control**
(2) **Current voltage regulator**

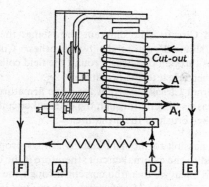

FIG. 16.3.

Compensated Voltage Control

This method of control usually employs the **single-contact** type of regulator; the **double-contact** regulator is sometimes used for commercial vehicles. The single-contact regulator (see Fig. 16.3) has vibrating contacts which control the strength of the field current and therefore the dynamo output. These contacts regulate the time that the resistance is in circuit with the dynamo field winding.

Current–Voltage Regulator

This method of control employs a current regulator and also a voltage regulator; both are of the single-contact type, see Fig. 16.4.

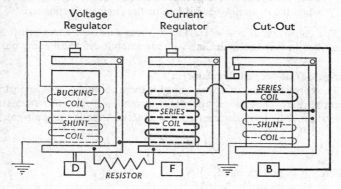

FIG 16.4.

The basic function of the current–voltage regulator is:

When the battery is discharged the current regulator permits charging at the maximum rated dynamo output until the battery reaches a charged condition. Control is then taken over by the voltage regulator, which maintains the voltage at a constant level and reduces the current to a low charge.

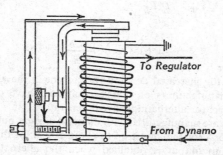

FIG. 16.5.

The Cut-out

The **cut-out** acts as an automatic switch in any charging circuit, see Fig. 16.5. Its purpose is as follows:

(1) To close the dynamo–battery charging circuit when the dynamo voltage exceeds the battery voltage.

(2) To prevent the battery from discharging through the dynamo when the dynamo voltage falls below the battery voltage, generally when the dynamo speed is low or the engine not running.

The construction and operation of these electrical components are described in text-books dealing with automobile electrical equipment.

Air-gaps (Cut-out and Regulator)

The correct setting of the air-gaps for these components is important because they depend on magnetic attraction (pull) for successful operation. The formula connecting magnetic attraction and air-gap is:

$$F = \frac{D^2 F_2}{d^2}$$

where $F =$ pull required, in N
$F_2 =$ known pull, in N
$D^2 =$ increased or decreased air-gap, in mm
$d^2 =$ present air-gap, in mm

Example. A certain cut-out has an air-gap, armature and core, of 0·625 mm; the points close when the magnetic pull reaches a value of 1·7 N.

Calculate the pull required when the air-gap is increased to 1·25 mm.

$$F = \frac{D^2 F_2}{d^2}$$

$$= \frac{1 \cdot 25^2 \times 1 \cdot 7}{0 \cdot 625^2} = \underline{6 \cdot 8 \text{ N}}$$

The Alternator

Because of the increased demand for current in the modern motor vehicle the manufacturers of vehicle equipment have developed the **alternator**, short for alternating-current generator.

Alternators are manufactured with different current outputs, ranging from about 25 A for the lowest up to about 200 A for the highest output. Maximum output is obtained when the alternator is cold, a desirable feature, because the battery usually needs a high charge after the engine has been started from cold. Fig. 16.6 shows the output characteristic curve of one type of alternator and a comparable type of generator when the battery is partly discharged.

The alternator can run safely at speeds of up to 12 500 rev/min, and so runs much faster than the average dynamo. Thus the alternator can be made to run fast enough to charge the battery all the time the engine is running, even when idling.

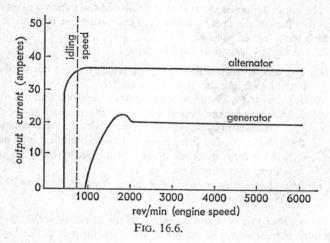

FIG. 16.6.

The principal parts of the alternator and their functions are as follows:

(*a*) An eight-pole **rotor** assembly houses the field windings, which are connected to two slip rings. The brushes are mounted on the slip-ring end bracket. A cooling fan is fitted at the driven end of the rotor shaft.

(*b*) A laminated **stator** which houses a three-phase winding; this is equivalent to the armature winding of a normal dynamo.

(*c*) **Silicon diode rectifiers** are housed in the slip-ring end bracket of the alternator. These rectifiers convert basic a.c. to the d.c. essential for charging the battery.

Alternator Control

The alternator is self-limiting in its current output, but a regulator is required to control the voltage output. This type of regulator is in circuit with the alternator field winding, so that the current in the field winding is varied to maintain the output voltage within close limits.

Transistors are used instead of vibrating contacts, and the regulator requires no maintenance.

The Starter Motor

The construction of the starter is similar to the dynamo except that the windings of the armature and field coils are made from thick wire which has a low resistance.

The principal parts of the starter are:

(1) The field coils (windings) through which current flows from the battery to create the main magnetic field.

(2) The armature, complete with brushes, and commutator, which collects the current, converts it to a.c. and passes it to the armature windings (a.c. is necessary to ensure continuous rotation of the armature). The brushes differ from the carbon type used in dynamos; they are made chiefly of copper in order to reduce resistance to current flow.

(3) Some form of drive to mesh with the flywheel ring gear; this will not be described.

In practice, the field and armature windings are in series, therefore battery current of the same value will pass through both. Fig. 16.7

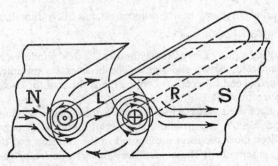

FIG. 16.7.

should enable starter operation to be understood and, to avoid confusion, only one armature coil is shown. The two field coils are arranged to have opposite polarity, as indeed they have in practice. The armature coil (placed horizontally between the field coils) and the field coils have current passed through them from the battery; the actual connections to the field coils, etc., are not shown. The lines of force round L are anticlockwise, but the lines of force round R are clockwise, and the main magnetic field lies between the field coils, N and S. The magnetic field round the armature coil and the main magnetic field of the field coils interact with each other and, in doing this, they tend to distort the lines of force below L and above R. These distorted lines of force endeavour to straighten; they exert a force on the armature coil and thus cause the armature to rotate in a clockwise direction. The torque of the armature can be increased by increasing the number of armature coils and the number of field coils; many starters are fitted with four field coils or **poles** as they are often called.

The torque developed by a starter is proportional to the product of the armature current and the field strength. When starting an engine, particularly from cold, a heavy current is 'drawn' from the battery, and the combined effect of the armature and main field produces a high torque. The heavy current 'draw' is, however, rapidly reduced, because as soon as the starter speeds up an e.m.f., known as a **back e.m.f.**, is produced in the armature due to its windings cutting the lines of force of the field coils. In effect, the starter becomes a dynamo and, as the back e.m.f. opposes the battery e.m.f., the current 'draw' is reduced. The faster the armature rotation, the less will be the current 'draw' from the battery.

Starter Calculations

Example. A starter having an efficiency of 60 per cent 'draws' 185 A when turning an engine. If the voltage at the starter terminals is 10, calculate the power of the starter.

$$\text{Watts} = E \times I$$

$$P = E\,I\,\text{(watts)}$$

$$= 10 \times 185 \text{ W}$$

$$= 1850 \text{ W}$$

Since $\quad \therefore$ Power $(P) = 1850 \times \dfrac{60}{100}$ W

$$= \underline{1110 \text{ W}}$$

Example. A starter having an efficiency of 55 per cent 'draws' 186·5 A when turning an engine at 150 rev/min through a reduction gear of

10 to 1. If the voltage at the starter terminals is 10, calculate: (*a*) the power of the starter; (*b*) the torque of the starter.

(*a*)
$$\text{Watts} = E \times I$$
$$P = E\,I \text{ (watts)}$$
$$= 10 \times 186.5 \text{ W}$$
$$= 1865 \text{ W}$$
$$\therefore \text{Power } (P) = 1865 \times \frac{55}{100}$$
$$= \underline{1025.75 \text{ W}}$$

(*b*) Let T = starter torque, in Nm

Then rev/min of starter = Engine rev/min × Gear reduction
$$= 150 \times 10 = 1500$$

Since
$$P = T \times 2\pi \times \frac{\text{rev/min}}{60}$$
$$1025.75 = T \times 2\pi \times \frac{1500}{60}$$
$$T = \frac{1025.75 \times 60}{1500 \times 2\pi}$$
$$= \underline{6.53 \text{ Nm}}$$

Example. Calculate the efficiency of a starter whose test figures are:

$$\text{Torque} = 12 \text{ Nm}; 1000 \text{ rev/min}; 4.2 \text{ V}; 200 \text{ A}$$
$$\text{Input power} = E \times I = 4.2 \times 200 = 840 \text{ W}$$
$$\text{Output power} = \frac{T \times 2\pi \times \text{rev/min}}{60}$$
$$= \frac{12 \times 2\pi \times 100}{60} = 1257 \text{ W}$$
$$\text{Efficiency} = \frac{\text{Output power}}{\text{Input power}} \times 100 \text{ per cent}$$
$$= \frac{840}{1257} \times 100 \text{ per cent}$$
$$= \underline{66.8 \text{ per cent}}$$

Measuring Instruments

The voltmeter, ammeter and ohmmeter were mentioned in Part 1. Now we shall examine the construction, operation and application of these meters.

The Voltmeter

The moving-coil type of test meter is used in motor-vehicle work for measuring voltage. Fig. 16.8 shows the construction and circuit layout of a voltmeter to read from zero to 30 V (full-scale deflection).

The needle is attached to the moving coil *a* and spindle assembly. Voltmeters usually have a very high resistance; the value of the combined series *b* and moving-coil resistance is up to about 1000 ohms/volt. Thus, only a very small current passes through the moving coil.

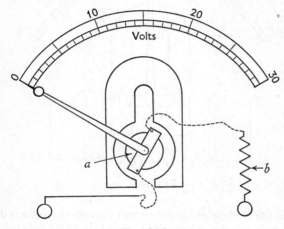

FIG. 16.8.

When in use, current passes through the moving coil and produces a magnetic field which interacts with the magnetic field produced by the permanent magnet. The coil and needle assembly is urged round by the magnetic forces, but is held steady by the hair springs, and the needle is deflected to a position corresponding to the value of the current passing through the moving coil; that is, the moving-coil current is proportional to the voltage applied to the meter.

A voltmeter is usually connected in parallel, but voltmeters are sometimes connected in series in order to detect a short-circuit.

The Ammeter

Test meters used in motor-vehicle work for measuring amps are also of the moving-coil type, but they are usually centre-zero reading instruments.

The construction of the ammeter is similar to that of the voltmeter, having a needle, moving-coil and spindle assembly, but a shunt or parallel resistance is connected across the main terminals of the meter, see Fig. 16.9.

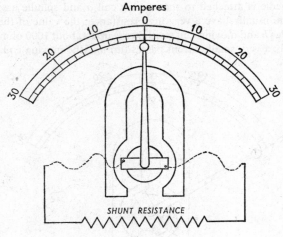

FIG. 16.9.

When in use the flow of applied current through the meter is divided proportionally between the moving coil and the shunt resistance. As the needle is deflected it indicates either a charge or a discharge reading according to the value of the current applied to the meter.

The ammeter used on the dash-board of a vehicle is also a centre-zero instrument, but is of the simple moving-iron type. Accurate readings are not usually obtained from this type of meter, and should be regarded as only approximate.

The Ohmmeter

Ohmmeters suitable for motor-vehicle work are self-contained direct reading instruments which measure the value of a given resistance in ohms.

The construction of the ohmmeter is similar to that of the moving-coil meter previously described. The movement assembly consists of a control coil, a deflecting coil and a needle. This assembly is pivoted so as to rotate in the annular gaps between the fixed iron core and the poles of the permanent magnet. The meter has its own voltage supply; a dry battery of about 4 V is housed in the casing of the meter.

The ohmmeter is operated as follows:

The resistance to be tested is connected in series. Because of the interaction between the magnetic field of the permanent magnet and the magnetic fields produced by the movement coils, the needle assembly is deflected from the zero position and the value of the resistance under test can be read directly from the scale.

Multi-range test sets are available which combine the voltmeter, the ammeter and the ohmmeter.

Exercise 16

1. Describe with the aid of diagrams one method of controlling the output from the dynamo of a motor vehicle. (C. and G.)

2. State the principles on which a dynamo works and describe how this principle is applied in the design and construction of an actual dynamo. (E.M.E.U.)

3. Explain the principal operations which change the low-tension electrical current of the battery to the high tension for the ignition of the gases in the engine cylinder. (E.M.E.U.)

4. Calculate the torque of a starter motor which gave the following results on test: $P = 1865$ W; rev/min 550. (32·36 Nm)

5. Describe a method of controlling the output of a dynamo in a charging circuit so that it is automatically adjusted to suit the state of charge of the battery. (E.M.E.U.)

6. Sketch and describe the construction of an ignition coil and explain how it operates. Why are the contact breaker and the distributor essential in the ignition system? (U.E.I.)

7. A dynamo has two circular field coils of approximately 75 mm mean diameter, wound of 0·9144 mm diameter copper wire. Each coil is found to have a resistance of 20 ohms at a room temperature of 15°C. About how many turns are there in each coil, assuming the resistance of 0·9144 mm diameter copper is 24 ohms per 1000 metres at 15°C?

The machine is run on full load for several hours until it is warmed up and the coil resistance is found to be 25 ohms. What is the temperature of the coil, assuming the resistance–temperature coefficient of copper wire is 0·00428 C? (3537 turns; 73·4°C) (C. and G.)

8. (*a*) Draw a circuit diagram for a generating system comprising the generator, battery, voltage and current regulators, cut-out, warning-light and ignition switch.

(*b*) State probable causes of, and the checks required to diagnose, the following faults: (i) generator not charging; (ii) discharged battery and low charging rate; (ii) fully charged battery and excessive charging rate. (C. and G.)

9. What are the advantages and disadvantages of the alternator when compared with the normal type dynamo?

10. (*a*) Define 'Resistivity'.

(*b*) Calculate the resistance of a piece of copper wire 15 metres long, having a cross-sectional area of 16 mm² and resistivity of 16 μΩ mm.

(0·015 ohm) (E.M.E.U.)

11. (*a*) Two 3-ohm resistances are wired in parallel, and one end is connected to a resistance of 10·5 ohms and the other end of this resistance is connected to a 12-volt battery. The other battery terminal is connected to the other end of the parallel resistance.

Draw the circuit diagram and calculate the total current from the battery. (*b*) A petrol engine's starter motor, rotating at 1350 rev/min, uses 150 A when the applied voltage is 11. If the efficiency of the starter motor is 70 per cent, calculate the starting torque being provided in Nm. (1 amp; 8·16 Nm)

This chapter contains principles and problems which cannot be conveniently included in any of the other chapters. A brief explanation of each principle is given, and the method of solving each problem is shown in detail.

Leaf Springs

In general, the adoption of thinner blades (leaves) reduces the stress in the individual blades and therefore reduces the stress in the whole of the spring.

Example. A laminated semi-elliptic spring is composed of eight blades each 6·58 mm in thickness. It is desired to replace the spring by one made from thinner and less highly stressed blades, each 5·58 mm in thickness.

Calculate the number of blades which will be required in order that the spring shall have the same load/deflection characteristics as the original one.

(C. and G.)

The number of blades varies as nt^3 where

$$n = \text{number of blades}$$
and
$$t = \text{thickness of one blade.}$$

Let x = number of blades in new spring, then

$$nt^3 = 8 \times 6\cdot58^3 \quad \text{and} \quad xt^3 = x \times 5\cdot58^3$$

$$\therefore x = \frac{8 \times 6\cdot58^3}{5\cdot58^3}$$

$$= \underline{13 \text{ blades}}$$

The Rhomboid Plan

The theory of the laminated (leaf) spring is based on the **rhomboid plan**.

To obtain the best results, the stress in a loaded spring should be the same throughout all its leaves.

Fig. 17.1 shows the plan view of a diamond-shaped plate (**rhombus**) or beam of constant thickness, supported at each end. When the beam

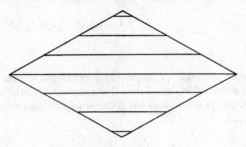

FIG. 17.1.

is loaded at its centre, then the bending moment at any point in the beam is proportional to the distance of that point from its nearest support.

To obtain constant stress throughout the beam, its width must vary in proportion to the bending moment. Thus, the beam is shown to be

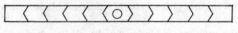

FIG. 17.2.

widest at the point where the bending is greatest. But the width of the beam tapers off towards the supports because the bending moment decreases.

To form a laminated spring, the beam is cut into strips as shown in

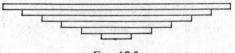

FIG. 17.3.

Fig. 17.2 and the strips are piled together as shown in Fig. 17.3; pairs of equal lengths are placed together so as to form an elementary laminated spring. The spring thus formed has the same load/stress characteristics as the diamond-shaped plate.

Valve Spring

Valve springs are designed to make the tappet follow the cam, but as the engine speed is increased a point is reached where the springs exert insufficient force and the valves 'clatter' or bounce.

Example. Assuming that with valve springs exerting 155 N the valve clatter speed is 4000 rev/min, calculate the spring force necessary to raise the clatter to 5000 rev/min. (C. and G.)

The spring force varies as engine rev/min squared.

Let $x =$ the spring force required, in N. Since 155 N is exerted at 4000^2 rev/min, then x N will be exerted at 5000^2 rev/min.

$$\therefore x = \frac{155 \times 5000^2}{4000^2} \text{ N}$$

$$= \underline{242 \cdot 18 \text{ N}}$$

Valve Force and Acceleration

The following example shows the application of formulae, given earlier, to a valve force and acceleration problem.

Example. A valve with its tappet, etc., of mass 0·2 kg, is lifted through the first 1·6 mm of its lift while the crankshaft turns through 24°. If the acceleration is assumed to be uniform for this period, calculate the force exerted by the cam on the tappet when the engine is running at 3000 rev/min. (C. and G.)

Since the crankshaft runs at 3000 rev/min, then the camshaft will run at 1500 rev/min. Therefore, when the crankshaft turns through 24°, the camshaft will turn through 12°.

The time taken for the valve to lift 1·6 mm will be:

$$1500 \text{ rev/min} = \frac{1500}{60} = 25 \text{ rev/s}$$

Since $360° = 1$ rev, then:

$$\text{Time taken to turn through } 1° = \frac{1}{25} \times \frac{1}{360} \text{ s}$$

$$\therefore \text{ time taken to turn through } 12° = \frac{1}{25} \times \frac{12}{360} = \frac{1}{750} \text{ s}$$

The acceleration of the valve must next be calculated.

Since $1{\cdot}6$ mm $= 0{\cdot}0016$ m and $s = \frac{1}{2}at^2$ (see Chapter 15, Part 1), then

$$a = \frac{2s}{t^2} = 2 \times 750^2 \times 0{\cdot}0016 \text{ m/s}^2$$

$$= 1800 \text{ m/s}^2$$

$F = ma$, where F is the required force and $m = 0{\cdot}2$ kg

$$= 0{\cdot}2 \times 1800 \text{ N} = \underline{360 \text{ N}}$$

Torque and Torque Reaction

The principle that action and reaction are equal and opposite can be applied to torque in the same way as for forces. Therefore, if an engine torque T is applied to the input shaft of a gear box, mounted separately in the frame, than a torque T and a torque reaction Tr is produced at the output shaft, where r is the gear-box reduction ratio in use. Now, of this total torque reaction Tr the greater portion, denoted by TR, i.e. $(Tr - T)$ or $T(r - 1)$, is taken by the gear-box casing; the remaining portion T is taken by the engine casing.

When in direct drive there is no torque reaction on the gear-box casing and the engine torque reaction is taken by the engine casing. Where an overdrive is fitted, however, there is a torque reaction on the gear-box casing. This is relatively small, since it is equal to the difference between the output torque and the engine torque which is now the greater.

When the engine and gear box are combined the engine torque reaction is equal and opposite to the engine torque when in direct drive, also the torque reaction at the input shaft of the gear box is equal and opposite to the torque reaction at the output shaft. Therefore, the resultant torque reaction in direct drive is engine torque reaction only.

In any gear, other than direct, the total torque reaction is:

Torque reaction = Engine torque + Torque created by gear reduction

$$= T + T(r - 1) = Tr$$

= Engine torque $\times$ Gear ratio

Example. Consider a gear box mounted separately in the frame and having a gear ratio of $4{\cdot}5$ to 1. Assume the torque entering the box from the engine is 130 Nm and calculate the torque at the output shaft.

Consider carefully and calculate the equilibrium torque reaction on the mounting points required to hold and prevent rotation of the gear box.

(C. and G.)

Let T = engine torque, in Nm

r = gear ratio

TR = torque reaction, in Nm

Neglecting friction losses, then:

$$\text{Output torque} = T \times r \text{ Nm}$$
$$= 130 \times 4\cdot5 \text{ Nm}$$
$$= \underline{585 \text{ Nm}}$$

Then,
$$TR = T(r - 1)$$
$$= 130(4\cdot5 - 1) \text{ Nm}$$
$$= \underline{455 \text{ Nm}}$$

Couples. When two equal and opposite forces act on either side of a pivot they form a **couple**. The turning moment or torque exerted by a couple is given by multiplying *one* of the forces by the perpendicular distance between the lines of action of the forces, see Fig. 17.4 (*a*).

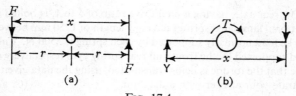

Fig. 17.4.

$$\text{Total moment of the forces} = Fr + Fr$$
$$= 2Fr$$
$$= F(2r)$$
$$= Fx$$

In the same way (see Fig. 17.4 (*b*)) a torque T will react on the points Y; the magnitude of these reactions is:

$$Y = \frac{T}{x} \text{ N where } T \text{ is in Nm}$$

Example. Let $T = 130$ Nm and $x = 500$ mm (0.5 m), then:

$$Y = \frac{130 \text{ Nm}}{0.5 \text{ m}}$$

$$= \underline{260 \text{ N}} \text{ on each point } Y$$

N.B. The *total* distance between the points Y was used.

Example. (a) An engine develops a torque of 120 Nm which is transmitted through a gear box, separately mounted in the frame. If the gear ratio of forward drive in use is 4 to 1, what is the torque reaction transmitted by the gear box to the frame?

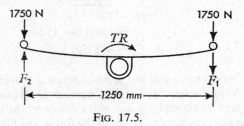

FIG. 17.5.

(b) The rear axle, having a final-drive ratio of 5 to 1, is bolted to two conventional laminated springs having a length of 1250 mm between the eyes. The load normally supported by each spring is 3500 N. Calculate the load supported by the front and rear spring eyes respectively during the time that the torque is being transmitted, using the data given in (a).

Illustrate your answer with a diagram.   (C. and G.)

(a) $$TR = T(r - 1)$$

$$= 120(4 - 1) \text{ Nm}$$

$$= \underline{360 \text{ Nm}}$$

(b)   Overall gear ratio $= 4 \times 5 = 20$ to 1

Torque in each axle shaft $= \dfrac{T \times \text{Overall gear ratio}}{2}$

$$= \frac{120 \times 20}{2} \text{ Nm}$$

$$= 1200 \text{ Nm}$$

Let F_2 and F_1 = load on front and rear spring eyes (see Fig. 17.5), then:

Vertical upward thrust on each front eye of spring $= \dfrac{1200 \text{ Nm}}{1 \cdot 25 \text{ m}}$

$= \underline{960 \text{ N}}$

Normal load on each front eye of spring = 1750 N

$\therefore$ Total load supported by each front eye F_2 = 1750 + 960 N

$= \underline{2710 \text{ N}}$

Vertical downward thrust on each rear eye of spring $= \dfrac{1200 \text{ Nm}}{1 \cdot 25 \text{ m}}$

$= 960 \text{ N}$

Normal load on each rear eye of spring = 1750 N

$\therefore$ Total load supported by each rear eye F_1 = 1750 − 960 N

$= \underline{790 \text{ N}}$

The following problems require for their solution the application of several principles already used.

Example. A car exerts a downward force of 12 750 N and has an engine which develops a maximum torque of 120 Nm. The rear-axle ratio is 5·2 to 1, and the effective diameter of the road wheels is 700 mm. If the driving wheels carry 60 per cent of the total weight and the coefficient of friction between tyres and road is 0·7, calculate the lowest gear-box ratio which can usefully be employed. Transmission losses may be neglected.　　　　　　　　　　　　　　　　　　　　(C. and G.)

Let T_e = Tractive effort at road wheels, in N

x = Gear-box ratio

Then, $\quad T_e = \dfrac{\text{Engine torque} \times \text{Rear-axle ratio} \times x}{\text{Wheel radius}} \text{ N}$

$= \dfrac{120 \times 5 \cdot 2 \times x}{0 \cdot 35}$

$= 1783 \, x \text{ N}$

Force on road wheels $= \dfrac{12\,750 \times 60}{100} \text{ N}$

Tractive resistance $(T_r) = \dfrac{12\,750 \times 60 \times 0 \cdot 7}{100} \text{ N}$

$= 5355 \text{ N}$

Now, T_e must at least equal T_r, thus:

$1783x = 5355$

$\therefore x = 5355 \div 1783 = \underline{3 \text{ to } 1}$

Example. A vehicle has a rear-axle which exerts a downward force of 6750 N, the wheels are 700 mm diameter and the coefficient of friction between tyres and road may be taken as 0·7. Fixed to the rear-axle casing and attached to the chassis by a ball-joint 1220 mm from the centre of the rear axle is a member whose function it is to transmit rear-axle thrust and to resist torque reaction. Assuming the member to be horizontal, determine the maximum resultant force that may act on the ball. (C. and G.)

$$\text{Tractive resistance } (T_r) = 6750 \times 0.7 \text{ N} = 4725 \text{ N}$$

$\therefore$ Tractive effort (T_e) at road wheels = 4725 N

Now, $\qquad$ Torque in axle shafts = $T_e \times$ Wheel radius

$$= 4725 \times 0.35 \text{ Nm}$$

Then:

Torque in axle shafts = Torque reaction (TR) on axle casing

$$\therefore TR = 4725 \times 0.35 \text{ Nm}$$

The upward force at ball = $TR \div$ Length of member, in metres

$$= 4725 \times 0.35 \div 1.22 \text{ N}$$

$$= 1355.5 \text{ N}$$

Using the triangle of forces (see Fig. 17.6) then:

Maximum resultant force $= \sqrt{1355.5^2 + 4725^2}$

$$= \underline{4914 \text{ N}}$$

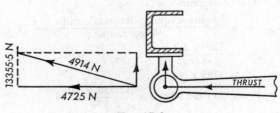

Fig. 17.6.

Universal Joints

One universal joint connecting two rotating shafts, which lie at an angle to each other, will produce a variation in speed of the driven shaft, even though the driving shaft rotates at a constant speed. The fitting of two universal joints in the same plane (in line) cancels out the variation in speed, e.g. open-type propeller shaft and final-drive pinion shaft. If these two joints are coupled incorrectly, e.g. at 90 degrees, then the speed of the pinion shaft becomes variable.

Example. A universal joint connects two shafts which are inclined at an angle of 20°. The speed of the driving shaft is 1000 rev/min. Find the maximum and minimum speeds of the driven shaft.

Let θ = angle of driven shaft to axis of driving shaft

ω = driving shaft speed (constant)

ω_1 = driven shaft speed (variable)

$$\text{Maximum speed } \frac{\omega^1}{\omega} = \frac{1}{\cos \theta}$$

$$\therefore \omega_1 = \frac{\omega}{\cos \theta}$$

$$\text{Minimum speed } \frac{\omega^1}{\omega} = \cos \theta$$

$$\therefore \omega_1 = \omega \cos \theta$$

$$\omega = \frac{2\pi 1000}{60} \text{ radians/s} = 104 \cdot 7 \text{ radians/s}$$

$$\text{Maximum value of } \omega_1 = \frac{\omega}{\cos 20°} = \frac{104 \cdot 7}{0 \cdot 9397}$$

$$= \underline{111 \cdot 4 \text{ radians/s}}$$

$$\text{Minimum value of } \omega_1 = \omega \cos 20°$$

$$= 104 \cdot 7 \times 0 \cdot 9397 = \underline{98 \cdot 3 \text{ radians/s}}$$

Assume that two universal joints are fitted incorrectly at 90 degrees, then:

$$\text{Maximum value of } \omega_1 = \frac{\omega}{\cos^2 \theta} = \frac{\omega}{\cos^2 20°}$$

$$= \frac{104 \cdot 7}{0 \cdot 9397^2} = \underline{118 \cdot 5 \text{ radians/s}}$$

$$\text{Minimum value of } \omega_1 = \omega \cos^2 \theta = \omega \cos^2 20°$$

$$= 104 \cdot 7 \times 0 \cdot 9397^2$$

$$= \underline{92 \cdot 4 \text{ radians/s}}$$

We can convert radians/s to rev/min. The last value of 92·4 radians/s equals 882·4 rev/min, which represents a considerable variation in speed.

Forces on Connecting Rod and Piston

During the power stroke of an engine with the piston in any position except t.d.c. and b.d.c., the obliquity or angularity of the connecting rod causes the piston to press against the cylinder wall (side thrust) and the cylinder wall to react against the piston. The effective force on the piston crown combines with the reaction on the cylinder wall to produce a thrust along the axis of the connecting rod. We can calculate these forces:

Let F_p = effective force on piston, in N

F_s = side thrust of piston, in N

F_c = thrust along connecting rod, in N

θ = crank angle, in degrees

ϕ = obliquity of connecting rod, in degrees

n = ratio of connecting-rod length to crank radius

The three forces F_p, F_s and F_c act at the centre of the gudgeon pin and form a parallelogram of forces as shown in Fig. 17.7.

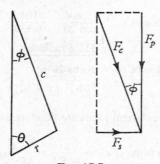

FIG. 17.7.

From this we see that

$$F_s = F_p \tan \phi$$
$$F_c = F_p \div \cos \phi$$

also $\qquad \sin \phi = \sin \phi \div n$ (Chapter 9, Part 1)

Example. An engine has a bore and stroke of 60 mm and 85 mm respectively with a connecting rod 170 mm long. When the crank is 60° past t.d.c. on the power stroke, the effective pressure on the piston is 1035 kN/m². Calculate: (*a*) the effective force on the piston; (*b*) the side thrust of the piston; (*c*) the thrust along the connecting rod.

(*a*) Force on piston F_p = Effective pressure × Bore area

$$= 1\ 035\ 000 \times \frac{\pi}{4} \times 0{\cdot}06^2 \text{ N}$$

$$= \underline{2927 \text{ N}}$$

(*b*) Thrust on piston $F_s = F_p \tan \phi = 2927 \tan \phi$

Since $\sin \phi = \sin \theta \div n$

∴ $\sin \phi = \sin 60° \div 4$

$$= 0{\cdot}8660 \div 4 = 0{\cdot}2165 \quad \therefore \phi = 12° \ 30'$$

Since $\tan \phi = \tan 12° \ 30' = 0{\cdot}2217$

then $F_s = 2927 \times 0{\cdot}2217 \text{ N}$

$$= \underline{648{\cdot}9 \text{ N}}$$

(*c*) Thrust along connecting rod $F_c = F_p \div \cos \phi$, (12° 30′)

$$= 2927 \div 0{\cdot}9763 \text{ N}$$

$$= \underline{2998 \text{ N}}$$

Torque or Twisting Moment at the Crankshaft

We have already seen that the effective force on the piston is transmitted through the connecting rod to the crankpin, thus causing a torque or twisting moment at the crankshaft. The torque produced is the product of the force acting along the connecting rod and the moment arm OC which is perpendicular to AB, see Fig. 17.8.

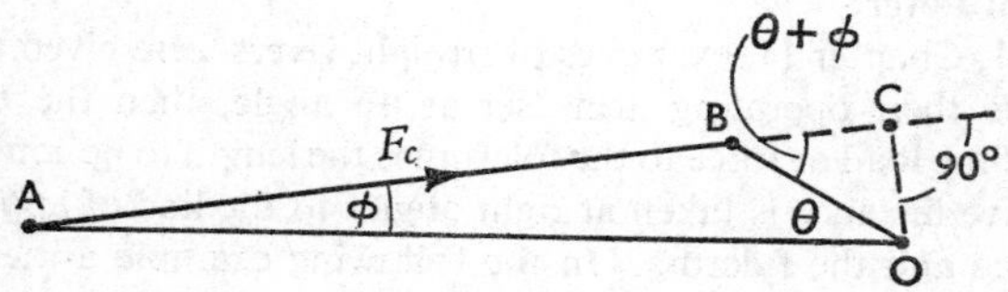

FIG. 17.8.

Using the same symbols as in the last example, with the addition of T which equals torque at crankshaft in Nm, then

$$T = F_c \times \text{OC}$$

The length of OC is calculated:

$$\text{Angle OBC} = \theta + \phi$$

then
$$\sin \theta + \phi = \frac{\text{OC}}{\text{OB}}$$

$$\therefore \text{OC} = \sin (\theta + \phi) \times \text{OB}$$

Example. An engine has a bore and stroke of 60 mm and 85 mm respectively, with a connecting rod 170 mm long. When the crank is 60° past t.d.c. on the power stroke the effective pressure on the piston is 1035 kN/m².

Calculate the twisting moment at the crankshaft.

$$\text{Twisting moment } T = F_c \times \text{OC}$$

From the last example we know that $F_c = 2998$ N

$$\text{The length OC} = \sin (\theta + \phi) \times \text{OB}$$

$$= \sin (60° + 12° \, 30') \times 0.0425 \text{ m}$$

$$= 0.9537 \times 0.0425 = 0.040 \, 53 \text{ m}$$

$$\therefore T = 2998 \times 0.040 \, 53 \text{ Nm}$$

$$= \underline{121.5 \text{ Nm}}$$

Forces on a Lever

In Part 1, Chapter 11, examples of straight levers were given. Where levers have their operating arms set at an angle, then the effective distance of the load or force to the fulcrum is the length to be considered. The effective distance is taken at right angles to the line of application of the force and the fulcrum. In the following example a method of calculating effective distances is shown.

Example. A clutch requires a force of 1575 N for disengagement. The operating mechanism consists of a pedal, rod and operating arms as shown in Fig. 17.9.

Calculate the force, applied at right angles to the pedal pad, required to disengage the clutch.

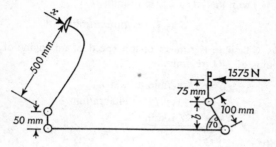

FIG. 17.9.

We must first find the effective distance b.

Then, $$\sin 70° = \frac{b}{4}$$

$$\therefore b = \sin 70° \times 0.1 \text{ m}$$

$$= 0.9397 \times 0.1 \text{ m}$$

$$= 0.093\,97 \text{ m}$$

Let $x =$ force required to disengage clutch, in N

Then $$x \times \frac{0.5}{0.05} = \frac{0.075}{b} \times 1575 \text{ N}$$

$$\therefore x \times \frac{0.5}{0.05} = \frac{0.075}{0.093\,97} \times 1575 \text{ N}$$

$$\therefore x = \frac{0.075 \times 1575 \times 0.05}{0.093\,97 \times 0.5} \text{ N}$$

$$= \underline{125.7 \text{ N}}$$

Piston Speed

The mean or average piston speed of modern engines is between 300 and 600 m/min. The mean piston speed is calculated as follows:

Let $\quad l =$ length of stroke, in m

rev/min $=$ rev/min of crankshaft

$\quad\quad S =$ mean piston speed, in m/min

then $\quad\quad\quad\quad\quad\quad\quad\quad S = 2l \text{ rev/min m/min}$

Example. Calculate the mean piston speed of an engine of 75 mm stroke running at 2400 rev/min.

$$S = 2l \text{ rev/min m/min}$$
$$= 2 \times 0{\cdot}075 \times 2400 \text{ m/min}$$
$$= \underline{360 \text{ m/min}}$$

Gas Velocity

The maximum mean gas velocity through the valve ports is about 48 m/s for the inlet port and about 74 m/s for the exhaust port.

The mean gas velocity is calculated as follows:

Let $D =$ diameter of cylinder bore, in mm or m

$\quad l =$ length of stroke, in mm or m

$\quad d =$ diameter of valve port, in mm or m

$\quad h =$ valve lift, in mm or m

$\quad v =$ mean velocity of gas through valve port, in m/s

$\quad S =$ mean piston speed, in m/s

The mean gas velocity through the valve port is to the mean piston speed as the piston (bore) area is to the valve-port area. But as the piston area is proportional to the square of the bore diameter and the valve-port area is proportional to the square of the valve-port diameter, then the mean gas velocity through the valve port is to the mean piston speed as the square of the bore is to the square of the port diameter, thus:

$$v : S = D^2 : d^2$$
$$\therefore v = S(D^2 \div d^2)$$
$$= S\left(\frac{D}{d}\right)^2$$

Example. An engine has a cylinder bore of 75 mm and stroke 100 mm and the inlet valve diameter is 32 mm. Making the conventional assumption that a volume of gas equal to the swept volume of the cylinder is drawn through the inlet valve during one-half revolution of the crankshaft, find the mean velocity of the gas in m/s through the inlet valve when the engine is running at 1500 rev/min.   (C. and G.)

$$S = 2l \text{ rev/min m/min (from piston speed formula)}$$
$$= 2 \times 0\cdot 1 \times 1500 \text{ m/min}$$
$$= 300 \text{ m/min}$$
$$v = \frac{S}{60}\left(\frac{D}{d}\right)^2$$
$$= \frac{300}{60}\left(\frac{0\cdot 075}{0\cdot 032}\right)^2 \text{ m/s}$$
$$= \underline{27\cdot 475 \text{ m/s}}$$

Using the data given in the last example, calculate the theoretical lift of the valve.

The lift of the valve should give an opening equal in area to that of the valve port. The area of the space round the valve seat, neglecting valve angle, will equal $\pi d \times h$ (lift of valve), and this should be equal to the valve-port area which is $\frac{\pi}{4}d^2$. Then:

$$h = \frac{\pi d^2}{4\pi d} \text{ mm}$$
$$= \frac{d}{4} \text{ mm}$$
$$= \frac{32}{4} \text{ mm}$$
$$= \underline{8 \text{ mm}}$$

Drilling Machine Speeds and Feeds
Spindle Speeds. The spindle speeds of drilling machines and the cutting speeds of drills are calculated as follows:

For spindle speeds the formulae shown on pp. 71 and 72 of this book are used.

$$\frac{N}{n} = \frac{d}{D} \text{ for belt drives}$$
$$\frac{N}{n} = \frac{t}{T} \text{ for gear-wheel drives}$$

Example. A sensitive drilling machine spindle has two pulleys, and thus two speeds, depending on which pulley is driven by the belt from the electric motor pulley. The motor pulley is 125 mm diameter and the pulleys on the machine spindle are 250 mm and 150 mm diameter. If the motor speed is 1200 rev/min, determine the two possible spindle speeds in rev/min.

Now
$$\frac{N}{n} = \frac{d}{D}$$

hence
$$\frac{1200}{n} = \frac{250}{125}$$

$$\therefore n = \frac{1200 \times 125}{250} = \underline{600 \text{ rev/min}}$$

$$\frac{1200}{n} = \frac{150}{125}$$

$$\therefore n = \frac{1200 \times 125}{150} = \underline{100 \text{ rev/min}}$$

Cutting Speeds

The cutting speed of drills is usually given in m/min, thus the drill diameter must be given in metres.

Now
$$S = nDD\pi$$

where $S =$ drill speed, in m/min

$n =$ spindle speed, in rev/min

$\pi = 3\frac{1}{7}$

$DD =$ drill dia., in m

Example. The speed of a drilling-machine spindle is 324 rev/min. Calculate the cutting speed, in m/min, of a 20 mm drill used at this speed.

Now
$$S = nDD\pi \text{ m/min}$$
$$= 324 \times 0.02 \times \frac{22}{7} \text{ m/min}$$
$$= \underline{20.365 \text{ m/min}}$$

Feeds

The following table gives the rate of feed to the size of drill:

Size of drill	Feed, mm/rev
Under 6 mm dia.	0·025–0·1
From 6 mm to 12·5 mm dia.	0·1–0·175
Over 12·5 mm dia.	=0·175–0·375

Exercise 17

1. A valve of a four-stroke engine is open while the crankshaft turns through 220° and is fully open for 28 degrees. The lift of the valve (ignoring clearance) is 9·5 mm, the times of opening and closing are equal, and the acceleration and deceleration are uniform. If the crankshaft speed is 1800 rev/min, calculate the valve acceleration assuming maximum velocity at half lift. (240·4 m/s²)

2. Calculate the torque exerted by an engine when it is developing 22·38 kW at 1500 rev/min.

What load does a torque of this amount produce on the side members of the frame if they are 1·37 m apart?

(142·5 Nm; 104 N)   (E.M.E.U.)

3. The outside diameter of a dry liner is given as $80 {\, + 0·0125 \atop \, - 0·0000}$ mm and the permissible interference fit in the block is between 0·038 mm and 0·0635 mm. What are the limits of size for the cylinder bore into which the liner is to be fitted?

(79·9365–79·9745 mm)   (E.M.E.U.)

4. A valve with its tappet, etc., of mass 0·225 kg, is lifted through 6·25 mm with an open period of 240°; the engine revolutions are 3000 rev/min. Calculate: (*a*) the valve acceleration; (*b*) the force required to produce the acceleration. ((*a*) 281·25 m/s²; (*b*) 63·28 N)

5. A six-cylinder engine is to develop 29·84 kW at 2500 rev/min, at which speed the b.m.e.p. is expected to be 825 kN/m². If the ratio of stroke to bore is to be 1·4, determine the bore and stroke of the engine.

(64 mm; 89·6 mm)   (C. and G.)

6. A petrol engine gives valve clatter at 3500 rev/min due to the valve springs having become weak. The 'full lift' load of each spring is found to be 133 N. What load will be required to raise the clatter speed to 4500 rev/min? (219·85 N)   (C. and G.)

7. A foot-brake pedal may be regarded as a lever 350 mm long. It is pivoted at one end and a push rod is connected 75 mm from the pivot and at right angles to the lever. The push rod is connected to the master-cylinder piston, which is 38 mm diameter. Calculate the fluid pressure in the system if a perpendicular foot pedal force of 222 N is applied to the lever. (913·3 kN/m²) (E.M.E.U.)

8. A volume of air 0·0005 m³ passes through a valve port 38 mm diameter in 0·0125 s. Find the velocity through the port in metres per second. (35·27 m/s) (C. and G.)

9. State the firing intervals and magneto-cam angles for a 50° twin engine. (410°; 310°; 205°; 155°)

10. A four-stroke engine, whose bore and stroke are 100 mm, is fitted with an inlet valve whose mean seat diameter is 38 mm. Assuming that a volume of gas equal to the swept volume of the cylinder is drawn in past the open inlet valve seat during one-half revolution of the crankshaft, find the mean gas velocity in m/s past the open inlet valve seat when the engine speed is 3000 rev/min. (69·24 m/s)

11. A cast-iron disc is 350 mm in diameter and 50 mm thick. It has a mass of 39 kg and, for balancing purposes, two holes each 25 mm diameter and 38 mm deep are drilled in one face of the disc and filled up flush with lead of density 11 350 kg/m³. Calculate the new mass of the disc and plugs. (39·121 kg) (U.E.I.)

12. A racing track is triangular in shape and 4·57 km in length. Let the turning points be A, B and C. Side BC is 0·85 of AB and 0·25 km shorter than CA.

What are the lengths of each side?

If the average speed for each side of the track is proportional to its length, what are these speeds when the lap speed is 90·6 km/h?

(AB = 1·6 km; BC = 1·36 km; CA = 1·61 km; AB = 95·17 km/h; BC = 80·89 km/h; CA = 95·76 km/h)

13. The Air Standard Efficiency of an engine working on a constant-volume cycle is given by the expression:

$$E = 1 - \left(\frac{1}{r}\right)^{\gamma-1}$$ where r is the compression ratio, γ is 1·4.

Find the percentage increase in the Air Standard Efficiency when the compression ratio of an engine is raised from 8·9 to 1 to 9·5 to 1.

(1·852 per cent)

14. A crankshaft has 50 mm diameter journals and is rotating in a bearing at 2100 rev/min. If the work lost in friction is equal to 746 W when the load on the bearing is 3370 N, determine the coefficient of friction. (0·04) (N.C.T.E.C.)

15. A single-plate clutch is designed to transmit 26 kW. If the mean radius of the lining is 100 mm, and the coefficient of friction 0·4, find (*a*) the torque transmitted at 3000 rev/min, (*b*) the total spring force in N.

((*a*) 82·74 Nm; (*b*) 1034·25 N)   (U.L.C.I.)

16. In an engine 25 per cent of the heat developed by the combustion of 1 kg of petrol, calorific value 47 500 kJ/kg, is absorbed by the cooling water. How many kg of cooling water are required per kg of fuel used if its temperature is raised from 10°C to 80°C? If this water is raised to boiling point and heated until it is all evaporated, how many additional kJ are absorbed? The latent heat of steam 2256 kJ/kg.

(40·5 kg; 94 759 kJ)   (E.M.E.U.)

17. The length of a spring when it is stretched by a force F (N) is l mm, and $l = 36 + 0·085F$. Determine (*a*) the length for a force of 48 N, (*b*) the force which will stretch the spring to a length of 48 mm, (*c*) the unstretched length of the spring.

((*a*) 39·34 mm; (*b*) 141·17 N; (*c*) 36 mm)   (E.M.E.U.)

18. The effort E required to lift a load W by means of a crane is $E = 0·05W + 28$. Rearrange the formula to make W the subject, and then calculate the load which can be lifted by an effort of 140 N.

Determine also the efficiency of the crane, using the formula: efficiency $= \dfrac{W}{20E}$.

(2240 N; 80 per cent)   (E.M.E.U.)

19. A quarter of a kilogramme of copper, of specific heat capacity 0·398, and at a temperature of 150°C is immersed in 1·12 kg of oil at 15°C. The final temperature of both is 25°C. What is the specific heat capacity of the oil? Assume no heat losses.   (1·331)   (E.M.E.U.)

20. If the relative density of aluminium is 2·6, and the relative density of cast iron is 7·8, what percentage mass is saved by replacing a cast-iron piston by one of the same dimensions made of aluminium?

(33·3 per cent)   (E.M.E.U.)

21. The cylindrical side wall of an oil drum is 500 mm high and the ends are 250 mm diameter. They are made from a rectangular sheet of steel measuring 525 mm by 1050 mm. What percentage of the steel will be scrap? Assume the parts to be welded together without overlaps.

(10·95 per cent)   (E.M.E.U.)

22. The pressure on a piston at various points in the stroke is as follows:

Pressure, kN/m²	1725	965	689·5	482·5	344·5
Distance of piston from beginning of stroke, m	0	0·05	0·075	0·10	0·125

Draw a work diagram and from it obtain the work done in J in a stroke of 0·125 m.   (111·4 J)   (E.M.E.U.)

23. An electric motor running at 1500 rev/min drives the spindle of a drilling machine. The motor shaft has a 32-tooth pinion keyed to it which meshes with a 51-tooth gear wheel splined on an intermediate shaft. Splined also to this shaft is a 45-tooth gear wheel driving a 35-tooth gear wheel fixed to the drill spindle.

Calculate the speed of the drill spindle in rev/min.   (1210 rev/min)

24. During a drilling operation 16 mm dia. holes are drilled. The electric motor running at 1440 rev/min has on its shaft a 35-tooth pinion which drives a 32-tooth gear wheel on the intermediate shaft. Also on the intermediate shaft is a 30-tooth pinion which drives a 42-tooth gear wheel on the spindle of the drilling machine.

Calculate: (*a*) the cutting speed of the drill in m/min; (*b*) the speed of the drill in rev/min.   ((*a*) 56·54 m/min; (*b*) 1125 rev/min)

25. The motion of a car of mass 1500 kg is opposed by a constant resistance of 900 N. The car starts from rest under the action of a variable driving force $F(N)$, whose value is given below for corresponding distances X metres moved by the car from the starting-point.

F	4450	4280	3650	3290	3200	3120	2670
X	0	2	4	6	8	10	12

Plot the curve connecting F and X. Determine the kinetic energy of the car after it has moved through 12 m and its speed in m/s at that point.   (31·5 kJ; 6·481 m/s)

26. A vehicle of mass 1500 kg is travelling at 36 km/h on the level. If, under the circumstances the total resistance to motion is 560 N and the total power available is 29·84 kW, calculate the maximum acceleration available.   (1·616 m/s)

27. A clutch of single plate type transmits a torque of 81 Nm. Six springs supply the clamping force. What force must each of these springs exert if the mean radius of the driven friction plate is 150 mm? The coefficient of friction of these faces is 0·5.   (90 N)

28. A car has a mass of 1 tonne. The pressure in each of the rear tyres is 190 kN/m^2 and in each of the front tyres 180 kN/m^2. The distance between the front and rear axles is 3 m. The centre of gravity of the car is 1·6 m to the rear of the front axle.

Calculate the area of contact between the road and each of the tyres.   (14 180 mm^2; 12 250 mm^2)

29. A car of total mass 1270 kg has an engine which develops a maximum torque of 114 Nm. The rear axle ratio is 5 to 1, the effective tyre diameter is 660 mm and the transmission efficiency is 90 per cent. Assuming that the driving wheels carry two-thirds of the total mass and that the coefficient of friction between the tyres and the road is 0·7, determine the lowest gearbox ratio that can be usefully employed.

(3·736 to 1)   (C. and G.)

30. A motor car of mass 1000 kg has a wheelbase of 2·4 m. The height of the centre of gravity above ground level is 0·75 m and the load distribution when at rest is 40 per cent front axle, 60 per cent rear axle.

If the coefficient of friction between the tyres and the road is 0·3, determine the maximum acceleration when the drive is by: (*a*) front axle; (*b*) rear axle.   (1·075 m/s²; 1·946 m/s²)   (C. and G.)

Appendix

The mass of a body depends on the number of particles or quantity of matter the body contains. The SI unit of mass is the **kilogramme (kg)**.

Mass must not be confused with **volume** because when the temperature of a body changes the volume of the body changes also, but its mass does not change. The SI unit of volume is the cubic metre (m^3).

Weight must not be confused with mass because the weight of a body is the amount of attraction the earth exerts on the body, i.e. the gravitational force. The SI unit of weight is the **newton (N)** and we can say that the weight of a body is $9.81m$ newtons where m is the mass of the body in kilogrammes.

Example

A metal block having a mass of 50 kg rests on a level bench. Calculate the downward force on the bench.

$$\text{Downward force on bench} = \text{weight of block}$$
$$= 50 \text{ kg} \times 9.81 \text{ N}$$
$$= \underline{490.5 \text{ N}}$$

When a beam balance is used to measure the mass of a body, another mass of known value is used as a comparison, thus the value of the gravitational pull of the earth will be the same on each body.

A **spring balance**, however, measures the **weight** of a body, since this records the force exerted by the earth on the body. But this force, and thus the weight of the body, will vary from place to place on the earth's surface.

Students should note that when the term **load** is used it may refer to either a mass (load) or weight (load).

LOGARITHMS

	0	1	2	3	4	5	6	7	8	9	1	2	3	4	5	6	7	8	9
10	0000	0043	0086	0128	0170	0212	0253	0294	0334	0374	4	8	12	17	21	25	29	33	37
11	0414	0453	0492	0531	0569	0607	0645	0682	0719	0755	4	8	11	15	19	23	26	30	34
12	0792	0828	0864	0899	0934	0969	1004	1038	1072	1106	3	7	10	14	17	21	24	28	31
13	1139	1173	1206	1239	1271	1303	1335	1367	1399	1430	3	6	10	13	16	19	23	26	29
14	1461	1492	1523	1553	1584	1614	1644	1673	1703	1732	3	6	9	12	15	18	21	24	27
15	1761	1790	1818	1847	1875	1903	1931	1959	1987	2014	3	6	8	11	14	17	20	22	25
16	2041	2068	2095	2122	2148	2175	2201	2227	2253	2279	3	5	8	11	13	16	18	21	24
17	2304	2330	2355	2380	2405	2430	2455	2480	2504	2529	2	5	7	10	12	15	17	20	22
18	2553	2577	2601	2625	2648	2672	2695	2718	2742	2765	2	5	7	9	12	14	16	19	21
19	2788	2810	2833	2856	2878	2900	2923	2945	2967	2989	2	4	7	9	11	13	16	18	20
20	3010	3032	3054	3075	3096	3118	3139	3160	3181	3201	2	4	6	8	11	13	15	17	19
21	3222	3243	3263	3284	3304	3324	3345	3365	3385	3404	2	4	6	8	10	12	14	16	18
22	3424	3444	3464	3483	3502	3522	3541	3560	3579	3598	2	4	6	8	10	12	14	15	17
23	3617	3636	3655	3674	3692	3711	3729	3747	3766	3784	2	4	6	7	9	11	13	15	17
24	3802	3820	3838	3856	3874	3892	3909	3927	3945	3962	2	4	5	7	9	11	12	14	16
25	3979	3997	4014	4031	4048	4065	4082	4099	4116	4133	2	3	5	7	9	10	12	14	15
26	4150	4166	4183	4200	4216	4232	4249	4265	4281	4298	2	3	5	7	8	10	11	13	15
27	4314	4330	4346	4362	4378	4393	4409	4425	4440	4456	2	3	5	6	8	9	11	13	14
28	4472	4487	4502	4518	4533	4548	4564	4579	4594	4609	2	3	5	6	8	9	11	12	14
29	4624	4639	4654	4669	4683	4698	4713	4728	4742	4757	1	3	4	6	7	9	10	12	13
30	4771	4786	4800	4814	4829	4843	4857	4871	4886	4900	1	3	4	6	7	9	10	11	13
31	4914	4928	4942	4955	4969	4983	4997	5011	5024	5038	1	3	4	6	7	8	10	11	12
32	5051	5065	5079	5092	5105	5119	5132	5145	5159	5172	1	3	4	5	7	8	9	11	12
33	5185	5198	5211	5224	5237	5250	5263	5276	5289	5302	1	3	4	5	6	8	9	10	12
34	5315	5328	5340	5353	5366	5378	5391	5403	5416	5428	1	3	4	5	6	8	9	10	11
35	5441	5453	5465	5478	5490	5502	5514	5527	5539	5551	1	2	4	5	6	7	9	10	11
36	5563	5575	5587	5599	5611	5623	5635	5647	5658	5670	1	2	4	5	6	7	8	10	11
37	5682	5694	5705	5717	5729	5740	5752	5763	5775	5786	1	2	3	5	6	7	8	9	10
38	5798	5809	5821	5832	5843	5855	5866	5877	5888	5899	1	2	3	5	6	7	8	9	10
39	5911	5922	5933	5944	5955	5966	5977	5988	5999	6010	1	2	3	4	5	7	8	9	10
40	6021	6031	6042	6053	6064	6075	6085	6096	6107	6117	1	2	3	4	5	6	8	9	10
41	6128	6138	6149	6160	6170	6180	6191	6201	6212	6222	1	2	3	4	5	6	7	8	9
42	6232	6243	6253	6263	6274	6284	6294	6304	6314	6325	1	2	3	4	5	6	7	8	9
43	6335	6345	6355	6365	6375	6385	6395	6405	6415	6425	1	2	3	4	5	6	7	8	9
44	6435	6444	6454	6464	6474	6484	6493	6503	6513	6522	1	2	3	4	5	6	7	8	9
45	6532	6542	6551	6561	6571	6580	6590	6599	6609	6618	1	2	3	4	5	6	7	8	9
46	6628	6637	6646	6656	6665	6675	6684	6693	6702	6712	1	2	3	4	5	6	7	7	8
47	6721	6730	6739	6749	6758	6767	6776	6785	6794	6803	1	2	3	4	5	5	6	7	8
48	6812	6821	6830	6839	6848	6857	6866	6875	6884	6893	1	2	3	4	4	5	6	7	8
49	6902	6911	6920	6928	6937	6946	6955	6964	6972	6981	1	2	3	4	4	5	6	7	8
50	6990	6998	7007	7016	7024	7033	7042	7050	7059	7067	1	2	3	3	4	5	6	7	8
51	7076	7084	7093	7101	7110	7118	7126	7135	7143	7152	1	2	3	3	4	5	6	7	8
52	7160	7168	7177	7185	7193	7202	7210	7218	7226	7235	1	2	2	3	4	5	6	7	7
53	7243	7251	7259	7267	7275	7284	7292	7300	7308	7316	1	2	2	3	4	5	6	6	7
54	7324	7332	7340	7348	7356	7364	7372	7380	7388	7396	1	2	2	3	4	5	6	6	7

LOGARITHMS

	0	1	2	3	4	5	6	7	8	9	1 2 3 4	5	6 7 8 9
55	7404	7412	7419	7427	7435	7443	7451	7459	7466	7474	1 2 2 3	4	5 5 6 7
56	7482	7490	7497	7505	7513	7520	7528	7536	7543	7551	1 2 2 3	4	5 5 6 7
57	7559	7566	7574	7582	7589	7597	7604	7612	7619	7627	1 2 2 3	4	5 5 6 7
58	7634	7642	7649	7657	7664	7672	7679	7686	7694	7701	1 1 2 3	4	4 5 6 7
59	7709	7716	7723	7731	7738	7745	7752	7760	7767	7774	1 1 2 3	4	4 5 6 7
60	7782	7789	7796	7803	7810	7818	7825	7832	7839	7846	1 1 2 3	4	4 5 6 6
61	7853	7860	7868	7875	7882	7889	7896	7903	7910	7917	1 1 2 3	4	4 5 6 6
62	7924	7931	7938	7945	7952	7959	7966	7973	7980	7987	1 1 2 3	3	4 5 6 6
63	7993	8000	8007	8014	8021	8028	8035	8041	8048	8055	1 1 2 3	3	4 5 5 6
64	8062	8069	8075	8082	8089	8096	8102	8109	8116	8122	1 1 2 3	3	4 5 5 6
65	8129	8136	8142	8149	8156	8162	8169	8176	8182	8189	1 1 2 3	3	4 5 5 6
66	8195	8202	8209	8215	8222	8228	8235	8241	8248	8254	1 1 2 3	3	4 5 5 6
67	8261	8267	8274	8280	8287	8293	8299	8306	8312	8319	1 1 2 3	3	4 5 5 6
68	8325	8331	8338	8344	8351	8357	8363	8370	8376	8382	1 1 2 3	3	4 4 5 6
69	8388	8395	8401	8407	8414	8420	8426	8432	8439	8445	1 1 2 2	3	4 4 5 6
70	8451	8457	8463	8470	8476	8482	8488	8494	8500	8506	1 1 2 2	3	4 4 5 6
71	8513	8519	8525	8531	8537	8543	8549	8555	8561	8567	1 1 2 2	3	4 4 5 5
72	8573	8579	8585	8591	8597	8603	8609	8615	8621	8627	1 1 2 2	3	4 4 5 5
73	8633	8639	8645	8651	8657	8663	8669	8675	8681	8686	1 1 2 2	3	4 4 5 5
74	8692	8698	8704	8710	8716	8722	8727	8733	8739	8745	1 1 2 2	3	4 4 5 5
75	8751	8756	8762	8768	8774	8779	8785	8791	8797	8802	1 1 2 2	3	3 4 5 5
76	8808	8814	8820	8825	8831	8837	8842	8848	8854	8859	1 1 2 2	3	3 4 5 5
77	8865	8871	8876	8882	8887	8893	8899	8904	8910	8915	1 1 2 2	3	3 4 4 5
78	8921	8927	8932	8938	8943	8949	8954	8960	8965	8971	1 1 2 2	3	3 4 4 5
79	8976	8982	8987	8993	8998	9004	9009	9015	9020	9025	1 1 2 2	3	3 4 4 5
80	9031	9036	9042	9047	9053	9058	9063	9069	9074	9079	1 1 2 2	3	3 4 4 5
81	9085	9090	9096	9101	9106	9112	9117	9122	9128	9133	1 1 2 2	3	3 4 4 5
82	9138	9143	9149	9154	9159	9165	9170	9175	9180	9186	1 1 2 2	3	3 4 4 5
83	9191	9196	9201	9206	9212	9217	9222	9227	9232	9238	1 1 2 2	3	3 4 4 5
84	9243	9248	9253	9258	9263	9269	9274	9279	9284	9289	1 1 2 2	3	3 4 4 5
85	9294	9299	9304	9309	9315	9320	9325	9330	9335	9340	1 1 2 2	3	3 4 4 5
86	9345	9350	9355	9360	9365	9370	9375	9380	9385	9390	1 1 2 2	3	3 4 4 5
87	9395	9400	9405	9410	9415	9420	9425	9430	9435	9440	0 1 1 2	2	3 3 4 4
88	9445	9450	9455	9460	9465	9469	9474	9479	9484	9489	0 1 1 2	2	3 3 4 4
89	9494	9499	9504	9509	9513	9518	9523	9528	9533	9538	0 1 1 2	2	3 3 4 4
90	9542	9547	9552	9557	9562	9566	9571	9576	9581	9586	0 1 1 2	2	3 3 4 4
91	9590	9595	9600	9605	9609	9614	9619	9624	9628	9633	0 1 1 2	2	3 3 4 4
92	9638	9643	9647	9652	9657	9661	9666	9671	9675	9680	0 1 1 2	2	3 3 4 4
93	9685	9689	9694	9699	9703	9708	9713	9717	9722	9727	0 1 1 2	2	3 3 4 4
94	9731	9736	9741	9745	9750	9754	9759	9763	9768	9773	0 1 1 2	2	3 3 4 4
95	9777	9782	9786	9791	9795	9800	9805	9809	9814	9818	0 1 1 2	2	3 3 4 4
96	9823	9827	9832	9836	9841	9845	9850	9854	9859	9863	0 1 1 2	2	3 3 4 4
97	9868	9872	9877	9881	9886	9890	9894	9899	9903	9908	0 1 1 2	2	3 3 4 4
98	9912	9917	9921	9926	9930	9934	9939	9943	9948	9952	0 1 1 2	2	3 3 4 4
99	9956	9961	9965	9969	9974	9978	9983	9987	9991	9996	0 1 1 2	2	3 3 3 4

ANTILOGARITHMS

	0	1	2	3	4	5	6	7	8	9	1	2	3	4	5	6	7	8	9
·00	1000	1002	1005	1007	1009	1012	1014	1016	1019	1021	0	0	1	1	1	1	2	2	2
·01	1023	1026	1028	1030	1033	1035	1038	1040	1042	1045	0	0	1	1	1	1	2	2	2
·02	1047	1050	1052	1054	1057	1059	1062	1064	1067	1069	0	0	1	1	1	1	2	2	2
·03	1072	1074	1076	1079	1081	1084	1086	1089	1091	1094	0	0	1	1	1	1	2	2	2
·04	1096	1099	1102	1104	1107	1109	1112	1114	1117	1119	0	1	1	1	1	2	2	2	2
·05	1122	1125	1127	1130	1132	1135	1138	1140	1143	1146	0	1	1	1	1	2	2	2	2
·06	1148	1151	1153	1156	1159	1161	1164	1167	1169	1172	0	1	1	1	1	2	2	2	2
·07	1175	1178	1180	1183	1186	1189	1191	1194	1197	1199	0	1	1	1	1	2	2	2	2
·08	1202	1205	1208	1211	1213	1216	1219	1222	1225	1227	0	1	1	1	1	2	2	2	3
·09	1230	1233	1236	1239	1242	1245	1247	1250	1253	1256	0	1	1	1	1	2	2	2	3
·10	1259	1262	1265	1268	1271	1274	1276	1279	1282	1285	0	1	1	1	1	2	2	2	3
·11	1288	1291	1294	1297	1300	1303	1306	1309	1312	1315	0	1	1	1	2	2	2	2	3
·12	1318	1321	1324	1327	1330	1334	1337	1340	1343	1346	0	1	1	1	2	2	2	2	3
·13	1349	1352	1355	1358	1361	1365	1368	1371	1374	1377	0	1	1	1	2	2	2	3	3
·14	1380	1384	1387	1390	1393	1396	1400	1403	1406	1409	0	1	1	1	2	2	2	3	3
·15	1413	1416	1419	1422	1426	1429	1432	1435	1439	1442	0	1	1	1	2	2	2	3	3
·16	1445	1449	1452	1455	1459	1462	1466	1469	1472	1476	0	1	1	1	2	2	2	3	3
·17	1479	1483	1486	1489	1493	1496	1500	1503	1507	1510	0	1	1	1	2	2	2	3	3
·18	1514	1517	1521	1524	1528	1531	1535	1538	1542	1545	0	1	1	1	2	2	2	3	3
·19	1549	1552	1556	1560	1563	1567	1570	1574	1578	1581	0	1	1	1	2	2	3	3	3
·20	1585	1589	1592	1596	1600	1603	1607	1611	1614	1618	0	1	1	1	2	2	3	3	3
·21	1622	1626	1629	1633	1637	1641	1644	1648	1652	1656	0	1	1	2	2	2	3	3	3
·22	1660	1663	1667	1671	1675	1679	1683	1687	1690	1694	0	1	1	2	2	2	3	3	3
·23	1698	1702	1706	1710	1714	1718	1722	1726	1730	1734	0	1	1	2	2	2	3	3	4
·24	1738	1742	1746	1750	1754	1758	1762	1766	1770	1774	0	1	1	2	2	2	3	3	4
·25	1778	1782	1786	1791	1795	1799	1803	1807	1811	1816	0	1	1	2	2	2	3	3	4
·26	1820	1824	1828	1832	1837	1841	1845	1849	1854	1858	0	1	1	2	2	3	3	3	4
·27	1862	1866	1871	1875	1879	1884	1888	1892	1897	1901	0	1	1	2	2	3	3	3	4
·28	1905	1910	1914	1919	1923	1928	1932	1936	1941	1945	0	1	1	2	2	3	3	4	4
·29	1950	1954	1959	1963	1968	1972	1977	1982	1986	1991	0	1	1	2	2	3	3	4	4
·30	1995	2000	2004	2009	2014	2018	2023	2028	2032	2037	0	1	1	2	2	3	3	4	4
·31	2042	2046	2051	2056	2061	2065	2070	2075	2080	2084	0	1	1	2	2	3	3	4	4
·32	2089	2094	2099	2104	2109	2113	2118	2123	2128	2133	0	1	1	2	2	3	3	4	4
·33	2138	2143	2148	2153	2158	2163	2168	2173	2178	2183	0	1	1	2	2	3	3	4	4
·34	2188	2193	2198	2203	2208	2213	2218	2223	2228	2234	1	1	2	2	3	3	4	4	5
·35	2239	2244	2249	2254	2259	2265	2270	2275	2280	2286	1	1	2	2	3	3	4	4	5
·36	2291	2296	2301	2307	2312	2317	2323	2328	2333	2339	1	1	2	2	3	3	4	4	5
·37	2344	2350	2355	2360	2366	2371	2377	2382	2388	2393	1	1	2	2	3	3	4	4	5
·38	2399	2404	2410	2415	2421	2427	2432	2438	2443	2449	1	1	2	2	3	3	4	4	5
·39	2455	2460	2466	2472	2477	2483	2489	2495	2500	2506	1	1	2	2	3	3	4	5	5
·40	2512	2518	2523	2529	2535	2541	2547	2553	2559	2564	1	1	2	2	3	4	4	5	5
·41	2570	2576	2582	2588	2594	2600	2606	2612	2618	2624	1	1	2	2	3	4	4	5	5
·42	2630	2636	2642	2649	2655	2661	2667	2673	2679	2685	1	1	2	2	3	4	4	5	6
·43	2692	2698	2704	2710	2716	2723	2729	2735	2742	2748	1	1	2	3	3	4	4	5	6
·44	2754	2761	2767	2773	2780	2786	2793	2799	2805	2812	1	1	2	3	3	4	4	5	6
·45	2818	2825	2831	2838	2844	2851	2858	2864	2871	2877	1	1	2	3	3	4	5	5	6
·46	2884	2891	2897	2904	2911	2917	2924	2931	2938	2944	1	1	2	3	3	4	5	5	6
·47	2951	2958	2965	2972	2979	2985	2992	2999	3006	3013	1	1	2	3	3	4	5	5	6
·48	3020	3027	3034	3041	3048	3055	3062	3069	3076	3083	1	1	2	3	4	4	5	6	6
·49	3090	3097	3105	3112	3119	3126	3133	3141	3148	3155	1	1	2	3	4	4	5	6	6

ANTILOGARITHMS

	0	1	2	3	4	5	6	7	8	9	1 2 3 4	5	6 7 8 9
·50	3162	3170	3177	3184	3192	3199	3206	3214	3221	3228	1 1 2 3	4	4 5 6 7
·51	3236	3243	3251	3258	3266	3273	3281	3289	3296	3304	1 2 2 3	4	5 5 6 7
·52	3311	3319	3327	3334	3342	3350	3357	3365	3373	3381	1 2 2 3	4	5 5 6 7
·53	3388	3396	3404	3412	3420	3428	3436	3443	3451	3459	1 2 2 3	4	5 6 6 7
·54	3467	3475	3483	3491	3499	3508	3516	3524	3532	3540	1 2 2 3	4	5 6 6 7
·55	3548	3556	3565	3573	3581	3589	3597	3606	3614	3622	1 2 2 3	4	5 6 7 7
·56	3631	3639	3648	3656	3664	3673	3681	3690	3698	3707	1 2 3 3	4	5 6 7 8
·57	3715	3724	3733	3741	3750	3758	3767	3776	3784	3793	1 2 3 3	4	5 6 7 8
·58	3802	3811	3819	3828	3837	3846	3855	3864	3873	3882	1 2 3 4	4	5 6 7 8
·59	3890	3899	3908	3917	3926	3936	3945	3954	3963	3972	1 2 3 4	5	5 6 7 8
·60	3981	3990	3999	4009	4018	4027	4036	4046	4055	4064	1 2 3 4	5	6 6 7 8
·61	4074	4083	4093	4102	4111	4121	4130	4140	4150	4159	1 2 3 4	5	6 7 8 9
·62	4169	4178	4188	4198	4207	4217	4227	4236	4246	4256	1 2 3 4	5	6 7 8 9
·63	4266	4276	4285	4295	4305	4315	4325	4335	4345	4355	1 2 3 4	5	6 7 8 9
·64	4365	4375	4385	4395	4406	4416	4426	4436	4446	4457	1 2 3 4	5	6 7 8 9
·65	4467	4477	4487	4498	4508	4519	4529	4539	4550	4560	1 2 3 4	5	6 7 8 9
·66	4571	4581	4592	4603	4613	4624	4634	4645	4656	4667	1 2 3 4	5	6 7 9 10
·67	4677	4688	4699	4710	4721	4732	4742	4753	4764	4775	1 2 3 4	5	7 8 9 10
·68	4786	4797	4808	4819	4831	4842	4853	4864	4875	4887	1 2 3 4	6	7 8 9 10
·69	4898	4909	4920	4932	4943	4955	4966	4977	4989	5000	1 2 3 5	6	7 8 9 10
·70	5012	5023	5035	5047	5058	5070	5082	5093	5105	5117	1 2 4 5	6	7 8 9 11
·71	5129	5140	5152	5164	5176	5188	5200	5212	5224	5236	1 2 4 5	6	7 8 10 11
·72	5248	5260	5272	5284	5297	5309	5321	5333	5346	5358	1 2 4 5	6	7 9 10 11
·73	5370	5383	5395	5408	5420	5433	5445	5458	5470	5483	1 3 4 5	6	8 9 10 11
·74	5495	5508	5521	5534	5546	5559	5572	5585	5598	5610	1 3 4 5	6	8 9 10 12
·75	5623	5636	5649	5662	5675	5689	5702	5715	5728	5741	1 3 4 5	7	8 9 10 12
·76	5754	5768	5781	5794	5808	5821	5834	5848	5861	5875	1 3 4 5	7	8 9 11 12
·77	5888	5902	5916	5929	5943	5957	5970	5984	5998	6012	1 3 4 5	7	8 10 11 12
·78	6026	6039	6053	6067	6081	6095	6109	6124	6138	6152	1 3 4 6	7	8 10 11 13
·79	6166	6180	6194	6209	6223	6237	6252	6266	6281	6295	1 3 4 6	7	9 10 11 13
·80	6310	6324	6339	6353	6368	6383	6397	6412	6427	6442	1 3 4 6	7	9 10 12 13
·81	6457	6471	6486	6501	6516	6531	6546	6561	6577	6592	2 3 5 6	8	9 11 12 14
·82	6607	6622	6637	6653	6668	6683	6699	6714	6730	6745	2 3 5 6	8	9 11 12 14
·83	6761	6776	6792	6808	6823	6839	6855	6871	6887	6902	2 3 5 6	8	9 11 13 14
·84	6918	6934	6950	6966	6982	6998	7015	7031	7047	7063	2 3 5 6	8	10 11 13 15
·85	7079	7096	7112	7129	7145	7161	7178	7194	7211	7228	2 3 5 7	8	10 12 13 15
·86	7244	7261	7278	7295	7311	7328	7345	7362	7379	7396	2 3 5 7	8	10 12 13 15
·87	7413	7430	7447	7464	7482	7499	7516	7534	7551	7568	2 3 5 7	9	10 12 14 16
·88	7586	7603	7621	7638	7656	7674	7691	7709	7727	7745	2 4 5 7	9	11 12 14 16
·89	7762	7780	7798	7816	7834	7852	7870	7889	7907	7925	2 4 5 7	9	11 13 14 16
·90	7943	7962	7980	7998	8017	8035	8054	8072	8091	8110	2 4 6 7	9	11 13 15 17
·91	8128	8147	8166	8185	8204	8222	8241	8260	8279	8299	2 4 6 8	9	11 13 15 17
·92	8318	8337	8356	8375	8395	8414	8433	8453	8472	8492	2 4 6 8	10	12 14 15 17
·93	8511	8531	8551	8570	8590	8610	8630	8650	8670	8690	2 4 6 8	10	12 14 16 18
·94	8710	8730	8750	8770	8790	8810	8831	8851	8872	8892	2 4 6 8	10	12 14 16 18
·95	8913	8933	8954	8974	8995	9016	9036	9057	9078	9099	2 4 6 8	10	12 15 17 19
·96	9120	9141	9162	9183	9204	9226	9247	9268	9290	9311	2 4 6 8	11	13 15 17 19
·97	9333	9354	9376	9397	9419	9441	9462	9484	9506	9528	2 4 7 9	11	13 15 17 20
·98	9550	9572	9594	9616	9638	9661	9683	9705	9727	9750	2 4 7 9	11	13 16 18 20
·99	9772	9795	9817	9840	9863	9886	9908	9931	9954	9977	2 5 7 9	11	14 16 18 20

NATURAL SINES

°	0′	6′	12′	18′	24′	30′	36′	42′	48′	54′	1′	2′	3′	4′	5′
0	·0000	0017	0035	0052	0070	0087	0105	0122	0140	0157	3	6	9	12	15
1	·0175	0192	0209	0227	0244	0262	0279	0297	0314	0332	3	6	9	12	15
2	·0349	0366	0384	0401	0419	0436	0454	0471	0488	0506	3	6	9	12	15
3	·0523	0541	0558	0576	0593	0610	0628	0645	0663	0680	3	6	9	12	15
4	·0698	0715	0732	0750	0767	0785	0802	0819	0837	0854	3	6	9	12	14
5	·0872	0889	0906	0924	0941	0958	0976	0993	1011	1028	3	6	9	12	14
6	·1045	1063	1080	1097	1115	1132	1149	1167	1184	1201	3	6	9	12	14
7	·1219	1236	1253	1271	1288	1305	1323	1340	1357	1374	3	6	9	12	14
8	·1392	1409	1426	1444	1461	1478	1495	1513	1530	1547	3	6	9	12	14
9	·1564	1582	1599	1616	1633	1650	1668	1685	1702	1719	3	6	9	11	14
10	·1736	1754	1771	1788	1805	1822	1840	1857	1874	1891	3	6	9	11	14
11	·1908	1925	1942	1959	1977	1994	2011	2028	2045	2062	3	6	9	11	14
12	·2079	2096	2113	2130	2147	2164	2181	2198	2215	2233	3	6	9	11	14
13	·2250	2267	2284	2300	2317	2334	2351	2368	2385	2402	3	6	8	11	14
14	·2419	2436	2453	2470	2487	2504	2521	2538	2554	2571	3	6	8	11	14
15	·2588	2605	2622	2639	2656	2672	2689	2706	2723	2740	3	6	8	11	14
16	·2756	2773	2790	2807	2823	2840	2857	2874	2890	2907	3	6	8	11	14
17	·2924	2940	2957	2974	2990	3007	3024	3040	3057	3074	3	6	8	11	14
18	·3090	3107	3123	3140	3156	3173	3190	3206	3223	3239	3	6	8	11	14
19	·3256	3272	3289	3305	3322	3338	3355	3371	3387	3404	3	5	8	11	14
20	·3420	3437	3453	3469	3486	3502	3518	3535	3551	3567	3	5	8	11	14
21	·3584	3600	3616	3633	3649	3665	3681	3697	3714	3730	3	5	8	11	14
22	·3746	3762	3778	3795	3811	3827	3843	3859	3875	3891	3	5	8	11	13
23	·3907	3923	3939	3955	3971	3987	4003	4019	4035	4051	3	5	8	11	13
24	·4067	4083	4099	4115	4131	4147	4163	4179	4195	4210	3	5	8	11	13
25	·4226	4242	4258	4274	4289	4305	4321	4337	4352	4368	3	5	8	11	13
26	·4384	4399	4415	4431	4446	4462	4478	4493	4509	4524	3	5	8	10	13
27	·4540	4555	4571	4586	4602	4617	4633	4648	4664	4679	3	5	8	10	13
28	·4695	4710	4726	4741	4756	4772	4787	4802	4818	4833	3	5	8	10	13
29	·4848	4863	4879	4894	4909	4924	4939	4955	4970	4985	3	5	8	10	13
30	·5000	5015	5030	5045	5060	5075	5090	5105	5120	5135	3	5	8	10	13
31	·5150	5165	5180	5195	5210	5225	5240	5255	5270	5284	2	5	7	10	12
32	·5299	5314	5329	5344	5358	5373	5388	5402	5417	5432	2	5	7	10	12
33	·5446	5461	5476	5490	5505	5519	5534	5548	5563	5577	2	5	7	10	12
34	·5592	5606	5621	5635	5650	5664	5678	5693	5707	5721	2	5	7	10	12
35	·5736	5750	5764	5779	5793	5807	5821	5835	5850	5864	2	5	7	10	12
36	·5878	5892	5906	5920	5934	5948	5962	5976	5990	6004	2	5	7	9	12
37	·6018	6032	6046	6060	6074	6088	6101	6115	6129	6143	2	5	7	9	12
38	·6157	6170	6184	6198	6211	6225	6239	6252	6266	6280	2	5	7	9	11
39	·6293	6307	6320	6334	6347	6361	6374	6388	6401	6414	2	4	7	9	11
40	·6428	6441	6455	6468	6481	6494	6508	6521	6534	6547	2	4	7	9	11
41	·6561	6574	6587	6600	6613	6626	6639	6652	6665	6678	2	4	7	9	11
42	·6691	6704	6717	6730	6743	6756	6769	6782	6794	6807	2	4	6	9	11
43	·6820	6833	6845	6858	6871	6884	6896	6909	6921	6934	2	4	6	8	11
44	·6947	6959	6972	6984	6997	7009	7022	7034	7046	7059	2	4	6	8	10

NATURAL SINES

°	0′	6′	12′	18′	24′	30′	36′	42′	48′	54′	1′	2′	3′	4′	5′
45	·7071	7083	7096	7108	7120	7133	7145	7157	7169	7181	2	4	6	8	10
46	·7193	7206	7218	7230	7242	7254	7266	7278	7290	7302	2	4	6	8	10
47	·7314	7325	7337	7349	7361	7373	7385	7396	7408	7420	2	4	6	8	10
48	·7431	7443	7455	7466	7478	7490	7501	7513	7524	7536	2	4	6	8	10
49	·7547	7559	7570	7581	7593	7604	7615	7627	7638	7649	2	4	6	8	9
50	·7660	7672	7683	7694	7705	7716	7727	7738	7749	7760	2	4	6	7	9
51	·7771	7782	7793	7804	7815	7826	7837	7848	7859	7869	2	4	5	7	9
52	·7880	7891	7902	7912	7923	7934	7944	7955	7965	7976	2	4	5	7	9
53	·7986	7997	8007	8018	8028	8039	8049	8059	8070	8080	2	3	5	7	9
54	·8090	8100	8111	8121	8131	8141	8151	8161	8171	8181	2	3	5	7	8
55	·8192	8202	8211	8221	8231	8241	8251	8261	8271	8281	2	3	5	7	8
56	·8290	8300	8310	8320	8329	8339	8348	8358	8368	8377	2	3	5	6	8
57	·8387	8396	8406	8415	8425	8434	8443	8453	8462	8471	2	3	5	6	8
58	·8480	8490	8499	8508	8517	8526	8536	8545	8554	8563	2	3	5	6	8
59	·8572	8581	8590	8599	8607	8616	8625	8634	8643	8652	1	3	4	6	7
60	·8660	8669	8678	8686	8695	8704	8712	8721	8729	8738	1	3	4	6	7
61	·8746	8755	8763	8771	8780	8788	8796	8805	8813	8821	1	3	4	6	7
62	·8829	8838	8846	8854	8862	8870	8878	8886	8894	8902	1	3	4	5	7
63	·8910	8918	8926	8934	8942	8949	8957	8965	8973	8980	1	3	4	5	6
64	·8988	8996	9003	9011	9018	9026	9033	9041	9048	9056	1	3	4	5	6
65	·9063	9070	9078	9085	9092	9100	9107	9114	9121	9128	1	2	4	5	6
66	·9135	9143	9150	9157	9164	9171	9178	9184	9191	9198	1	2	3	5	6
67	·9205	9212	9219	9225	9232	9239	9245	9252	9259	9265	1	2	3	4	6
68	·9272	9278	9285	9291	9298	9304	9311	9317	9323	9330	1	2	3	4	5
69	·9336	9342	9348	9354	9361	9367	9373	9379	9385	9391	1	2	3	4	5
70	·9397	9403	9409	9415	9421	9426	9432	9438	9444	9449	1	2	3	4	5
71	·9455	9461	9466	9472	9478	9483	9489	9494	9500	9505	1	2	3	4	5
72	·9511	9516	9521	9527	9532	9537	9542	9548	9553	9558	1	2	3	4	4
73	·9563	9568	9573	9578	9583	9588	9593	9598	9603	9608	1	2	2	3	4
74	·9613	9617	9622	9627	9632	9636	9641	9646	9650	9655	1	2	2	3	4
75	·9659	9664	9668	9673	9677	9681	9686	9690	9694	9699	1	1	2	3	4
76	·9703	9707	9711	9715	9720	9724	9728	9732	9736	9740	1	1	2	3	3
77	·9744	9748	9751	9755	9759	9763	9767	9770	9774	9778	1	1	2	3	3
78	·9781	9785	9789	9792	9796	9799	9803	9806	9810	9813	1	1	2	2	3
79	·9816	9820	9823	9826	9829	9833	9836	9839	9842	9845	1	1	2	2	3
80	·9848	9851	9854	9857	9860	9863	9866	9869	9871	9874	0	1	1	2	2
81	·9877	9880	9882	9885	9888	9890	9893	9895	9898	9900	0	1	1	2	2
82	·9903	9905	9907	9910	9912	9914	9917	9919	9921	9923	0	1	1	2	2
83	·9925	9928	9930	9932	9934	9936	9938	9940	9942	9943	0	1	1	1	2
84	·9945	9947	9949	9951	9952	9954	9956	9957	9959	9960	0	1	1	1	1
85	·9962	9963	9965	9966	9968	9969	9971	9972	9973	9974	0	0	1	1	1
86	·9976	9977	9978	9979	9980	9981	9982	9983	9984	9985	0	0	1	1	1
87	·9986	9987	9988	9989	9990	9990	9991	9992	9993	9993	0	0	0	0	0
88	·9994	9995	9995	9996	9996	9997	9997	9997	9998	9998	0	0	0	0	0
89	·9998	9999	9999	9999	9999	1·000	1·000	1·000	1·000	1·000	0	0	0	0	0

NATURAL COSINES

°	0′	6′	12′	18′	24′	30′	36′	42′	48′	54′	1′	2′	3′	4′	5′
0	1·000	1·000	1·000	1·000	1·000	1·000	**·9999**	**9999**	**9999**	**9999**	0	0	0	0	0
1	·9998	9998	9998	9997	9997	9997	9996	9996	9995	9995	0	0	0	0	0
2	·9994	9993	9993	9992	9991	9990	9990	9989	9988	9987	0	0	0	0	0
3	·9986	9985	9984	9983	9982	9981	9980	9979	9978	9977	0	0	1	1	1
4	·9976	9974	9973	9972	9971	9969	9968	9966	9965	9963	0	0	1	1	1
5	·9962	9960	9959	9957	9956	9954	9952	9951	9949	9947	0	1	1	1	1
6	·9945	9943	9942	9940	9938	9936	9934	9932	9930	9928	0	1	1	1	2
7	·9925	9923	9921	9919	9917	9914	9912	9910	9907	9905	0	1	1	2	2
8	·9903	9900	9898	9895	9893	9890	9888	9885	9882	9880	0	1	1	2	2
9	·9877	9874	9871	9869	9866	9863	9860	9857	9854	9851	0	1	1	2	2
10	·9848	9845	9842	9839	9836	9833	9829	9826	9823	9820	1	1	2	2	3
11	·9816	9813	9810	9806	9803	9799	9796	9792	9789	9785	1	1	2	2	3
12	·9781	9778	9774	9770	9767	9763	9759	9755	9751	9748	1	1	2	3	3
13	·9744	9740	9736	9732	9728	9724	9720	9715	9711	9707	1	1	2	3	3
14	·9703	9699	9694	9690	9686	9681	9677	9673	9668	9664	1	1	2	3	4
15	·9659	9655	9650	9646	9641	9636	9632	9627	9622	9617	1	2	2	3	4
16	·9613	9608	9603	9598	9593	9588	9583	9578	9573	9568	1	2	2	3	4
17	·9563	9558	9553	9548	9542	9537	9532	9527	9521	9516	1	2	3	4	4
18	·9511	9505	9500	9494	9489	9483	9478	9472	9466	9461	1	2	3	4	5
19	·9455	9449	9444	9438	9432	9426	9421	9415	9409	9403	1	2	3	4	5
20	·9397	9391	9385	9379	9373	9367	9361	9354	9348	9342	1	2	3	4	5
21	·9336	9330	9323	9317	9311	9304	9298	9291	9285	9278	1	2	3	4	5
22	·9272	9265	9259	9252	9245	9239	9232	9225	9219	9212	1	2	3	4	6
23	·9205	9198	9191	9184	9178	9171	9164	9157	9150	9143	1	2	3	5	6
24	·9135	9128	9121	9114	9107	9100	9092	9085	9078	9070	1	2	4	5	6
25	·9063	9056	9048	9041	9033	9026	9018	9011	9003	8996	1	3	4	5	6
26	·8988	8980	8973	8965	8957	8949	8942	8934	8926	8918	1	3	4	5	6
27	·8910	8902	8894	8886	8878	8870	8862	8854	8846	8838	1	3	4	5	7
28	·8829	8821	8813	8805	8796	8788	8780	8771	8763	8755	1	3	4	6	7
29	·8746	8738	8729	8721	8712	8704	8695	8686	8678	8669	1	3	4	6	7
30	·8660	8652	8643	8634	8625	8616	8607	8599	8590	8581	1	3	4	6	7
31	·8572	8563	8554	8545	8536	8526	8517	8508	8499	8490	2	3	5	6	8
32	·8480	8471	8462	8453	8443	8434	8425	8415	8406	8396	2	3	5	6	8
33	·8387	8377	8368	8358	8348	8339	8329	8320	8310	8300	2	3	5	6	8
34	·8290	8281	8271	8261	8251	8241	8231	8221	8211	8202	2	3	5	7	8
35	·8192	8181	8171	8161	8151	8141	8131	8121	8111	8100	2	3	5	7	8
36	·8090	8080	8070	8059	8049	8039	8028	8018	8007	7997	2	3	5	7	9
37	·7986	7976	7965	7955	7944	7934	7923	7912	7902	7891	2	4	5	7	9
38	·7880	7869	7859	7848	7837	7826	7815	7804	7793	7782	2	4	5	7	9
39	·7771	7760	7749	7738	7727	7716	7705	7694	7683	7672	2	4	6	7	9
40	·7660	7649	7638	7627	7615	7604	7593	7581	7570	7559	2	4	6	8	9
41	·7547	7536	7524	7513	7501	7490	7478	7466	7455	7443	2	4	6	8	10
42	·7431	7420	7408	7396	7385	7373	7361	7349	7337	7325	2	4	6	8	10
43	·7314	7302	7290	7278	7266	7254	7242	7230	7218	7206	2	4	6	8	10
44	·7193	7181	7169	7157	7145	7133	7120	7108	7096	7083	2	4	6	8	10

Figures in **bold type** show change of integer   SUBTRACT

NATURAL COSINES

°	0′	6′	12′	18′	24′	30′	36′	42′	48′	54′	1′	2′	3′	4′	5′
45	·7071	7059	7046	7034	7022	7009	6997	6984	6972	6959	2	4	6	8	10
46	·6947	6934	6921	6909	6896	6884	6871	6858	6845	6833	2	4	6	8	11
47	·6820	6807	6794	6782	6769	6756	6743	6730	6717	6704	2	4	6	9	11
48	·6691	6678	6665	6652	6639	6626	6613	6600	6587	6574	2	4	7	9	11
49	·6561	6547	6534	6521	6508	6494	6481	6468	6455	6441	2	4	7	9	11
50	·6428	6414	6401	6388	6374	6361	6347	6334	6320	6307	2	4	7	9	11
51	·6293	6280	6266	6252	6239	6225	6211	6198	6184	6170	2	5	7	9	11
52	·6157	6143	6129	6115	6101	6088	6074	6060	6046	6032	2	5	7	9	12
53	·6018	6004	5990	5976	5962	5948	5934	5920	5906	5892	2	5	7	9	12
54	·5878	5864	5850	5835	5821	5807	5793	5779	5764	5750	2	5	7	9	12
55	·5736	5721	5707	5693	5678	5664	5650	5635	5621	5606	2	5	7	10	12
56	·5592	5577	5563	5548	5534	5519	5505	5490	5476	5461	2	5	7	10	12
57	·5446	5432	5417	5402	5388	5373	5358	5344	5329	5314	2	5	7	10	12
58	·5299	5284	5270	5255	5240	5225	5210	5195	5180	5165	2	5	7	10	12
59	·5150	5135	5120	5105	5090	5075	5060	5045	5030	5015	3	5	8	10	13
60	·5000	4985	4970	4955	4939	4924	4909	4894	4879	4863	3	5	8	10	13
61	·4848	4833	4818	4802	4787	4772	4756	4741	4726	4710	3	5	8	10	13
62	·4695	4679	4664	4648	4633	4617	4602	4586	4571	4555	3	5	8	10	13
63	·4540	4524	4509	4493	4478	4462	4446	4431	4415	4399	3	5	8	10	13
64	·4384	4368	4352	4337	4321	4305	4289	4274	4258	4242	3	5	8	11	13
65	·4226	4210	4195	4179	4163	4147	4131	4115	4099	4083	3	5	8	11	13
66	·4067	4051	4035	4019	4003	3987	3971	3955	3939	3923	3	5	8	11	13
67	·3907	3891	3875	3859	3843	3827	3811	3795	3778	3762	3	5	8	11	13
68	·3746	3730	3714	3697	3681	3665	3649	3633	3616	3600	3	5	8	11	14
69	·3584	3567	3551	3535	3518	3502	3486	3469	3453	3437	3	5	8	11	14
70	·3420	3404	3387	3371	3355	3338	3322	3305	3289	3272	3	5	8	11	14
71	·3256	3239	3223	3206	3190	3173	3156	3140	3123	3107	3	6	8	11	14
72	·3090	3074	3057	3040	3024	3007	2990	2974	2957	2940	3	6	8	11	14
73	·2924	2907	2890	2874	2857	2840	2823	2807	2790	2773	3	6	8	11	14
74	·2756	2740	2723	2706	2689	2672	2656	2639	2622	2605	3	6	8	11	14
75	·2588	2571	2554	2538	2521	2504	2487	2470	2453	2436	3	6	8	11	14
76	·2419	2402	2385	2368	2351	2334	2317	2300	2284	2267	3	6	8	11	14
77	·2250	2233	2215	2198	2181	2164	2147	2130	2113	2096	3	6	9	11	14
78	·2079	2062	2045	2028	2011	1994	1977	1959	1942	1925	3	6	9	11	14
79	·1908	1891	1874	1857	1840	1822	1805	1788	1771	1754	3	6	9	11	14
80	·1736	1719	1702	1685	1668	1650	1633	1616	1599	1582	3	6	9	11	14
81	·1564	1547	1530	1513	1495	1478	1461	1444	1426	1409	3	6	9	12	14
82	·1392	1374	1357	1340	1323	1305	1288	1271	1253	1236	3	6	9	12	14
83	·1219	1201	1184	1167	1149	1132	1115	1097	1080	1063	3	6	9	12	14
84	·1045	1028	1011	0993	0976	0958	0941	0924	0906	0889	3	6	9	12	14
85	·0872	0854	0837	0819	0802	0785	0767	0750	0732	0715	3	6	9	12	14
86	·0698	0680	0663	0645	0628	0610	0593	0576	0558	0541	3	6	9	12	15
87	·0523	0506	0488	0471	0454	0436	0419	0401	0384	0366	3	6	9	12	15
88	·0349	0332	0314	0297	0279	0262	0244	0227	0209	0192	3	6	9	12	15
89	·0175	0157	0140	0122	0105	0087	0070	0052	0035	0017	3	6	9	12	15

NATURAL TANGENTS

°	0'	6'	12'	18'	24'	30'	36'	42'	48'	54'	1'	2'	3'	4'	5'
0	·0000	0017	0035	0052	0070	0087	0105	0122	0140	0157	3	6	9	12	15
1	·0175	0192	0209	0227	0244	0262	0279	0297	0314	0332	3	6	9	12	15
2	·0349	0367	0384	0402	0419	0437	0454	0472	0489	0507	3	6	9	12	15
3	·0524	0542	0559	0577	0594	0612	0629	0647	0664	0682	3	6	9	12	15
4	·0699	0717	0734	0752	0769	0787	0805	0822	0840	0857	3	6	9	12	15
5	·0875	0892	0910	0928	0945	0963	0981	0998	1016	1033	3	6	9	12	15
6	·1051	1069	1086	1104	1122	1139	1157	1175	1192	1210	3	6	9	12	15
7	·1228	1246	1263	1281	1299	1317	1334	1352	1370	1388	3	6	9	12	15
8	·1405	1423	1441	1459	1477	1495	1512	1530	1548	1566	3	6	9	12	15
9	·1584	1602	1620	1638	1655	1673	1691	1709	1727	1745	3	6	9	12	15
10	·1763	1781	1799	1817	1835	1853	1871	1890	1908	1926	3	6	9	12	15
11	·1944	1962	1980	1998	2016	2035	2053	2071	2089	2107	3	6	9	12	15
12	·2126	2144	2162	2180	2199	2217	2235	2254	2272	2290	3	6	9	12	15
13	·2309	2327	2345	2364	2382	2401	2419	2438	2456	2475	3	6	9	12	15
14	·2493	2512	2530	2549	2568	2586	2605	2623	2642	2661	3	6	9	12	16
15	·2679	2698	2717	2736	2754	2773	2792	2811	2830	2849	3	6	9	13	16
16	·2867	2886	2905	2924	2943	2962	2981	3000	3019	3038	3	6	9	13	16
17	·3057	3076	3096	3115	3134	3153	3172	3191	3211	3230	3	6	10	13	16
18	·3249	3269	3288	3307	3327	3346	3365	3385	3404	3424	3	6	10	13	16
19	·3443	3463	3482	3502	3522	3541	3561	3581	3600	3620	3	7	10	13	16
20	·3640	3659	3679	3699	3719	3739	3759	3779	3799	3819	3	7	10	13	17
21	·3839	3859	3879	3899	3919	3939	3959	3979	4000	4020	3	7	10	13	17
22	·4040	4061	4081	4101	4122	4142	4163	4183	4204	4224	3	7	10	14	17
23	·4245	4265	4286	4307	4327	4348	4369	4390	4411	4431	3	7	10	14	17
24	·4452	4473	4494	4515	4536	4557	4578	4599	4621	4642	4	7	11	14	18
25	·4663	4684	4706	4727	4748	4770	4791	4813	4834	4856	4	7	11	14	18
26	·4877	4899	4921	4942	4964	4986	5008	5029	5051	5073	4	7	11	15	18
27	·5095	5117	5139	5161	5184	5206	5228	5250	5272	5295	4	7	11	15	18
28	·5317	5340	5362	5384	5407	5430	5452	5475	5498	5520	4	8	11	15	19
29	·5543	5566	5589	5612	5635	5658	5681	5704	5727	5750	4	8	12	15	19
30	·5774	5797	5820	5844	5867	5890	5914	5938	5961	5985	4	8	12	16	20
31	·6009	6032	6056	6080	6104	6128	6152	6176	6200	6224	4	8	12	16	20
32	·6249	6273	6297	6322	6346	6371	6395	6420	6445	6469	4	8	12	16	20
33	·6494	6519	6544	6569	6594	6619	6644	6669	6694	6720	4	8	13	17	21
34	·6745	6771	6796	6822	6847	6873	6899	6924	6950	6976	4	9	13	17	21
35	·7002	7028	7054	7080	7107	7133	7159	7186	7212	7239	4	9	13	18	22
36	·7265	7292	7319	7346	7373	7400	7427	7454	7481	7508	5	9	14	18	23
37	·7536	7563	7590	7618	7646	7673	7701	7729	7757	7785	5	9	14	18	23
38	·7813	7841	7869	7898	7926	7954	7983	8012	8040	8069	5	9	14	19	24
39	·8098	8127	8156	8185	8214	8243	8273	8302	8332	8361	5	10	15	20	24
40	·8391	8421	8451	8481	8511	8541	8571	8601	8632	8662	5	10	15	20	25
41	·8693	8724	8754	8785	8816	8847	8878	8910	8941	8972	5	10	16	21	26
42	·9004	9036	9067	9099	9131	9163	9195	9228	9260	9293	5	11	16	21	27
43	·9325	9358	9391	9424	9457	9490	9523	9556	9590	9623	6	11	17	22	28
44	·9657	9691	9725	9759	9793	9827	9861	9896	9930	9965	6	11	17	23	29

NATURAL TANGENTS

°	0'	6'	12'	18'	24'	30'	36'	42'	48'	54'	1'	2'	3'	4'	5'
45	1·0000	0035	0070	0105	0141	0176	0212	0247	0283	0319	6	12	18	24	30
46	1·0355	0392	0428	0464	0501	0538	0575	0612	0649	0686	6	12	18	25	31
47	1·0724	0761	0799	0837	0875	0913	0951	0990	1028	1067	6	13	19	25	32
48	1·1106	1145	1184	1224	1263	1303	1343	1383	1423	1463	7	13	20	26	33
49	1·1504	1544	1585	1626	1667	1708	1750	1792	1833	1875	7	14	21	28	34
50	1·1918	1960	2002	2045	2088	2131	2174	2218	2261	2305	7	14	22	29	36
51	1·2349	2393	2437	2482	2527	2572	2617	2662	2708	2753	8	15	23	30	38
52	1·2799	2846	2892	2938	2985	3032	3079	3127	3175	3222	8	16	24	31	39
53	1·3270	3319	3367	3416	3465	3514	3564	3613	3663	3713	8	16	25	33	41
54	1·3764	3814	3865	3916	3968	4019	4071	4124	4176	4229	9	17	26	34	43
55	1·4281	4335	4388	4442	4496	4550	4605	4659	4715	4770	9	18	27	36	45
56	1·4826	4882	4938	4994	5051	5108	5166	5224	5282	5340	10	19	29	38	48
57	1·5399	5458	5517	5577	5637	5697	5757	5818	5880	5941	10	20	30	40	50
58	1·6003	6066	6128	6191	6255	6319	6383	6447	6512	6577	11	21	32	43	53
59	1·6643	6709	6775	6842	6909	6977	7045	7113	7182	7251	11	23	34	45	56
60	1·7321	7391	7461	7532	7603	7675	7747	7820	7893	7966	12	24	36	48	60
61	1·8040	8115	8190	8265	8341	8418	8495	8572	8650	8728	13	26	38	51	64
62	1·8807	8887	8967	9047	9128	9210	9292	9375	9458	9542	14	27	41	55	68
63	1 9626	9711	9797	9883	9970	**0057**	**0145**	**0233**	**0323**	**0413**	15	29	44	58	73
64	2·0503	0594	0686	0778	0872	0965	1060	1155	1251	1348	16	31	47	63	78
65	2·1445	1543	1642	1742	1842	1943	2045	2148	2251	2355	17	34	51	68	85
66	2·2460	2566	2673	2781	2889	2998	3109	3220	3332	3445	18	37	55	73	92
67	2·3559	3673	3789	3906	4023	4142	4262	4383	4504	4627	20	40	60	79	99
68	2·4751	4876	5002	5129	5257	5386	5517	5649	5782	5916	22	43	65	87	108
69	2·6051	6187	6325	6464	6605	6746	6889	7034	7179	7326	24	47	71	95	118
70	2·7475	7625	7776	7929	8083	8239	8397	8556	8716	8878	26	52	78	104	130
71	2·9042	9208	9375	9544	9714	9887	**0061**	**0237**	**0415**	**0595**	29	58	87	116	145
72	3·0777	0961	1146	1334	1524	1716	1910	2106	2305	2506	32	64	96	129	161
73	3·2709	2914	3122	3332	3544	3759	3977	4197	4420	4646	36	72	108	144	180
74	3·4874	5105	5339	5576	5816	6059	6305	6554	6806	7062	41	81	122	163	203
75	3·7321	7583	7848	8118	8391	8667	8947	9232	9520	9812	Use interpolation				
76	4·0108	0408	0713	1022	1335	1653	1976	2303	2635	2972					
77	4·3315	3662	4015	4373	4737	5107	5483	5864	6252	6646					
78	4·7046	7453	7867	8288	8716	9152	9594	**0045**	**0504**	**0970**					
79	5·1446	1929	2422	2924	3435	3955	4486	5026	5578	6140					
80	5·6713	7297	7894	8502	9124	9758	**0405**	**1066**	**1742**	**2432**					
81	6·3138	3859	4596	5350	6122	6912	7720	8548	9395	**0264**					
82	7·1154	2066	3002	3962	4947	5958	6996	8062	9158	**0285**					
83	8·1443	2636	3863	5126	6427	7769	9152	**0579**	**2052**	**3572**					
84	9·5144	6768	8448	10·02	10·20	10·39	10·58	10·78	10·99	11·20					
85	11·43	11·66	11·91	12·16	12·43	12·71	13·00	13·30	13·62	13·95					
86	14·30	14·67	15·06	15·46	15·89	16·35	16·83	17·34	17·89	18·46					
87	19·08	19·74	20·45	21·20	22·02	22·90	23·86	24·90	26·03	27·27					
88	28·64	30·14	31·82	33·69	35·80	38·19	40·92	44·07	47·74	52·08					
89	57·29	63·66	71·62	81·85	95·49	114·6	143·2	191·0	286·5	573·0					

Figures in **bold type** show changes of integer

Index

ABSOLUTE pressure, 123
  temperature, 124
Acceleration, angular, 215
  centripetal, 216
  due to gravity, 212, 221
  valve, 339
Additives, 49
Adhesion, 20
Adiabatic compression, 136
  expansion, 136
Advantage, mechanical, 99, 100
Air consumed, measurement of, 191
Air gaps, 328
Air resistance, 226
Allowance, bearing, 56
Alternating current (a.c.), 323
Alternator, 328
Aluminium, 301
  alloys, 301
Ammeter, 333
Ampere-hour, 318
Amplitude, 263
Angle of friction, 21
Angular acceleration, 213
Angular velocity, 215
Annealing, 312
Annulus, 78
Anti-detonators, 161
Archimedes' principle, 151
Atmospheric pressure, 121
Atomic mass, 158

Balancing, engine, 272
  road wheel, 271
Banked track, 252
Bearing, ball and roller, 64
  metals, 302
  plain, 57
  pressure calculations, 59

Belt drive, 69
Bending diagrams, 286
Bending moment, 280
Bernoulli's Law, 155
Boyle's Law, 129
Brake power, 173, 175
  m.e.p., 181
  thermal efficiency, 181
Brake shoe, leading and trailing,
  theory of, 36
Brazing, 314
Brinell test, 307

Calorific value of fuels, 161
Cantilever bending moment, 280
Capacitance, 322
Centistoke, 46
Centre of gravity, 245
Centrifugal force, 244
Cetane number, 162
Chain drive, 69
Charles' Law, 131
Chemical formulae, 158
Clearance, bearing, 57
Clutches, 30
Coefficient, of contraction, 149
  of discharge, 149
  of friction, 22
  of velocity, 149
Combustion calculations, 165
Compression ratios, 125
Condenser, 322
Conservation of energy, 241
Conversion, angular to linear velo-
  city, 214
Copper and its alloys, 299
Coulomb, 318
Couples, 341
Current–voltage regulator, 327

Cut-out, 327

Density, 152
Detergents, 49, 50
Diesel engine, 159
Differential pulley block, 105
Displacement, 211
Drilling machine speeds and feeds, 352
Dynamic balance, 271
Dynamo, 323

Efficiency, mechanical, 185
  of a machine, 99
  thermal, 186
  volumetric, 191
Elastic limit, 304
Electrical measuring instruments, 332
Energy, kinetic, 238
  mechanical, 236
  potential, 236
Engler degrees, 46
E.P. oils, 51
Epicyclic gearing, 78
Evolution, 14

Factor of safety, 295
Fatigue failures, 310
Ferrous metals, 294
Fit, force, 56
  free, 56
Flash point, 48, 160
Flow of oil, gear-type pump, 151
Force ratio, 99, 100
Friction, angle of, 21
  boundary, 20
  coefficient of, 22
  dry, 20
  fluid, 21
  force of, 20
  kinetic, 21
  static, 21
  torque, 28, 32
Fuel consumption, 186
Fuels, 159
  liquid, 157
  non-volatile, 157
  properties of, 160
  volatile, 157

g, determination of, 218
Gas analysis, 203
Gas velocity, 350
Gases, compression of, 136
  expansion of, 136
  pressure of, 121, 136
  properties of, 121
  specific heat of, 136
  temperature of, 124
  volume of, 124, 136
Gauge, pressure, 123
Gear, double-reduction, 83
  drive, 69
  terms, 73
  trains, compound, 77; simple, 76
  types, 70
  velocity ratio, 70
Gear-box ratios, 77
Gradient resistance, 222
Gyration, radius of, 242

Heat balance, 199
Heat treatment, 311
Hydraulic jack, 108
Hydraulic power, 106
Hydraulic press, 108
Hypoid gears, 89
Hypoid oils, 51

Ignition quality, 162
Ignition system, 321
Impact test, 309
Impulse, 232
  direct, 234
Inclined plane, 23, 102
Indicated power, 177, 180, 181
Indicators, 182
  cathode-ray, 183
  Farnboro, 182
Interference, 57
Involution, 10
Isothermal, 136
Izod test, 309

Journal bearing, 27

Kelvin, 125
Kinetics, 211
King-pin bearings, 62

Law of a machine, 113
Linear speed, 91
Liquids, flow of, 148
  head of, 147
  pressure in, 146
Logarithms, 1–8
Log–log, 15
Lubrication, 43

Machine calculations, 100
Machines, 99
Mass, 218
  Atomic, 158
  Molecular, 158
Mechanical advantage, 99, 100
M.e.p., 181
Metals, 294
  ductility of, 294
  fatigue resistance of, 295
  hardness of, 295
  malleability of, 295
  mechanical properties of, 294
  testing of, 302
  toughness of, 295
Meters, 332
  moving-coil, 333
  moving-iron, 334
Modulus of section, 283
Molecular mass, 158
Molybdenum, 299
Moment of inertia, 241
Momentum, 231
Morse test, 185
Movement ratio, 100
Multi-grade oils, 51

Newton's laws of motion, 220
Nickel, 298
Nitriding, 312
Nominal dimension, 57
Non-ferrous metals, 294
Normalizing, 312
Nylon, 58

Obliquity, angle of, 346
Octane values, 161
Ohmmeter, 334
Oscillation, 264
Overdrive, 80
Overturning of a vehicle, 248, 254

Periodic motion, 264
Piston speed, 350
Plane, inclined, 23
Planet carrier, 79
Planet wheels, 79
Power, available, 230
  brake, 173
  friction, 185
  indicated, 177
  required, 230
Pressure, bearing, 59
  clutch plate, 33
Projected area, 59

Radian, 214
Ratios, compression, 125
  gear-box, 77
  overall, 84
  rear-axle, 82
Reduction in area, 305
Redwood viscometer, 44
Regulators, 326
Relative density, 153
Resistance, air, 226
  gradient, 222
  rolling, 221
Rhomboid plan, 337
Road wheels, balancing of, 271
  load distribution on, 256

S.A.E., 46
Saybolt viscometer, 45
Screw jack, 102
Shearing forces, 285
Silicon, 299
Simple harmonic motion (s.h.m.), 264
Skidding, 250
Slide rule, 16
Solders and soldering, 313
Specific resistance, 318
Speed, 211
Springs, 265, 337
Standard temperature and pressure (s.t.p.), 135
Starter motor, 330
Static balance, 271
Steering-box calculations, 93
Sun wheel, 79

Tables, use of, 2
Temperature coefficient, 318
Temperature/pressure curves for
  boiling point of water, 140
Tensile strength, 294
Testing, engine, 173
  brake power, 177
  metals, 302
Thermodynamic temperature, 124
Tolerance, 57
Torsion (twisting), 288
Torsional stiffness, 291
Torsional vibration, 277
Tractive effort, 90, 228
Tractive resistance, 228
Tungsten, 299

Universal joints, 344

Vacuum measurement, 124
Velocity, 211
  angular, 214
  ratio, 100
  relative, 213

Vena contracta, 148
Venturi principle, 154
Vibration, 264
  damper, 278
  torsional, 278
Vickers Diamond Pyramid test,
  308
Viscometer, 44
Viscosity, 44
  index, 47
  numbers, 46
  temperature effect on, 45
Volatility, 160
Voltmeter, 333
Volumetric efficiency, 191

Water gauge, 123
Welding, 314
  symbols, 315
Weston differential chain blocks, 105
Willan's line, 201
Worm wheel, 103

Yield point, 304